DUDLEY PUBLIC LIBRARIES

The loan of this book may be renewed if not required by other readers, by contacting the library from which it was borrowed.

6/3/20

D0625490

000003036237

Midwives on Call

Midwives on Call: Stealing the Surgeon's Heart

ANNE FRASER

MARION LENNOX

FIONA LOWE

MILLS & BOON

First Published in Great Britain 2020
By Mills & Boon, an imprint of HarperCollins*Publishers*
1 London Bridge Street, London, SE1 9GF

MIDWIVES ON CALL: STEALING THE SURGEON'S HEART
© 2020 Harlequin Books S.A.

Spanish Doctor, Pregnant Midwife © 2009 Harlequin Books S.A.
The Surgeon's Doorstep Baby © 2013 Marion Lennox
Unlocking Her Surgeon's Heart © 2015 Harlequin Books S.A.

Special thanks and acknowledgement are given to Anne Fraser for her contribution to the *Brides of Penhally Bay* series.

Special thanks and acknowledgement are given to Fiona Lowe for her contribution to the *Midwives On-Call* series.

ISBN: 978-0-263-28069-2

0220

MIX
Paper from
responsible sources
FSC www.fsc.org **FSC™ C007454**

This book is produced from independently certified FSC™ paper to ensure responsible forest management.

For more information visit: www.harpercollins.co.uk/green

Printed and bound in Spain
by CPI, Barcelona

SPANISH DOCTOR, PREGNANT MIDWIFE

ANNE FRASER

CHAPTER ONE

ANNIE slid into a pew of the cool, cavernous Spanish church and let the peace wash over her bruised and battered soul.

In two days' time, her holiday would be over and she would be returning to England and Penhally Bay. Which meant work and reality.

Despite her parents' entreaties that she join them on at least part of their Christmas and New Year worldwide cruise, Annie had insisted that she wanted to take this break on her own. Once and for all, she had told them gently, she needed to put her heartache behind her, including the break-up with her fiancé Robert and especially the horribly cruel reason behind it. The last thing she needed was to be on a luxury liner filled with happy families or, even worse, spend Christmas in Scotland with her sister Fiona and her young family. Even staying in Penhally Bay for the holiday season would be more than she could bear.

But her holiday to the small whitewashed village in Andalucia *had* helped. She had spent the days tramping the narrow streets and walking the hills, tiring herself out until she had fallen into bed too exhausted even to dream. Although nothing would ever take away the terrible void in her life, she was beginning to feel she could face the future. Whatever it might bring.

A group of excited children accompanied by a heavily pregnant woman disturbed the silence. As Annie looked at the brown-faced children with their heads of shiny dark hair, she felt her heart tighten. One little girl in particular caught her attention. Unlike the others, she was subdued, her thumb stuck in her mouth as she looked about her with wide-eyed solemnity. She hung back from the rest of the group, resisting the pregnant woman's attempts to pull her into the circle.

Annie followed the youngsters with her eyes, wondering once more what it would have been like if she had been able to have children of her own. She eyed the expectant mother's bump enviously. She must be nearly at term and Annie would have given anything to be in her position.

She would even have been prepared to adopt. God knew, there were enough children out there who needed the pent-up love Annie had to give and she knew she would have made a good mum, if only she had been given the chance. She sighed. But men didn't seem to think that way. Was it so very different for them? After she had accepted that she'd never be able to conceive naturally, she had suggested to Robert that they consider adoption. But he had been horrified at the idea, and over the following months he had withdrawn from her bit by bit until she had finally forced the truth out of him. He couldn't face a future without children. His *own* children. It had been a double blow to her when he had left. She had thought he had loved her. Well, no more. From now on it was just her, by herself. And she would manage. More than manage, she told herself firmly. She would throw herself into her work at Penhally Bay. She would make a good life on her own. It was the start of a new year and a new beginning. Of that she was determined.

Squaring her shoulders, Annie slung her bag over her shoulder and stood up. She had only taken a few steps when she heard a cry of pain ringing out and she swung round to see the heavily pregnant woman bent over, clutching at her stomach.

Instantly, Annie was by her side.

'What is it?' she asked. 'Are you okay?'

The woman stared at Annie with enormous brown eyes stretched with pain and fear.

'*Bebé,*' she gasped. And then doubled over again.

'When is your baby due?' Annie asked, keeping her voice calm, but the woman just frowned at her and shook her head. It was obvious she spoke no English. Annie bit back a sigh of frustration. Although she had learned a few words of Spanish, it wasn't up to the demands of the occasion. She needed someone to translate. And soon.

'She say the baby is coming. Now.'

Annie placed a hand on the woman's abdomen and felt the contractions. She counted slowly. They were coming one after the other, at two-minute intervals. She was absolutely right. The baby was on its way.

Annie lowered herself to the level of the little girl. 'What's your name, sweetheart?'

'Maria.' She gestured to the woman. 'This is my cousin, Señora Lopez.' She removed her thumb for only as long as it took to impart the information.

'Okay, Maria, I need you to be my helper. Can you do that?' When the little girl nodded her head, Annie continued, raising her voice above the babble of excited voices.

'Has your cousin other children?'

Maria nodded again. 'Three.'

'Ask her if they were normal deliveries. Then find out if anyone has a phone. We need to call an ambulance.'

An older woman with a nut-brown face pulled a mobile out of the pocket of her cavernous overall and, muttering something frustratingly incomprehensible to Annie, punched numbers into the phone. Hopefully she was calling an ambulance.

In the meantime, Maria had spoken to the labouring woman and listened to her reply.

'She say her other children all come quickly. This baby not supposed to be here for another few weeks.'

'Okay Maria, Well done. I need to find somewhere private for Mrs Lopez to lie down. Could you ask if there is such a place?'

As Maria spoke to the watching, chattering audience, Annie felt her hand being squeezed tightly as another contraction racked Señora Lopez's body. It was clear that the baby was going to be born right here. Annie guessed it would take time they didn't have for the ambulance to get here from the nearest town. The narrow, winding roads weren't built for speed.

Suddenly the crowd of chattering women parted and a dark-haired man pushed his way through. Annie only had time to note deep brown eyes and high cheekbones. The man spoke in rapid Spanish to the distraught woman holding Annie's hand and Annie saw her visibly relax.

'*Mi hijo,*' the older woman with the mobile said, nodding down at him. '*Médico.*'

My son. Doctor. Annie felt a wash of relief. At least she wasn't on her own any more. She prayed he could speak English. It would take the responsibility of translating from Maria. Although the little girl was doing her best, waiting for her questions and commands to be translated was frustratingly slow.

The man bent over and scooped the woman into his arms as if she weighed nothing. His mother gestured him to follow her while the other women took control of the children. Annie noticed that little Maria followed behind, obviously feeling as if she had a stake in the drama.

'I'm a midwife,' Annie said as she followed the dark-haired man with his burden to the rear of the church. 'Do you speak English?'

For a second, he stopped and looked at Annie. His mouth quirked. '*Sí*. Yes, I speak English. I am Dr Raphael Castillo, obstetrician. My mother has called an ambulance, but it will be some time before it gets here. It has to come from the city and the roads aren't very good. Have you made an assessment?'

'I haven't had a chance to examine her properly, but the contractions are coming one after the other. She could deliver at any time.'

He nodded. 'I think you are correct.' He smiled, flashing even white teeth. 'Looks like it is going to be you and me delivering this baby—right here.'

As he spoke, Señora Lopez cried out again, followed by a string of Spanish words. Dr Castillo responded in the same language as he laid her down on a couch in the priest's room.

'She says the baby is coming,' he said, stripping off the jacket of his suit and rolling up the sleeves of his white shirt. 'There is no more time.'

Noticing a sink at one end of the room, Annie crossed to it and began to scrub her hands. Dr Castillo, speaking to Señora Lopez over his shoulder, joined her. It was obvious from the look on Señora Lopez's face that she knew that the baby was going to be delivered in this tiny room. At least it wasn't a stable, Annie thought wryly. Then while the dark-haired doctor finished rinsing the soap from his hands, Annie examined the woman.

'The head is crowning, Dr Castillo,' she called over. 'I'll deliver the baby if you tell her what to do.' She turned to Maria, who had slipped in beside them. 'Go and see if you can find some towels, sheets anything. Something to wrap the baby in.'

As Maria ran off, Annie turned to him. 'How many weeks is she?'

'Thirty-nine,' he said. Although heavily accented, his English was perfect.

'How sure of her dates is she?'

'She is certain. By the way, her name is Sophia.' Then he turned back and said something to Sophia. Annie didn't need to understand the words to know that he would be telling her to push.

Just as Maria and the doctor's mother appeared at the door with a bundle of shawls and scarves, the baby's shoulder appeared. But then, to Annie's horror, the baby's progress down the birth canal halted. It was stuck. She felt her own heart rate rise. Where was that ambulance? But in the same moment Annie realised that even if it turned up in the next few minutes, it wouldn't help. Sophia was in no position to be moved right now.

She looked up and found Raphael Castillo's calm brown eyes on hers.

'What is it?' he asked quietly.

'The baby's stuck,' she said. 'I think we have a shoulder dystocia.' Seeing the answering look of concern in Raphael's eyes, Annie knew he grasped the gravity of the situation. If they were in a hospital, it would be serious enough, but here, without instruments, not even a pair of forceps, there was every chance they could lose the baby. She stood aside to let him examine Sophia while Maria and the older woman watched silently from the doorway. Sensing something was wrong, the labouring woman called out in panic. Raphael's mother rushed to her side and spoke softly to her. What ever she said seemed to reassure the woman and she flopped back down.

After another couple of minutes of Sophia pushing and the baby not making any progress, Annie was certain they were in serious trouble. It seemed as if Raphael had arrived at the same conclusion.

'I'm going to ask my mother to help me pull Sophia's legs above her shoulders. Then I want you to press down just above the pubic bone as hard as you can.' His expression was grim, but his voice was calm. Somehow Annie felt confident that if anyone could save mother and child, he could.

As soon as Sophia's legs had been manoeuvred into position, Annie followed his instructions. With a cry of pain, Sophia gave a final push and the baby slithered into the Annie's arms, giving a gusty cry a few seconds later. Annie and Raphael's eyes locked over the exhausted mother. He grinned widely, his eyes crinkling at the corners, and Annie's world tilted.

'A healthy baby girl,' he said, repeating the words in Spanish to the new mother.

Quickly Annie checked that the baby's breathing was un-restricted before wrapping the tiny infant in a shawl and passing Sophia her daughter to hold.

'*Gracias, gracias,* Raphael,' Sophia whispered, nuzzling her newborn. She looked up at Annie. '*Gracias, Señora.*' In the distance Annie could hear the sound of a siren approach-ing. They just had time to deliver the placenta before the am-bulance crew hurried in.

Raphael spoke to the paramedics as they prepared to transfer Sophia to the hospital, and Annie studied him surreptitiously. He really was the most gorgeous-looking man she had ever seen in her life! His black wavy hair was worn slightly too long and a lock fell across his eyes. He swept it away impatiently with long, tapered fingers. He had high cheekbones, an aquiline nose and his olive complexion showed off even white teeth. He wasn't overly tall, but every muscle was clearly defined under his white shirt. Tailored trousers clung to thighs that looked as if they had been honed by hours in the gym. All in all he exuded sex appeal. Annie had never met anyone like him before. Quite simply, he took her breath away.

'Well done,' he said to Annie over the cries of the infant. 'I am sorry, I don't even know your name.'

'It's Annie,' she said. 'Annie Thomas. And there's no need to thank me. I was glad to help. Although I'm relieved you appeared when you did. I'm not sure I would have coped—even with my two helpers here.' She nodded at the older woman and the young girl, who were now fussing over the baby.

'My mother—' he indicated the older woman with a nod of his head '—called me. Fortunately, I was waiting for her in a café nearby. She wanted to say a prayer before we went home for lunch.'

His mother glanced up from Sophia and the baby and Raphael introduced them. Señora Castillo nodded vigorously and said something to her son in rapid Spanish.

'She says you must come for lunch too.' By this time Sophia and her baby were being loaded onto a stretcher, with Raphael helping.

'Shouldn't we go with them to the hospital?' Annie asked.

He looked at her and grinned. 'I will go with them. There is no room for you. Anyway, you are on holiday, no? I am sure you have other things you would like to do. Even if you don't care to join my family for lunch.'

Annie felt unreasonably disappointed. But whether it was because she wouldn't be able to follow up her patient as she was used to doing, or whether it was because Raphael was about to disappear from her life for good, she didn't know. Not that she was in any mood for romance. Not when she had just decided to get her life back on track. The last thing she needed was more complications in her life.

'What about this little one?' Annie asked, indicating Maria, who remained watching with enormous brown eyes.

Raphael laughed and chucked the little girl under her chin. 'Maria is staying with my mother. She will go home with her. Everyone will be there. It is our New Year family gathering. Maybe you will think about coming and I will see you there later?' He quirked an eyebrow in enquiry and Annie felt a shiver dance down her spine. How on earth was this man having this effect on her? She had only just met him, for goodness' sake! Maybe it was something to do with those intense brown eyes and that body, an inner voice whispered. Maybe it's because she'd never met anyone who looked like him before. Everything about him sent warning signals flashing in Annie's head and she knew the wisest thing she could do was put as much distance as possible between her and this man—and the sooner the better.

As she opened her mouth to protest that she couldn't possibly intrude, Raphael smiled again. 'Actually, you can't say no. Mama will not let you, so you might as well give in now. My mother is—how do you say? Formidable. But, look, I must go. The ambulance is about to leave.' He stared down at her for a long second, holding her gaze with the intensity of his own. 'I hope you will decide to come.' And then he was walking away, leaving Annie reeling.

Sure enough, Mama Castillo was tugging at Annie's arm, making it clear that she expected her to follow. Silently Maria slipped her hand into Annie's and it seemed that she was going for lunch whether she wanted to or not. Well, it wasn't as if she had anything else planned for the rest of the day, and, if she was honest with herself, she'd had enough of her own company. Moreover, hadn't it been one of her New Year resolutions to try and experience more of life? She refused to let herself think too long about the real reason she wanted to go. The thought of seeing Raphael again was irresistible, no matter what the sensible part of her brain was telling her. What could it hurt? She was leaving soon and she would never see any of them again. And what was the point of being wise anyway? Right now, she had nothing left to lose.

'Okay. I'd love to,' she said, finally throwing her hands up in surrender. When Maria translated for her an enormous grin lit up the tiny woman's weatherbeaten face.

They stepped outside just as the ambulance sped away. Although it was winter, the sun was high in the sky and Annie could feel it warming her skin. She felt a shiver of anticipation. This holiday was turning out to be not at all what she had expected!

Unsure of where they were going or how they were going to get there, Annie was dismayed when Mama Castillo lifted her voluminous skirts and climbed onto a small moped, indicating that Annie should jump on behind her.

Annie looked to Maria for confirmation.

'She says she will take you. I will walk. It is not far. Just up there.' Maria pointed up a narrow road towards a cluster of whitewashed houses. 'In the hills,' she added.

'Could I not walk with you?' Annie said doubtfully. But Maria shook her head decisively. 'No, you must go with Grandma. She says it is too far for an English woman to walk in this sun. I am used to it. It is better if you go on the bike.'

It seemed to Annie as if she had little choice in the matter. Mama Castillo looked in no mood to debate the matter. Reluctantly Annie climbed on the moped and hoped for the best.

In the event Annie kept her eyes closed as they raced up the hill, scattering chickens and goats in all directions. For the whole of the ten-minute journey, Mama Castillo didn't slow down once, not even for a group of men trudging up the hill in front of them. It was obvious to Annie that she only had one speed, and nothing and no one was going to slow her down.

When they eventually stopped outside a farmhouse perched on the side of the hill, Annie felt a huge wave of relief. There had been moments when she'd been sure that she wasn't going to survive the journey.

As soon as they climbed off the moped they were surrounded by what seemed to Annie to be most of the village. There were a number of young men, at least two of whom bore a striking resemblance to Raphael, as well as half a dozen women. There were also children, almost too many to count, running around the large courtyard, squealing and laughing.

Overwhelmed by the noise, Annie stood back, feeling suddenly shy. Why on earth had she agreed to come here? she wondered. After a few minutes a stunning woman with thick wavy hair and hazel eyes detached herself from the crowd and came across to Annie holding out her hand.

'Welcome to our home,' she said. 'Mama told me you helped Sophia and her baby today. Sophia is a cousin of my father's so we all are in your debt.' So this dark-haired beauty must be Raphael's sister. Annie could see the resemblance in the high cheekbones and sensuous mouth.

'It was nothing,' Annie replied. 'I was glad to help.'

'My name is Catalina.' The woman continued. 'I heard Raphael was there too.' She stood on tiptoe, looking over Annie's shoulder. 'So where is my brother now? He promised to be here.'

'He went with Sophia and the baby to the hospital. To make sure there were no complications. He said he would come as soon as he was finished there.'

Catalina pouted. 'That's Raphael for you, always working. We don't see him very often. He is supposed to be on holiday with us, just for these few days, but we've hardly seen him. Pah! But seeing as it is our cousin he is attending to, I won't tell him off when he comes.'

And then, before Annie had a chance to say anything, she was being led into an enormous farmhouse kitchen where a large table had been laid out as if to feed the five thousand. It was covered with bowls of fruit and olives and large platters of paella as well as other Spanish dishes that Annie couldn't identify, but which smelled delicious. Soon she was part of the chattering group, absorbed into their friendly warmth that needed little translation. Catalina made some introductions, but there were too many for Annie to possibly remember all their names. It seemed that she had guessed right and the two men she had thought were Raphael's brothers turned out to be just that. Apart from Catalina, there were another two women who were his sisters. Annie had just been guided into a seat at the table when Maria, smiling shyly appeared silently at her side where, after squeezing in beside her, she remained for the rest of the meal. Gazing around the crowded table, Annie couldn't be sure who Maria belonged to. As far as she could tell, all the children appeared to be shared.

During a spell when no one's attention was on her, Annie wondered wistfully what it would be like to be part of a family just like this one, and in an instant the sadness came flooding back. She squeezed her eyes closed, forcing back the never-far-away tears. She would never know.

When she opened her eyes again, it was to find Raphael looking down at her, his dark-winged brows knotted in puzzlement. His eyes had an intensity that made her feel as if he could see into her soul, and as he held her gaze Annie thought she recognised an answering sadness in their depths, but knew she had to be mistaken. What could this vibrant, gorgeous man have to feel unhappy about? As far as Annie could see, he had everything. Her eyes swept the happy chattering family again; at least, everything that mattered.

He leaned over her. 'Don't be so sad,' he murmured in her ear.

She could smell his aftershave and his breath on her cheek was like a caress. Her heart gave an involuntary leap. What *was* it about him that made her feel like a schoolgirl with her first crush? She couldn't remember the last time she'd had such an instant and powerful response to a man. In fact, she couldn't remember responding like this to a man ever—and that included Robert. Maybe it was the Spanish sunshine and the couple of glasses of sangria that had been served with lunch. Whatever it was, she couldn't deny she was pleased that he was back before she had made her excuses and left.

'I'm not sad,' she retorted. There was a sudden lull in the conversation and her words rang out around the table. To her acute embarrassment, all eyes swivelled her way. There was a moment of deathly silence before everyone resumed their conversations. Annie felt herself blush to the tips of her ears.

'How is Sophia?' she asked, determined to change the subject.

'Mother and baby are doing fine,' he said. 'She told me to thank you again.' Then he turned towards the others and said something in Spanish to which they all raised their glasses. 'To Sophia! To Annie!' If it were possible, Annie felt more self-conscious than ever, and it seemed by the broad grin on his face that Raphael was enjoying her discomfort.

All of a sudden she wanted nothing more than to put as much distance between herself and this man as possible. She stood, almost knocking over her wineglass in her haste to get away. 'Thank you for the meal, but I really think I should be going,' she said breathlessly. 'I've taken enough of your family's kind hospitality.' She stumbled as her head spun with the sudden movement.

His hand shot out and grasped her wrist, steadying her. The touch of his fingertips seemed to burn her skin.

'I will take you. Where are you staying?'

'Oh, no, it's quite all right. I'm sure I can find my own way. My apartment is opposite the church. It won't take me more than half an hour to walk back. And after that meal, I could do with the exercise.' She was miserably aware that she was babbling on, but she seemed powerless to halt the words erupting from her mouth. The longer she was in his company, the more she felt like a star-struck schoolgirl.

'Anyway, you haven't had a chance to eat yet.' She checked her watch. 'It's almost 5.30! You must be starving by now. Please don't worry about taking me.'

'It is no trouble. My mother would never forgive me my poor manners if I didn't see you home. I told you how formidable she can be. I wouldn't put it past her to—how do you say?—box my ears!'

Annie laughed, suddenly relaxing. 'Okay, then. I wouldn't want to be responsible for that,' she said. 'But I insist you have something to eat before we leave.'

'Only if you promise me you will stay a little longer.' Then he frowned. 'But forgive me, I am stupid. You are sure to have someone waiting for you? Back at your apartment?'

'No,' Annie said heavily. 'I'm on my own, so there isn't really a need for me to rush away.' If she were honest with herself, the last thing she felt like doing was returning to the little flat she had rented. After two weeks of her own company, she was heartily sick of it. Besides, there was something about this family group that made her feel warm and wanted. Perhaps just for tonight she could pretend she belonged and forget about her life back home?

Raphael looked puzzled. 'You are here in Spain on your own? Over Christmas? And New Year! How can that be?'

Annie had no intention of telling him the truth. The last thing she wanted was his sympathy. 'I thought a little bit of winter sun would be nice,' she said.

If anything, Raphael looked even more perplexed. 'It is winter here, too,' he said.

"At home, right now it's snowing.' Annie had to laugh. 'I can assure you there is no comparison.'

'Whatever,' he said, grinning back at her. 'I for one am glad you came to Spain.' There was something in the force of his gaze that sent shivers of anticipation up Annie's spine. 'And I know Sophia is, too,' he added.

The last comment was a reality check. Of course, Annie thought. Why would a man like Raphael Castillo be interested in someone as ordinary as her?

It was growing dark by the time they left and Annie felt a pang as she was subjected to dozens of warm embraces and repeated pleas to return and see them again. All in all, it had been a magical afternoon, and she wished she could stay for ever. But, of course, that wasn't possible. She had her own life to return to even if it was a lonely and barren one—in more ways than one. Just as Raphael opened the wrought-iron gate to the road, Maria came running over and flung herself into Annie's arms, burying her face in Annie's shoulder. Annie felt her heart contract as she cuddled the little girl, breathing in the scent of oranges on her skin. What she would give to be able to hold her own child in her arms.

She released the little girl as Mama Castillo called to her with softly spoken words and Annie watched Maria cuddle up, the inevitable thumb back in her mouth, in the older woman's lap. Regretfully Annie gave a final wave, before following Raphael down the dirt road away from the house.

'Who does Maria belong to?' she asked. 'She is such a sweetheart, but she seems so…I don't know…lost.'

'Ah, little Maria,' Raphael said slowly. 'Her mother, my cousin, died suddenly a few months ago. Her father…' he sucked in his breath, his mouth tightening with disapproval. 'He is weak. He left Maria behind. What kind of man is that? If Maria were my child, I would do everything I could to keep her with me.'

Suddenly the warmth drained from his eyes and Annie

shivered. Instinctively she knew that Raphael was not the kind of man to give up anything he thought he had a right to. He was not the kind of man she would ever want to cross swords with.

'He must have been in some state to abandon his child. People do all sorts of things that are out of character when they are hurting,' Annie said. But she couldn't really understand how any father could abandon his child—especially when that child had just lost her mother. It was too cruel.

'There is no excuse,' Raphael said curtly. 'A father has his duty. How he feels is of no importance when it comes to the child.' He looked away, but not before Annie read the bleakness in his eyes. 'So now she lives with my family. She loves my mother but she still grieves for her own,' Raphael went on. 'She is sad—like you—but every day she is getting stronger.'

There it was again. The reference to her sadness. Was she so transparent? Or did this man just seem to be able to see into her soul?

They walked along the narrow road, the scent of the heavily laden orange trees that edged the pavement drifting in the still air, the velvet sky punctuated with stars. He asked her about her job, and she told him about Penhally Bay, how much she loved living there and how much she enjoyed her job at the hospital. He listened closely, then he told her about his job in Barcelona. That he missed the countryside and regretted that he wasn't able to see his family more often. He grinned down at her.

'As you can tell, we Spaniards are big on family. What about you?'

'I have my parents and a brother as well as a sister. They both have small children. My brother lives in Australia and my parents are going to stay with him there for a few months after their cruise. My sister is in Scotland with her family.' She slid a glance at him. 'I envy you, having your family all so close,' she admitted.

Once again, she thought she saw a shadow pass across his face. But when he smiled she knew she must have been mistaken.

'It's not all good. I have to put up with my sisters and my mother wanting to know everything about my life. *Dios*, they never give me peace.'

Before Annie knew it, they were outside her apartment. The nearby houses were draped in Christmas lights, lighting the cobbled street.

She didn't want the evening to end and it seemed as if Raphael didn't either. He hesitated then said, 'If you are not too tired, there is this little restaurant a few minutes' walk away. It has the most excellent tapas. And I am suddenly hungry again. Will you come with me?'

She let her gaze sweep his muscular frame. There wasn't an ounce of fat on it as far as she could see. Where did he put all that food?

'Okay,' she said softly. 'It's my last night. I might as well make the most of it.'

He steered her towards a small restaurant behind the church. It was packed inside, but there was no one sitting at the outside tables in the plaza.

'Do you mind if we sit here?' Annie asked.

'Of course. If that is what you want.' He took off the thin sweater he had been wearing, revealing a short-sleeved shirt. 'But I insist you put this on.'

Sensing that it would be useless to argue, Annie slipped the sweater on over her shoulders. It smelled faintly of a mix of citrus aftershave and the warm tang of his scent. It was much too large, falling almost to her knees and slipping off her shoulder. Her breath caught in her throat as he leant forward and turned up the cuffs. The gesture was both tender and erotic and as his fingers lightly brushed against her bare skin, Annie felt darts of electricity tingle up her arms.

Raphael studied her slowly, his smile turning up the corners of his mouth and creasing the corner of his eyes. Annie thought yet again that she had never seen a man so gorgeous yet so sure of his masculinity. A part of her, sensing danger, wanted to run from him as fast as she could, but at the same time she knew that she couldn't bear to see him walk out of her life. At least, not yet.

When their order of seafood arrived, it felt like the most natural thing in the world for Raphael to feed her small morsels of lobster and shrimp with his fingers. The touch of his hands on her lips sent small explosions of desire racing through her body.

Then, without saying anything, they stood and Raphael took her hand again. She led him back up the path to the front door of her apartment. Knowing that what was about to happen was beyond her control, she opened the door and, keeping her hand in his, went inside.

'Are you sure?' he said. He looked into her eyes and it was as if he knew her most hidden thoughts. Despite the ready smile, she saw something in the depths of his ebony eyes that mirrored her own pain. All she wanted was to give comfort and to be comforted in return. The rest of her life could take care of itself.

'It's not too late to change your mind.' His voice was soft, yet there was an undercurrent that caused her pulse to leap.

'No,' she said, stunned by her brazenness. 'It's what I

want.' She knew she was risking danger. Not that she didn't trust him—she instinctively knew he would never harm her. But she could no more resist her need for him than she could walk back to Penhally Bay.

He picked up her hand and pressed it to his lips. She shivered as shock waves of desire coursed through her body. She had never experienced lust like it before, but she wasn't naive. She knew what those dark brown eyes were asking her. She didn't want to play games. All she felt was an overriding need to be held in his arms—to have her femininity reaffirmed. It had taken such a beating in the last few months. Surely just this once she could throw caution to the wind and take a chance?

He dropped her hand and pulled her hard against him, one hand on her hip, the other cupping her bottom. She could feel every muscle of his hard chest through his T-shirt and the pressure of his thighs on hers. Flames of desire flooded her body and she turned her face up to his, seeking his mouth. He brought it down on hers, gently at first and then harder as he seemed to draw her very soul. She snaked her hands around his neck, pulling him closer. She was drowning, her legs weak with her need for him.

He pulled away. She could see that he too was shaken by the strength of their mutual desire.

'Are you sure?' he asked gently. It was all she could do to nod, then with a triumphant smile he picked her up and, holding her close in his arms, he carried her up the stairs and into their own private world.

Later, when the sun was beginning to lighten the sky, she lay on one elbow, looking down on him. Asleep he looked softer, more vulnerable somehow. He had been a passionate but considerate lover, taking his time with her, waiting until she cried out with her need to have him inside her before he took her. She smiled. Several times he had taught her things about her own body that she hadn't known. Time and time again he had brought her to a climax that had left her shuddering and almost tearful with release. She traced a finger over his lips, memorising the contours of his face, knowing she would never see him again. But it was almost all right. In one wonderful night he had managed to heal something inside her that she'd thought was beyond repair. And for that, she would never forget him.

CHAPTER TWO

ANNIE read through the case notes again to refresh her memory. Not that she needed to. She had seen Claire and Roy several times already and knew their history well. Satisfied that she was completely up to date, she sat back and waited for them to arrive.

The rain pattered depressingly against the window and Annie felt her mind drifting back to the magical last night of her Spanish holiday. Almost four months had passed and yet her memories of Raphael and the time they had spent together hadn't diminished. She could still remember his every touch, their every kiss. It was as if she had found the missing part of herself. The man she had been waiting for all her life. Her soulmate. She hadn't believed that such a person existed— but now she knew differently.

Her heart lurched. Sometimes she wished she had never met him. Because it had made being alone all the more painful, as if she'd left half of herself back in Spain. Annie sighed wistfully, remembering his last words to her.

'Cariño,' he had said huskily the morning she had left. 'If only you had come into my life before. But now it's too… complicated.' She hadn't pressed him to explain. What would have been the point? Still, she couldn't help trying to fathom out what he had meant. Was he married? No—she was sure if he was, his family would have made some reference to it. In love with someone else, committed in a relationship? Perhaps. But it didn't matter. Even if he had begged her to stay with him, she wouldn't have said yes. Not so soon after Robert and all their problems. No, much better to lock the memory of him in her heart. Much safer.

Annie pulled her gaze away from the window and swung her chair back round to her desk. There was no point in thinking of Raphael. She had to get on with her life. Hadn't she vowed to do just that? Besides, the irony of not being able to conceive made her a better midwife. At least she could console herself with that realisation. And her work in Penhally was more than satisfying and enjoyable. It was what got her up each morning, determined to put her own heart-ache behind her and help the couples who streamed through her door hoping to realise the dream that she would never have.

Like her next two patients—Roy and Claire Dickson, who were being ushered in. Annie greeted them warmly, knowing they were nervous. The couple had been trying for years to have a baby, and finally with the help of IVF had succeeded. Their initial scan had shown not one but two healthy heart-beats and now Annie, who had a special responsibility for mothers with high-risk pregnancies, was following them up regularly.

'How have you been feeling?' she asked Claire, while checking her blood pressure.

'As if I'm on cloud nine!' Claire smiled with delight. 'Apart from that, nauseous and tired and more than a little bit scared.'

'The nausea will pass. Take it as a good sign in the meantime,' Annie said.

Although she shared the couple's joy, Annie couldn't help a pang of envy. How she would love to be in Claire's shoes, looking forward to her first babies with a loving supportive husband by her side. But she wasn't even a candidate for IVF, she thought sadly. And it wasn't as if there was a rush of people wanting to marry her either, but at least she could help this couple experience what she never could. And she found comfort in that.

'Your blood pressure is absolutely fine, but I want to keep an eye on you and these little ones. I'm sure you both know that the first twelve weeks are the riskiest.' Catching Claire's look of alarm, she hastened to reassure her. 'But you're well past that now. It's just that twin pregnancies are riskier over the whole of the pregnancy. But we are going to do everything possible to deliver two healthy babies and right now everything appears to be going fine.'

'They gave us a choice at the IVF clinic,' Roy said, as if Annie didn't already know, 'about whether we wanted one or two embryos put back. They explained the pros and cons, that there was a greater risk with twins, but we decided to take a chance and have two embryos replaced. This way we'll have a complete family in one go, and Claire doesn't have to put herself through it all again.' His grin almost split his face in two. 'I still can't believe it,' he said, patting his wife's tummy with a proprietary air. 'Two babies. Isn't she clever?'

Annie saw the happy couple to the front door of the maternity wing, and watched Claire struggling to open the umbrella over her head as she battled against the slanting rain, She was delighted for them, but it was early days yet. Twin pregnancies had a greater risk of problems developing and although that had been explained to the couple, she wondered if they really understood.

Annie felt a wave of fatigue wash over her. She always felt so caught up with her patients, sharing their see-saw emotions as she followed them through their pregnancies. Although she loved being part of the team that looked after high-risk pregnancies at St Piran Hospital, sometimes it was hard to remember that most women sailed through their pregnancies and gave birth to healthy babies without medical intervention.

But today was different and Annie knew it wasn't just concern for her patients that was bothering her. She couldn't continue to ignore what was staring her in the face, no matter how much she wanted to. She hadn't had a period for months now and she had begun to put weight on around her middle. All the symptoms of an early menopause.

Unreasonably, even though she knew she couldn't conceive naturally, there had always been a faint glimmer of hope that one day she might have a child. No matter how much she had tried to convince herself otherwise. But with the menopause, any hope would be completely extinguished. Annie was painfully aware that she had to see someone about it, but there was only one person she really trusted and who would understand exactly how she was feeling. She would pop in to see Kate Althorp, the senior midwife at Penhally Bay Surgery, on her way home.

Annie enjoyed working with Kate and her colleague Chloe, who were both midwives based at the surgery. To begin with, they had discussed patients they shared over the phone, but over time they had become friends and Annie would often drop in at the surgery on her way home from hospital for a chat. Occasionally the three women would meet up for coffee or supper too.

Making up her mind, Annie picked up her coat. Kate would know what her next step should be. It was time for Annie to face up to whatever the future had in store. Hadn't she made that promise to herself just months before?

Annie found Kate in her office, catching up with paperwork. The older midwife looked up and smiled when she noticed Annie standing in the doorway.

'Grief, is it that time already?' She looked at her watch. 'Six o'clock! I'm due to pick Jem up from football practice in forty minutes.' She glanced back at Annie and something in Annie's expression must have alerted the experienced nurse. 'But time for some coffee before then. You look a bit peaky, methinks.'

As Kate fished out a couple of mugs, Annie wondered whether there was any point in confiding her fears. But if she was right, she would need to consider whether to start hormone replacement therapy and wanted to discuss the option with Kate before she saw Dr Nick Tremayne, her GP and also the senior partner at the practice.

'Hey.' Kate turned and looked at her closely, her brown eyes warm with concern. 'So, what's up? Is Claire's pregnancy going okay? I know she and Roy were seeing you today.'

'Oh. No, that's fine. I intend to keep a close eye on them, but so far—touch wood—everything seems to be going as expected.'

'It's good to see them so happy. They've been waiting for this for so long. I'll call round and see Claire tomorrow,' Kate said handing a mug to Annie. 'But back to you. Something's bothering you. You didn't come here just to tell me about Claire and Roy, did you? C'mon, whatever it is, out with it.'

Annie hesitated. Once she told Kate, it would be the same as having it confirmed. Was she really ready for that?

Kate came over to Annie and dragged a chair across so she was sitting beside her. 'You don't have to tell me, but perhaps I can help?' she said gently. The older woman was always the one everyone went to with their problems. Annie wasn't sure why—perhaps because she always made time to listen and never seemed to judge. Annie felt tears sting her eyes and she blinked furiously. She wouldn't cry. She had shed enough tears to last her a lifetime.

'I never told you this, but I can't have children,' Annie blurted. 'I'm infertile.'

'Oh, Annie, I'm so sorry. Are you sure?'

'Positive,' Annie said, trying to keep her voice steady. 'You know I told you that I was seeing someone before I came back to Penhally Bay?'

Kate nodded and waited for Annie to continue.

'Robert and I were together for five years. We were in love—or so I thought. We planned to marry and started trying for a family. But after six months, when nothing had happened, I went to one of the doctors I worked with who specialised in infertility and he suggested we get tested. There was nothing wrong with Robert but they have a new blood test that they use to check a woman's fertility. Well, the result came back. My ovarian reserve, you know the number of eggs I have left, was so low as to be immeasurable.' Annie's voice broke. She remembered the day she had been given the news as if it were yesterday.

Kate put her arm around Annie's shoulder. Her silent sympathy gave Annie the strength to continue. 'The test is very reliable. A pregnancy, even with IVF, would be almost impossible for me. They also warned me that it was likely that I would have an early menopause.' She steadied her voice. 'Well, I think it's happening,' she said, trying not to show how much it hurt her to say the words. 'I haven't had a period since...' She thought back. 'Well, before New Year. And,' she continued, 'I don't know how else to describe this, but I kind of feel all hormonal, as if my emotions are all over the place. You know it took me all my willpower not to cry when I saw how relieved and happy Claire and Roy are, and that's not like me. Not that I don't care about them, of course I do, but I don't usually let it get to me like this.'

'But it's understandable, isn't it?' Kate said softly. 'It's bound to remind you of your own loss. And losing the ability to have a family is a loss. Just as much as a death.'

'I know all that,' Annie said, 'but I've been feeling so much happier since I came back from Spain. When I was over there, I knew I had to stop looking back and try and think positively about the future. Accept that children weren't on the cards for me and make something of my life. Be happy with what I have, instead of hankering for what can never be. But if I'm right and I'm experiencing the onset of the menopause, it's like having to deal with it all over again.'

'And you are certain that that's what's happening?' Kate said thoughtfully.

'There can't be another explanation. Missed periods. Emotions all over the place, and I swear I'm starting a middle-age spread. I could hardly get into my jeans the other day.' Annie tried a smile.

Kate looked at her sharply. 'All this since your holiday? Hmm. I don't suppose you had a holiday romance while you were away?'

Annie felt a blush creep up her cheeks. Seeing it, Kate

grinned. 'You did, didn't you? Well, good for you. It's about time you let yourself have some fun.' Then she frowned. 'If it was fun. Oh, dear, I didn't mean for it to come out that way. You know what I mean.'

Annie felt her blush deepen as she thought back to that night. Fun? Yes, but now one of her most precious memories.

'And, if you had sex, did you use contraception?' That was typical Kate. Straight to the point.

'Yes, I mean…no.' Annie blushed again. 'I mean, I told him it wasn't necessary and he just assumed I was on the Pill.' Oh, dear, this was so embarrassing. Although she felt comfortable discussing most things with Kate, there really was a limit.

'What I'm getting at,' Kate said gently, still looking thoughtful. 'I don't suppose you've taken a pregnancy test?'

Annie was stunned. A pregnancy test! The thought simply hadn't occurred to her. She had accepted that it was impossible, so hadn't even considered it. Not even for a second.

'Well, no. It's hardly likely is it? Not with my history.' Suddenly she felt dizzy. 'You don't think? It couldn't be? Could it?' Although she knew it was impossible, the sudden leap of hope was almost too much to bear.

Kate stood up, all business. 'It wouldn't hurt to make sure, would it? Come on.' She rooted around in a cupboard. 'Off you go to the Ladies and produce a specimen and we'll do a quick test. At the very least we'll be able to rule it out.'

Ten minutes later, Annie was sitting stunned in front of Kate. 'You're sure?' she said. 'There couldn't be some mistake?'

'I'm sure,' Kate replied smiling widely. 'We'll arrange a scan just to be absolutely certain, but there is no doubt in my mind. You are pregnant. Apart from the test, I could feel something when I palpated your tummy. I've seen it happen before. Just when a woman thinks a baby is out of the question. Then bam.'

Annie felt a wave of pure joy suffuse her soul. A baby! She was going to have a baby. She had longed for this moment for so long, and now it was here, she could hardly bring herself to believe it. Now the tiredness, the roller-coaster emotions, the hormonal mood swings all made perfect sense. She hugged herself, barely able to contain her delight.

'I assume you're not still in touch with the father? I mean, you've never mentioned him,' Kate was saying.

Raphael! Of course it must be his. He was the only man she had slept with since Robert.

'No. I haven't spoken to him since, well, you know.' How *would* Raphael feel about it? Was there any point in telling him? She neither expected nor wanted anything from him and his silence had made it perfectly clear that he wanted nothing from her, either. Her head reeled. She would have to take time off work, of course, at least for the first few months after the birth, but she had a small inheritance from her grandfather that would supplement her maternity pay. One way or another she would cope. One thing was for sure—her baby wouldn't be short of love.

'God, should I tell him? I don't know. I'm still trying to take it all in. I can hardly believe it myself. But I suppose he has the right to know.'

Annie thought she saw something move behind Kate's eyes, but almost as quickly it was gone. She knew Kate had brought up her child, Jem, on her own since the death of her husband, James. Although it must have been a struggle, Kate had had no choice. James had died before he had even known she was pregnant. All this must be bringing back painful memories for the older woman.

'Only you can make that decision,' Kate replied gently. 'Whatever is right for you.'

'I don't know if I want him in my life, Kate. It's a complication I could do without. Besides, he lives in Spain. Even if he wants to get to know his child, it won't be easy.'

Once again, Annie thought she saw a shadow cross Kate's face, but Annie knew her friend well enough not to ask. Although always willing to offer guidance and support, Kate rarely discussed her own personal life.

'As I said, it's up to you,' Kate said. 'But if you don't tell him, what will you say to your child when he asks about his father?'

Instinctively, Annie knew Kate was right. Whatever the consequences, telling Raphael was the right thing to do, even if he then wanted nothing to do with the baby. One day her child might want to seek out his father. How could she tell the child that its father didn't even know they existed? And if Raphael wanted contact, it wouldn't be right to deny her child the opportunity to know his father. But she had so much to think about right now, the decision could wait. The important thing was that she, Annie Thomas, ordinary woman with an ordinary life, had had this extra-ordinary thing happen to her. And for that alone she would always be grateful to Dr Raphael Castillo.

After Kate had seen a deliriously happy Annie out, she sat deep in thought. She remembered the day she had found out she was pregnant with Jem. A day infused with happiness but also regret and profound sadness. Her son had been conceived the night she had lost her husband to the first big storm almost eleven years ago. But Jem hadn't been her husband's child. While James had been out there fighting for his life, she had been in the arms of senior partner Nick Tremayne, and the guilt had haunted her every day since. She hadn't been able to tell Nick that Jem was his when she'd found out she was pregnant. It wouldn't have been fair. He had still been married to Annabel with children of his own, but he had found out the truth anyway and in the worst possible way when he had overheard her telling pathologist Eloise Haydon.

Kate rose and went across to the window. It was dark outside and the glass pane reflected back her blurred image, softening the faint lines that had started to appear around her eyes. Although she was no longer in her first bloom of youth, she still remembered in minute detail the passion her younger self had felt all these years ago, and, if she was honest with herself, the feelings had never truly faded.

What if she had told Nick that Jem was his as soon as she had found out? Would he have accepted Jem as his child then? But it was no use thinking like that. Rightly or wrongly she had made her decision and had lived with the consequences. Now Annie had to make up her own mind whether to tell the father of *her* child. Kate just hoped that her story would have a different outcome from hers.

After leaving Kate, Annie had spent the rest of the night telephoning her parents and siblings with her exciting news.

'Oh, darling, that's wonderful news!' her mother had said. 'I can only imagine how delighted you must be. I can't wait to tell Dad and David. They're all down at the beach at the moment with the children.'

Annie had felt a pang. She would have loved to share her news face to face with her family. Instead, they were thousands of miles away.

'Do you want us to come back?' her mother had added anxiously.

'Of course not, Mum. I know how long you and Dad have been looking forward to this trip. Anyway, you'll be back in August. In plenty of time for the actual birth.'

There had been silence for a few moments.

'Does that mean you and Robert are back together?' her mother asked. Annie could hear the caution in her voice. She had never really taken to Robert and when he had left Annie after hearing she couldn't have children, she had admitted as much to her daughter. 'Any man who behaves the way he did isn't worthy of you, darling,' she had said. 'You are better off without him.'

Annie knew she'd be thinking back to her words.

'It's not Robert's baby,' Annie said quietly. Once again the silence stretched down the phone line. Annie knew her mother was dying to know who the father was, but wouldn't ask.

'The father is someone I met in Spain—a doctor,' Annie said uncomfortably. 'Not someone I'll ever see again.' She felt her toes curl with embarrassment. How could she possibly explain to anyone, even her mother, about Raphael? How he had made her feel as if they were meant to be together? And how hopelessly wrong she had been?

'As long as you're happy, darling,' her mother had said finally, gently and without judgement. 'And you won't be alone. Dad and I will be back to help you with the baby.' After a few more minutes of conversation Annie had rung off and phoned her sister Fiona. The conversation had followed a similar pattern except Fi, while thrilled for her, had in typical fashion come straight to the point.

'Does your Dr Castillo know?'

It was a timely reminder to Annie that there was more than her involved in the life growing joyously inside her.

'Not yet,' Annie admitted. 'I'm planning to tell him, but…' She let the words tail off. It wasn't a conversation she was looking forward to, especially over the phone. There was no way of knowing what his reaction would be. He would be shocked, but would he be pleased? Angry? Disinterested?

'But you will tell him,' Fi prompted. 'You know it's the right thing to do.'

'Yes,' Annie replied heavily. 'And we both know I always do the right thing.'

But she had kept putting the telephone call off. She hadn't spoken to Raphael since the morning she had left Spain, although she thought of him often, hugging the memory of the night they had spent together. If she was honest, she had hoped he would get in touch with her. There had been such a connection between them, she just couldn't believe he hadn't felt it too. But if he had, he would have found a way to contact her, wouldn't he? But he hadn't and Annie had resigned herself to never hearing from him, concentrating instead on making a life for herself that was rich and varied and relied on no one.

After a couple of days of prevaricating, she made up her mind. She looked up the number of the hospital in Barcelona and, after taking a few deep breaths to calm her nerves, dialled and asked to be put through to Dr Castillo.

As she waited for the switchboard to page him, her heart thumped painfully. How would he take the news? It was bound to be a shock, however he felt about it. When they had made love, she had told him that there was no need for contraception, although she hadn't told him why.

She chewed on her nail until suddenly she heard his unmistakable voice on the other end of the phone.

'*Hola!* Raphael Castillo.'

Immediately memories came flooding back. She could see his face in her mind, almost feel the touch of his fingers on her skin.

Her hands were shaking so hard she thought she might drop the phone. 'Raphael, it's Annie.' There was a long pause on the other end of the line. Whether it was because he couldn't remember who she was or because he was shocked to hear from her, she couldn't tell.

'How are you? Is something wrong? ' His voice sounded cautious.

'No, nothing's wrong. At least…' She let the words hang in the air. Nothing was wrong as far as she was concerned, but how would he feel? 'I'm sorry to call you at the hospital, Raphael, but I didn't know how else to contact you.'

'*De nada,*' he said. 'Please, go on.' He sounded brusque, almost distracted, as if speaking to Annie had been the last thing on his mind. She couldn't help the way her spirits dipped. How could she expect anything else? If he had wanted to get in touch with her before now, well, he knew where she worked. That night obviously hadn't meant as much to him as it had to her, but it didn't matter, she told herself firmly. She didn't need him. She had all she ever wanted growing inside her.

All of a sudden she couldn't remember the words she had rehearsed, but she knew she had to say something as he was waiting for her to speak.

'I'm pregnant,' she blurted finally, not at all how she had planned to tell him.

There was another pause, longer this time.

'Pregnant? I thought you said…'

'That I couldn't get pregnant,' she finished for him. She had told him it was safe for them to have sex. He had assumed she was on the Pill and there had been no point in disabusing him.

'I didn't think it could happen, but it did!' She couldn't keep the joy out of her voice. Every time she said the words she felt a fresh burst of happiness.

When he spoke again his voice was cold. 'Is it mine?'

Annie reeled. What was he suggesting? That she was passing off some other man's child as his? Or that she slept with so many men she couldn't possibly know which one was the father? She felt the first stirring of anger.

'Yes, it's yours. It couldn't be anyone else's. You were the only man…' She hesitated, feeling a blush steal up her cheeks. It was so difficult to talk about this over the phone. At least he couldn't see how mortified she was. 'You are the only man I've slept with since…' Once more she stumbled over the words. 'It can only be yours.'

Another long silence. Why hadn't she just written to him? It would have been so much easier. But she had never been one to take the easy way out.

'You must be over three months by now in that case,' he said slowly. The pause must have been while he had worked the timing out in his head. 'Why didn't you let me know sooner? I'm assuming you're going to keep it.' His voice was cool. He seemed so utterly different from the man she had met in Spain.

'Of course I'm going to keep it! I would hardly be telling you now if I wasn't. I've only recently found out myself.' She stumbled over the words. 'Just a few days ago, but…' She took a deep breath. How could she explain the conflicting thoughts she had had about telling him? 'I just didn't realise I was pregnant. It didn't occur to me that I could be before then.' She could only imagine what he was thinking. How could a midwife not know she was pregnant? But she didn't really want to get into her medical history over the phone. As far as she was concerned, she had done her duty in telling him.

'And?' His voice was heavy, almost suspicious. 'Why exactly are you telling me now? What do you want from me?'

Annie felt a wave of anger wash over her. She hadn't expected him to be pleased, but this reaction, as if he didn't believe or trust her, as if she had ulterior motives for contacting him, wasn't what she had expected either.

'I'm just phoning to let you know. I thought you had a right.' She laughed but the sound was mirthless even to her own ears. 'But don't worry, I don't want anything from you. Not a thing. In fact, I want to be clear that this baby is my responsibility and mine alone,' she continued. 'I don't intend to keep secrets from my child. I plan to be honest about everything from as soon as they can understand. It might be that one day, when they are older, he or she may want to find you. That's why I'm telling you. No other reason.'

'*If* it is my baby—' he emphasised the first word '—then, of course, you were right to tell me. But how can I be sure?'

Annie felt as if she'd been slapped. But to be fair he wasn't to know she didn't make a habit of sleeping with strangers, especially not men she met on holiday. She took another breath to calm herself.

'It's yours. There is absolutely no doubt. But if you don't want to accept that, it's entirely up to you. I have done my bit. I'll say goodbye now.'

She thought she heard him say, 'Wait, Annie,' as she replaced the receiver, but she was in no mood to continue the discussion. As far as she was concerned, Raphael would play no part in her or her baby's life. And that was fine by her.

Raphael replaced the phone thoughtfully. It had been a shock hearing Annie's voice after all these months. He remembered every cadence of her soft accent and as soon as he had heard her speak, it had been as if she had been back in his arms.

It wasn't as if he hadn't thought about her every day since the night they had met. He hadn't been able to get her striking pale green eyes out of his mind, her wounded mouth, her pale skin a striking contrast to her luxurious dark brown hair and that deep but unmistakable air of sadness. How could he forget the curve of her hips, the sweep of her thighs, her tiny waist? He groaned aloud at the memory. He had done his best to put her out of his mind, and now, when he least expected it, she was back in his life. Because she was pregnant. With his baby. Or so she said.

He started pacing. There was no reason for Annie to lie about such a thing and she had made it perfectly clear that she wanted nothing from him. But he had been lied to before and he knew he couldn't trust his heart. It was why he had stayed away from her in the first place, even when every part of him had longed to be with her again. He swore under his breath. If she was lying, he would find out. But if there was any chance she was carrying his child, any chance at all…

He clenched his jaw against the painful memory of Sebastian. *Dios!* This time no one was going to take his child from him. He had to know the truth and there was only one way to find out.

CHAPTER THREE

OVER the next week, Annie mulled over her conversation with Raphael. She wondered if there had been any point in telling him she was pregnant. It might have been the right thing to do, but it had obviously made no difference. She hadn't heard a peep from him since the call and that was fine by her. What he chose to do with the information was up to him.

Nevertheless, she couldn't help acknowledge that she felt sad about his response. Not for herself, but for the child growing inside her. One day, he—or she—might want to know about their father and she would have to find a way of telling her child that his father had shown no interest.

Everyone at work knew about her pregnancy and it was all Annie could do to stop herself accosting strangers in the street and telling them that she was expecting a baby. She was so happy she wanted to shout it from the rooftops. But as far as who the father was, that would be her secret. Somehow explaining about Raphael would make it sound like a casual fling—when it had been anything but. Besides, as he had shown no interest, there was no reason for anyone, apart from her immediate family, to know his identity. She would be raising this child on her own and that was fine by her.

Annie chewed her lip. She looked around her tiny home with its double bedroom, minute single bedroom, kitchen and lounge. She loved it. It was so cosy, especially in the winter when she would light a fire and cuddle up on the sofa with a good book, but it wasn't really big enough for her and a baby. The second bedroom would only just be large enough for a cot and a changing table. However, it would have to do. Despite the small inheritance from her grandfather, money was bound to be tight after her maternity pay came to an end. But what did money or any material possessions matter when balanced against having a baby? It didn't. She would have happily given up everything she owned if she'd had to just to be in this position.

A knock on the door interrupted her thoughts. Annie wasn't expecting anyone. Sunday was a day that everyone she knew spent with their families. Puzzled, she opened the door to find the last person she expected standing there, a half-smile on his face.

Raphael! It couldn't be! What on earth was he doing here, in Penhally Bay? And why did her heart feel as if it had stopped beating?

Speechless, Annie stood aside to let him enter, and as he passed her she felt her skin prickle. Her breath caught in her throat as instantly she was transported back to the night she had spent in his arms.

She waved at a chair, still unable to speak, but he shook his head. Instead, he paced her small house with nervous energy.

'I had to come,' he said simply.

'Why?' she said, dry-mouthed. 'I told you there was no need.'

'Because if there is a chance you are having my baby,' he

said, sounding incredulous, 'I want to be here for him. He will need a father. I don't even know if you can look after a child.'

Annie felt her temper rise. Just who did he think he was, coming here to check up on her, questioning not only her morals but her ability to look after *her* child?

'Believe me, I am having *your* baby, and I'm perfectly able to look after it by myself. I certainly didn't expect you to come charging over here like a knight on a white horse.'

'But now I am here to find out if it is really mine.'

Annie swallowed, forcing herself to stay calm. 'You have to make up your own mind whether you believe me or not—although I can't think why you imagine I'm lying to you. As far as I'm concerned, I've told you. What you do with the information is up to you.'

He looked at her with flat eyes.

'You told me it was safe for us to have sex. Why did you tell me that if it wasn't true?'

'I thought it was safe. I never dreamt I could fall pregnant,' Annie replied, trying to keep her voice even. 'Look, I don't care whether you believe me or not. I'm not asking anything from you, so you are hardly in a position to demand proof from me!'

Suddenly the tension left Raphael's face. He grinned, the lopsided smile reminding Annie once again of the man she had met back in Spain.

'Please forgive me. I didn't come to make you angry with me. I want to believe it is mine and as long as there is that chance, I'm staying. Right here. In Penhally Bay.'

'You're staying here?' Annie said incredulously. 'But what about your job back in Spain?'

Raphael shrugged. 'I managed to persuade them to give me a six-month sabbatical. And I have a post for that time in the hospital at St Piran.' He nodded in the vague direction of the hospital a good thirty minutes up the road.

'You have a job? At St. Piran's?' Annie was only too aware that she was repeating his words parrot fashion. But it was all such a shock. At the very most, she'd imagined her staying in touch with him by phone, at least until the baby was born. Then the odd visit. But it seemed she had totally underestimated the man.

'How on earth did you manage to get a job at the hospital so soon? I only phoned you last week.'

'I know many people,' he said. 'I have many connections through my work. In the end it was not too difficult.' He smiled, a flash of white against his bronzed skin. 'And I specialise in high-risk pregnancies. So they were happy to have me on their team.'

Annie sat down in the chair. He could stand if he liked, but she needed something more solid to support her legs, which seemed to have turned to rubber again. He specialised in high-risk pregnancies. That meant they'd be working together. Every day.

'I need to know everything is all right with the baby,' he continued. 'You must be in your second trimester by now. Have you had a scan? Is everything normal? Have you been taking folic acid?' He fired the questions at Annie as if he were an interrogating officer of a hostile army.

'Perhaps you'd like to know what size feet I have while you're at it,' Annie muttered under her breath. Whatever he said, these weren't the questions of a man who doubted that he was the father. Suddenly she relented. He was here now and he was entitled to know how her pregnancy was progressing.

'Please, Raphael, sit down,' Annie said quietly. She

couldn't think straight while he was prowling around her like a lion circling its prey. For once he did as she asked and sat down in her armchair, still eyeing her warily.

'Everything is normal, and, yes, I have had a scan.' She stood up, relieved to find that her legs could support her, crossed over to her bookshelf and pulled out the photograph of her scan. Silently she passed it over to him.

She watched as Raphael studied the photograph carefully. A kaleidoscope of emotions crossed his face ranging from awe to intense interest. Then he looked at her and it was if the shutters came down.

'Good,' he said flatly. 'Everything looks as it should. Is it a boy or a girl?'

Annie hid a smile. He seemed determined not to show her how affected he was, but pride—or was it possessiveness?—was written all over his face. Suddenly she felt uneasy.

'I don't know the sex,' she said. 'I want it to be a surprise. Look, Raphael, if you wanted to check up on how the pregnancy was going, you could have phoned me, come for a visit even, but from what you've told me, you're planning to stick around. For the next six months at least.'

'If it is my child,' he said, 'then it needs a father as well as a mother. I don't have to stay here, you can come back with me to Spain. It will be better. You can stop work, stay with my family.'

Annie shook her head, dismayed. 'You can't be serious.' She gave a small laugh. 'Why on earth would I want to do that? My life is here. My job, my friends, my family. My baby will be born here and live here. We don't need you to support us. Is that the reason you think I called? So you would come running with financial support?'

Annie was trying hard to keep her tone even. Just who did

he think he was to come barging back into her life? Hadn't she made her position perfectly clear?

Suddenly Raphael looked contrite. 'I am sorry,' he said. 'I came in here like a bull in a…how do you say? Field? Shop?'

'China shop,' Annie answered automatically.

'Whatever. Forgive me?' he said, the boyish grin back on his face. 'It is just that I too want this child very much. I have to be part of his life. Can understand?'

'Yes. Of course. It's just that I wasn't expecting you to come rushing over here, taking a job. Speaking of which, what happens after your job comes to an end?'

'Oh, I will not go back to Spain—not until I can take my child with me. Until then, I will stay here. It is settled.'

'You plan to live here? Permanently?' Annie said shocked. Whatever she had been expecting, it wasn't this.

Raphael crossed his arms across his chest and nodded emphatically. 'If I have to.'

'I suppose I can't stop you,' Annie said slowly. 'But I want to make one thing clear—this baby is my responsibility.'

'And mine.' His mouth was set in a determined line.

'I am happy to be on my own. I don't want any thing from you—least of all a relationship. Although I guess the fact that you never tried to contact me means that it was never an option as far as you were concerned, either.'

Raphael narrowed his eyes at her. 'We never made any promises, either of us. There were things…' He paused, shaking his head. 'It just couldn't be.'

He was right, of course. There hadn't been any promises on either side, but that hadn't stopped her hoping he would get in touch, even while she knew she had nothing to offer him.

'Where will you live?' Annie asked, dragging her thoughts back to the present.

'I have taken a room in a hotel near the hospital for the time being, but I will look for a place here in Penhally Bay. I want to keep an eye on you and the pregnancy.'

Annie's thoughts were all over the place. He was here and if that wasn't a big enough shock, he was planning to stay.

'I should tell you that I have consulted a lawyer, in Spain as well as in the UK. I'm going to ask for shared access. No one is going to stop me seeing my child.'

Annie looked at him, aghast. Her growing feeling of unease was spot on. He was here and determined to interfere with her life. It was one thing letting him know he was going to be a father, quite another him demanding legal access. Too late, the memory of the words he had spoken in Spain came rushing back. 'If she were my child,' he had said referring to Maria, 'nothing and no one would stop me claiming what belongs to me.' At the time his words had meant little but now they burnt into her brain, sending a frisson of fear down her spine. What on earth had she done? And what could she do about it now?

CHAPTER FOUR

ANNIE studied the CTG of the pregnant woman whose labour she was monitoring for the umpteenth time. Although the contractions were still several minutes apart, the baby's heartbeat kept slowing down. Over the last couple of hours it had returned to normal within a few seconds, but this time the baby's heart rate stayed slow. The baby was clearly in distress and Annie knew that the mother should be delivered right now. Making up her mind, she asked one of the staff midwives to page the on-call consultant and let them know they were needed straight away.

While she waited, Annie explained to her patient that it was likely she would need to have a C-section.

Audrey looked at her with frightened eyes. 'I really wanted a natural birth,' she said.

'I know you did,' Annie said softly. She had been involved with Audrey's pregnancy all the way through and had helped her put a birth plan together.

'But sometimes things don't turn out the way we'd hoped. This is the best for your baby. And that's what's important in the end, isn't it? We should be able to give you a spinal, so at least you'll be awake to welcome your child into the world.'

Audrey sought her husband's hand. 'Of course you're right. All that matters is that my baby is okay.' She grimaced as another contraction hit her. 'I trust you to decide what's right for us,' she told Annie once the wave of pain had passed.

During the contraction, Annie had been watching the baby's heartbeat on the monitor. As before, it slowed down, but this time it was almost three minutes before the heart rate returned to normal. Where was the obstetrician? She tried to remember who was on call for labour ward, but couldn't. There had been so many changes recently with people going on leave, it was hard to keep up

Just as she was about to ask Julie, her fellow midwife, to call the consultant again, Raphael strode into the room.

'Someone paged me,' he said, seemingly oblivious to the fact that Annie was in the room. Although she had known she'd bump into him sooner rather than later, she was unprepared for the way her heart started pounding in her chest.

'It was me, Dr Castillo,' Annie said, thankful her voice didn't betray the unsteady beating of her heart. 'Audrey's baby is having repeated prolonged decelerations. She's only 5 cms. I think we need to get her delivered straight away.' She handed the CTG printout to Raphael, who studied it for a few moments before nodding.

'You're absolutely right,' he said. 'We need to get Audrey to theatre straight away. Could someone let the anaesthetist know we need him to do a spinal? Come on, let's get going.' As everyone reacted to his words, he bent over Audrey. 'Try not to worry. We'll have your baby out and in your arms shortly.'

There wasn't time in the next few minutes for Annie to think about anything except her patient. Quickly she and Julie, with a few words of reassurance to Audrey and her husband, started wheeling the bed down to theatre. Minutes later, Annie was washing her hands next to Raphael while he scrubbed up.

'Excellent call,' he said approvingly. 'It's good that you didn't wait any longer before calling me.'

'I have been a midwife for several years, Dr Castillo.'

Raphael arched an eyebrow but said nothing. Annie followed him into theatre.

Annie stood back ready to receive Audrey's baby while Raphael, after checking with the anaesthetist that Audrey's lower body was suitably numb, cut into the abdomen and then into the uterus. They all waited with bated breath as he pulled out the baby. There was a second of complete stillness before a lusty cry of rage broke the silence. Everyone smiled. Raphael passed the baby across to Annie who promptly wrapped it in a blanket before checking that the airway was clear.

'You have a beautiful baby boy,' she said to Audrey, passing her the newborn to hold. 'And he's absolutely perfect.'

While Raphael was suturing the wound in Audrey's abdomen, Annie, a lump in her throat, watched as Audrey and her husband cooed over their son. No matter how many times she delivered a baby, it always got to her, but for the first time in as long as she could remember there was no stab of envy as she watched a mother with her baby. In a few months' time, she would be holding a child of her own.

Glancing up from the happy trio, she found Raphael's speculative eyes on hers and wondered if he was thinking the same thing.

'We'll get you up to recovery as soon as Dr Castillo has finished closing,' she told Audrey. 'I'm just going to weigh your son and then I'll give him right back to you. Then you can try giving him a feed.' As soon as she finished checking the baby over, she passed him back to Audrey, and helped her settle her son onto the breast. Happily the tiny infant got the hang of it straight away and was soon sucking contentedly. Annie felt her throat constrict. Damn the tears that were never far away these days. At least these were the right kind of tears.

As soon as she had settled mother and baby in the postnatal ward, she headed off to the staff room. She needed to find a place where she could be alone with her thoughts. How on earth was she going to cope over the next few months, seeing Raphael every day? Yesterday she had asked him to leave, promising that they would talk again, but what could she say to him? That she had never stopped thinking about him and the night they had shared together? That it had taken all her willpower not to call him and that seeing him again had made her greedy for more? That suddenly she wanted it all—a child, yes, but also someone who loved them…both. But she knew that wasn't going to happen. If that night had meant anything at all he would have found her before now, despite what they had told each other.

As she tried to concentrate on her paperwork she became aware of someone watching her. She looked up to find Raphael studying her with an odd expression in his eyes.

'Hola,' he said softly. 'Can I come in?'

'It's not really a good time. I have to finish this paperwork before my afternoon clinic.'

He ignored her and, frowning, stepped into the room. 'When, then?' he demanded. 'When would be a good time? Because you and I need to talk about this baby,' he said. A muscle twitched in his cheek. He wasn't quite as casual as he had first seemed.

'I'm not sure that there's anything left to talk about,' Annie said. Then she relented. It had been a shock seeing him again, but now he was here, and she would be working closely with him over the coming months, she could hardly ignore him.

'Look,' she said. 'Why don't you come over this evening? Around seven? We can talk then, okay?'

He crossed the room and leaned over the table, his brown eyes drilling into hers. Annie felt like a moth trapped in a light and it was all she could do to stop herself from leaping up and moving away. Somehow she found the resolve to return his look steadily. He searched her face for a moment.

'Okay,' he said. 'Until tonight.' And, turning on his heel, he was gone.

As soon as Annie got home, she rushed around tidying up before jumping in the shower. As she soaped her body, she felt the small burgeoning lump of her pregnancy under her fingers and smiled. Then, as she let the hot water ease away the tiredness, her thoughts focused on Raphael. How would she cope, seeing him every day? Especially when the rapid beating of her heart every time she looked at him told her that the connection she had felt with him in Spain was still there. It hadn't just been the Mediterranean sun after all, though she had always known it had been much more than that.

Finishing her shower, she went to slip on a pair of jeans, but to her dismay, and secret delight, she couldn't do up the button. It was time to go shopping for some maternity clothes. She hadn't allowed herself to think that far ahead until now. A little suspicious side of her was afraid of tempting fate. She discarded the too-tight jeans in favour of a simple dress. Then she brushed her long dark hair until it shone, before adding a touch of eye shadow and lipstick. She refused to ask herself why she was taking so much time with her appearance.

The late spring evening was unseasonably warm, so she opened the window and the smell of her climbing roses floated in on the breeze. Should she offer him a meal? she wondered. What was the polite way to behave when meeting the father of your child after a one-night stand? Once again, she felt her face grow warm at the memory. She thought about phoning Fiona to tell her Raphael had turned up, and asking her for advice, but before she had the chance, there was a knock on her door. She felt a tingle of apprehension dance up her spine as she opened the door.

Raphael stood in the doorway, holding a bunch of tulips. She couldn't read the expression on his face, and before she could say anything, he handed her the flowers.

'Thank you,' she said simply, burying her nose in their fragrance. 'They're lovely.' She stood aside to let him enter. Once again she was dismayed at the way her heart was thumping.

'I thought we could go for a walk,' Annie said, feeling the need for neutral territory. 'I could show you Penhally Bay.'

'I would like that.'

Annie draped a sweater over her shoulders and soon they were following the road down to the harbour.

'How are your family?' she asked. 'And little Maria? I have thought of her often.'

'They are all well. Maria asks after the British woman with the sad green eyes often.' He stopped and turned towards her. 'But you don't look so sad to me any more.' He traced a finger down the line of her jaw. 'You look happy.'

'I am. Very happy.'

They continued following the road until they came to the lighthouse. They stood looking across the harbour to the sea beyond.

'It's hard to believe right now, when everything is so calm, but there was a bad storm here,' Annie said. 'It caused a lot of damage and there are still a lot of repairs being carried out to some of the buildings. A couple of people lost their lives. It's a small community and everybody feels it when something so awful happens.'

'It must have been hard on everyone. It is like this where my mother lives in Spain. Everybody knows and helps each other. It is a good way to live.'

'It's quiet now,' Annie continued. 'But you wouldn't believe how busy it gets in the summer months. I love it here.'

'In my country, we are always outdoors.' Raphael stopped and looked at her intently. 'It is a good country for a child to live. They can be outside playing instead of inside playing computer games, like so many of the children in this country.'

It seemed their walk was just another opportunity for Raphael to try and convince her to come and live in Spain, she thought, unable to prevent a stab of disappointment. Couldn't he see it was out of the question?

'Children here in Penhally Bay have a good life too,' she said. 'Many of them surf or sail, and there's always the beach for the younger ones. I loved it here when I was a child. It is a good place, a safe place for children. The community looks out for each other. Admittedly it attracts thousands of tourists in the summer, but that is a good thing too. It means that there is plenty going on for teenagers as well as adults. We have a very low crime rate here.'

'It is beautiful,' Raphael admitted, his eyes sweeping the bay. 'Almost as beautiful as where I live. But the weather.' He spread his hands. 'It is cold. And the rain. In Spain, there is always family around. The children spend time with their grandparents and aunts and uncles as well as cousins. Like you say, there are always people to watch out.'

They carried on walking, falling into step alongside each other. 'What about your family?' he asked. 'Don't you mind being far away from them?'

'I go to see my parents and my sister often and sometimes they come here. I'd always planned go to Australia to see my brother and his family, but I guess I'll have to shelve that plan for a while.' She smiled, thinking of the reason a visit to Australia would be out of the question for some time. 'We lived in Penhally Bay until I was about seven, when we moved to Edinburgh, so it always felt like a second home.'

'Why did you come back? Did you not like Edinburgh?'

'I'm not really a city girl. I love being able to open my front door and let the sea air in. I love the way everyone knows everyone else here—even if it does mean people know more about your business than you'd like.'

She slid a glance at him, wondering if he realised that the pair of them were bound to become a source of gossip. Not that it would be malicious, but people were bound to speculate eventually about the pregnant midwife and the Spanish doctor.

'So, they will talk about us,' Raphael said, shrugging his shoulders. 'It is of no importance. I am not ashamed.'

'Look, Raphael, can we talk about why you're here?' Annie was panting slightly as she spoke. Raphael placed a hand on her arm, indicating a bench with a tip of his dark head and leading her towards it.

They sat in silence for a few minutes, watching the surfers out at sea. The waves were a decent size and a number of people were making the most of it.

'You told me you've spoken to the lawyers about access. You didn't need to do that. I wouldn't stop you from seeing your child, not as long as you came to see him when you were supposed to. The only thing I don't want is a father who flits in and out of my child's life. A father who can't be depended on. I would much rather you have no involvement than that. But it scares me that you are consulting lawyers. I don't really understand why you seem to feel the need. I would have done anything to have a child. The last thing I would do is to take it away from you.'

Raphael brought his eyebrows together. 'Is that what happened, Annie? You wanted a child and you used me to have one?'

'It wasn't like that!' Annie insisted. 'You don't understand…'

He turned cool brown eyes on her. 'What is there to understand? You have what you want,' he said. 'Now I will have what is mine.'

Annie shivered. There was no mistaking the determination in the set of his mouth.

'In which case,' she replied, 'if that is what you think of me, I don't think there is anything left to say.'

She stood, leaving him sitting there staring out to sea.

At the top of the page, partially visible (ghosted) text bleeding through from another page:

CHAPTER FIVE

OVER the next week Annie kept bumping into Raphael but apart from his pointed enquiries into how she was feeling, their contact was limited to clinical discussions. When she saw him with his patients she was struck by his easygoing manner and they all seemed to love the way he managed to achieve the right balance between casual joking and interested concern. However, when he looked at her, his expression turned cool.

And it wasn't just the patients. He was causing quite a stir among the other female members of staff too. Annie was constantly overhearing conversations speculating about whether Dr Castillo was involved with anyone. Thankfully no one guessed that Annie and Raphael had met before, let alone that she was carrying his baby.

Annie was looking forward to a couple of days off over the weekend. She loved her job, but she hadn't been sleeping well the last few nights. Not since Raphael had turned up, in fact, and she was longing for an early night in bed with a good book.

She only had one more patient to see before she called it a day. Morgan was an anxious-looking woman who had come for her first antenatal appointment. She had taken a home pregnancy test and estimated she was about eight weeks pregnant.

'We'll just do another one here,' Annie said. 'If that's okay with you?'

'Is that necessary? I mean, there's no doubt I'm pregnant. The test was positive and my breasts are tender and I've even developed a bump already.' She dropped her hand to her stomach, a dreamy smile on her face. But there was something that was sending alarm bells ringing for Annie. She couldn't quite put her finger on it, but she knew she'd be happier when she repeated the test herself.

When she looked at the stick, she knew that her instincts had been correct. The test was negative. Not even the faintest blue line. Her heart sank. She hated days like these when she had to be the bearer of bad news. If Morgan had been pregnant, she wasn't any longer. Just to make absolutely sure, Annie decided to ask Raphael to come and see her.

Morgan must have seen the look on her face when she came back into the room. Her face puckered.

'I am so sorry,' Annie said gently. 'But the test is negative.' She could feel every word pierce the woman like an arrow.

'But I have to be! I've wanted this for so long. And I have all the symptoms. Your test must be wrong.'

'I don't think it is, but just in case, I'm going to ask Dr Castillo to scan you. He has the most experience of scanning women in early pregnancy.'

Morgan started to cry and Annie's heart went out to her. She paged Raphael, hoping that he hadn't left for the day. She was relieved when he answered, and when she told him about her concerns he said that he would come immediately.

Annie had only enough time to prepare her patient for the scan when Raphael arrived. As usual he looked breathtakingly handsome, but Annie, still reeling from his revelation about consulting a lawyer, told herself that she couldn't care less how he looked. Any man who suggested that she had used him to get pregnant and in the same breath threatened to take her child from her wasn't a man she wanted anything to do with. How she could have fooled herself into thinking that they were some kind of kindred spirits was beyond her. And if he made her heart tumble every time she saw him, that was just physical attraction and she would get over it.

Annie brought him up to speed and Raphael took Morgan by the hand and looked into her eyes.

'I am just going to have a look at your uterus,' he said softly. 'If there is a baby in there, I will find it. Have you had any bleeding?' Morgan shook her head silently.

Raphael waited while Annie squirted some ultrasound gel on Morgan's belly. Then he glided the probe over her tummy while watching the monitor intently. Finally he shook his head.

'I'm sorry, but there is no baby there. In fact, there is no evidence you have been pregnant recently.'

'But I am,' Morgan wailed. 'Please look again. It must be there. I swear I even felt it move yesterday.'

Raphael and Annie shared a look across the top of Morgan's head. Annie was bewildered. What was going on here?

Raphael took Annie outside while their patient got dressed again.

'I think she has a ghost pregnancy,' he said.

'You mean a phantom pregnancy?' Annie was astonished. She had never come across one of those before, although she had read about them. Apparently it could happen when women so desperately wanted to be pregnant they managed to convince themselves that they were.

Raphael nodded. 'She must want a child very much.'

Annie could understand Morgan's feelings and her heart ached for her. She knew what it was like to yearn for a baby, to feel that something was missing from life. Although she had never imagined herself to be pregnant, she would have done anything to have a child.

Annie almost smiled at the irony of it. Robert hadn't loved her enough to want to adopt a child with her and now here was a man who was determined to be a father to her child, and she wasn't sure she wanted him around.

'I need to talk to Morgan,' she said.

'Would you prefer me to?' Raphael asked.

'No, she's my patient. It's my job,' Annie said heavily. 'But I wish I were about to tell her something different.'

Annie saw a distraught but resigned Morgan out a little later, and after finishing her paperwork for the day left for home herself. She was surprised to find Raphael waiting by the hospital exit. She nodded a goodnight in his direction, but he caught up with her and walked beside her.

'Are you okay?' he asked, searching her face. 'That must have been difficult for you.'

'I'm fine. It's all part of the job after all, isn't it? Most of the time our work has a happy outcome, but sometimes…' She shrugged. 'Things don't work out the way we want.'

'But it upset you. You tried not to show it, but I could see it on your face.'

There it was again. This man's uncanny ability to perceive every emotion she felt. Even when she did her best to hide her feelings. Everyone thought nothing ruffled her, that she was able to keep herself emotionally detached, and she let them think that. Not least because it was the opposite of the truth. Her colleagues would be dismayed if they knew just how keenly she felt her patients' pain.

Perhaps it was because she understood their longing for a child only too well.

'Yes, it did upset me. But I'll put it behind me. And move on.'

'Can you? Can you really put your feelings aside? Just like that?' He placed his hands on her shoulders, stopping her in her tracks before turning her around and looking into her eyes. She felt a dizzying sense of being caught up in his aura like a leaf in the wind. The rest of the world seemed to recede until it was just the two of them, in a bubble of their own. 'I need to know that you are okay,' he said roughly, breaking the spell and bringing her back to reality.

For a second Annie thought he was talking about her, but as his eyes dropped to her stomach she realised he was talking about her baby. Of course. Well, he had never pretended he was interested in her. As far as he was concerned, she was just a walking incubator for his child. She felt a flash of temper.

She sighed. 'Don't worry, Raphael. *I'm* still pregnant. And I will let you know if there is a problem.' However, seeing the look on his face, she took pity on him. It must be difficult to be a man sometimes. To feel excluded. But that wasn't her concern. He would just have to deal with it.

'The baby's fine, honestly,' she said. Then she couldn't help herself. 'I think I might have felt it move yesterday for the first time.'

His eyes glowed and he dropped a hand to her stomach. He left it there for a second. Once again Annie felt electrifying shocks shoot through her body and her knees turned to jelly.

She stepped away from him as if she'd been stung. 'Hey, you'd have to stand there for a long time if you're waiting to feel it move.' She looked around the car park. Although it was almost empty, there was always a chance somebody would see them and what they'd make of Dr Castillo with his hand on her belly was anyone's guess. One thing was for sure, though, she wasn't ready for anyone to know that he was the father of her child. Not yet, at any rate.

'You haven't told anyone, have you?' she said, suddenly horrified at the possibility that the identity of the father of her child was no longer a secret.

'No, just my mother. She is delighted that she is going to be a grandmother again. She remembers you well, the way you were with Maria, and thinks you will make a very good mother. She is looking forward to meeting her grandchild in a few months' time.'

Annie decided to let that pass. At least for the time being. She had no intention of letting her baby out of her sight and certainly not to Spain. Not without her at any rate. She had heard too many scary stories about kidnapped children and the way Raphael was about this baby, she'd put nothing past him.

She started back to her car. She didn't want to be rude but all she wanted to do was get home and gather her thoughts.

'Do you need a lift?' Annie asked. 'Or have you sorted yourself out with a car as well as a job?' She hadn't meant it to come out quite so waspishly, but the way this man was organising his life around her baby was unsettling her.

'Yes.' He waved in the direction of a sleek silver sports car. 'I drove it from Spain. And I have found a house in the village to live in, just ten minutes from your home.' He quirked an eyebrow at her, as if gauging her reaction to his news.

'So you're definitely staying, then?'

He looked surprised. '*Sí.* I told you I was. I accepted this job at the hospital. I cannot leave now, even if I wanted to.'

He took a step towards Annie. 'You have to accept it. I am not going anywhere without my child.'

The next day was Saturday and Annie had been invited to a barbecue at Lucy and Ben's home. She didn't know Lucy, who was one of the doctors at the surgery and Nick's daughter, and who had gone on maternity leave before Annie had started at St Piran's, but she knew Ben, who was an A and E consultant at the hospital. She hadn't wanted to go, not sure she was ready to field questions about her own pregnancy, but Kate had pressed her.

'You should get to know more people in Penhally, Annie. I know your friends and family are far away, and once you have the baby, you'll appreciate knowing more of the mothers. It's helpful to have someone to compare notes with.'

Annie waited until she knew the barbecue would be almost over. Sure enough, by the time she arrived, the guests with young children were already beginning to leave, although there was still loads of food. Tables had been laid out on the lawn, which overlooked the sea, and the scent of grilling sausages filled the air.

There were a few familiar faces as well as some that she didn't recognize, but there was one in particular that made her heart thump. She hadn't expected to see Raphael there.

As she greeted the other guests she watched Raphael from the corner of her eye. He looked completely at ease, as if he'd known everyone for years. It seemed as if he felt her eyes on him, because he turned and stared directly at her. Annie felt her breath catch in her throat. He really was the most beautiful man she had ever met, with his Latin colouring emphasised by his crisp white T-shirt and the faded jeans that clung to the contours of his thighs. Once again the memory of the night they had shared came rushing back. She remembered only too well the touch of his hands and mouth on her body, the way he had made her feel as if she were the only woman in the world, and the most beautiful woman he had ever held in his arms. And the intensity in his deep brown eyes told her he was remembering too. She felt a heat low in her body and she almost groaned aloud. Why did he have to come back into her life right now, when she thought she had everything all planned out?

Kate must have noticed her hovering on the fringe of the party. The older midwife came over and touched her briefly on the arm. 'Are you okay, Annie? You look as if you've seen a ghost. Do you want a drink of water or something?'

'No, I'm fine,' Annie said, summoning a smile, rubbing her lower back. A niggling ache had started that morning. She had put it down to the added weight of the baby putting a strain on her lower muscles, but an underlying anxiety that something was wrong wouldn't go away. For a split second she wondered whether to ask Kate's advice, but immediately dismissed the idea. She was probably just being over-anxious. Besides, she didn't want to draw attention to herself or ruin her friend's day off.

'I just feel a bit tired. You know how we are always telling our pregnant patients that it's normal to feel exhausted? It's quite different to experience it yourself.'

'You don't have to stay long,' Kate said. 'Lucy and Ben will understand.'

'Thanks, Kate. I'll probably just say hello to everyone, then make my excuses. But I'm dying to see little Josh again.'

She picked up an orange juice from a table and sipped the drink, happy to have something to distract her from Raphael. She glanced around.

Ben and Lucy were showing off their latest arrival, baby Josh, to a group of admirers. Apart from Chloe and her husband Oliver, a GP at Penhally Bay Surgery, there was Nick Tremayne with a blonde woman Annie hadn't seen before. Dragan Lovak, another of the partners, was there too, with his stunning wife, the village vet. Their young son sat at their feet, playing.

Annie went over to join them. It was the first time that she had been able to see a baby without feeling a wash of regret and she was happy to join in the crowd fussing over the cheerful, plump baby. Nevertheless, as she watched Oliver stand with his wife wrapped in the circle of his arms, she felt a sharp stab that she and her baby would never be part of a loving unit. She moved away, wanting to be alone with her thoughts.

How would it be to have Raphael around—a permanent part of her child's life, if not hers?

As if he could read her mind, Raphael excused himself from whatever conversation he'd been having with Ben and came towards her. For a moment she wanted to run away. Her heart was pattering away inside her chest and she was finding it difficult to breathe. Her symptoms only increased as he came to stand beside her.

'Dr Castillo,' Annie greeted him formally, aware of Kate's speculative gaze. 'I didn't expect to see you here.'

'Dr Carter—Ben—asked me. We met at the hospital. He thought it would be good for me to meet some of the locals. He knows I am far from home.'

'Everyone is very welcoming here. It's a small community.' Annie let her eyes sweep the garden. Usually she avoided gatherings such as this one. Everyone always brought their children, and until now she had avoided occasions where she would see loving couples proudly showing off their offspring. But now everything was different. For the first time she could admire the babies without the tiniest bit of envy.

'Are you all right? You look pale,' Raphael asked, his eyes dropping to her belly. Once again Annie was reminded that, as far as he was concerned, she was little more than a human incubator for his unborn child. She felt a crippling stab of disappointment. But what else did she expect?

He was watching her, his brown eyes glinting, and she shivered. She wondered if he knew how much he affected her. He wasn't to know that the night they had spent together had been the most exhilarating night of her life, one she knew she would treasure for ever. He wasn't to know that she had been unable to get him out of her mind ever since. Thank God.

'I'm okay,' she said. 'If a little tired. I don't plan on staying long.'

Again there was a sharp look from eyes the colour of the mountains in the evening. His eyes raked her body.

He bent over and whispered in her ear. She could smell the tang of his aftershave and feel the heat of his breath on her neck. It took all her willpower not to shiver with delight. 'Pregnancy suits you,' he said softly. 'You are all curves and your face…' He hesitated as if searching for the right words. 'Your face is glowing. You don't look tired. You look beautiful.'

This time Annie couldn't prevent the blood staining her cheeks. There was something intimate in the way he spoke to her that made her feel as if they were the only two people in the world. 'If you want to leave,' he said, 'I will walk you home.'

'We don't want people to talk,' Annie managed through a dust-dry mouth. He had walked her home that night in Spain and look where that had led! Was he suggesting that they pick up where they had left off? Was he *flirting* with her? No, the idea was ridiculous.

Raphael looked around in surprise at the people gathered in the room. 'But they will have to know some time. Do you think you can keep us a secret for ever?'

'There is no "us",' she reminded him coolly.

'But there is. You, me and our child. I will be proud to be known as the father. And I am certain you are proud to be pregnant.'

'Of course I am, and everyone at the hospital knows about the baby already—I'm booked in at St Piran's after all. Kate, Chloe and Nick all know obviously, Kate's my midwife as well as my friend and Nick is my GP. But as for them knowing who the father is? Can't we keep that under wraps for the time being? Please?'

Raphael frowned. Then he smiled gently. 'If you wish. For the *time being*.' He echoed her words. 'It will give us a chance to get to know each other properly. Now, would you let me walk you home? It will give us the chance to talk.'

Suddenly Annie wanted nothing more than the comfort of her own house. Her mind was whirling, whether from Raphael's proximity or the promise in his words she couldn't be sure. As he had pointed out they did need to get to know each other—so that they could reach some sort of arrangement for their child. And she was curious to know more about this enigmatic man. For her baby's sake, of course.

'I just need to visit the bathroom first,' she said, trying to sound casual.

Since they'd been talking the dull ache she'd been experiencing earlier had grown in intensity. Her heart thudding, she told Raphael that she wouldn't be a minute, and hurried away.

When she made it to the toilet she was distraught to

discover that she had begun to bleed. Not huge amounts admittedly, but enough to scare her witless. Was she having a miscarriage? She slid down onto the bathroom floor and hugged her knees to her chest, gasping as a wave of terror and shock raked her body. She *couldn't* lose this baby. Not now. Not when the dream she had longed for, had thought was out of her reach, had finally come true. But hadn't she, deep in her soul, known that it was too good to be true? That somehow it wasn't in her destiny to be a mother?

She didn't know how long she had sat there when she heard a soft tap at the door.

'Annie, are you all right?' Raphael's deep tones penetrated the fog of grief and fear. She scrambled to her feet. He would know what to do. He would help her.

She opened the door and Raphael took one look at her face before gathering her into his arms.

'What is it? What is wrong?' he demanded. He held her at arm's length, forcing her to look at him. 'Is it the baby?'

Annie nodded, unable to speak. His face paled and she saw her anguish reflected in his eyes.

'What is happening?' he coaxed gently. 'Tell me exactly.'

Annie drew strength from him. 'I'm bleeding,' she said simply, and then in a rush the tears came and she was crying in his arms. 'My baby,' she gulped between the sobs that racked her body. 'I can't lose my baby.'

Raphael scooped her into his arms and carried her, still sobbing into his chest, past the startled glances of the other guests. Everyone stopped speaking for a moment and then Annie and Raphael were surrounded. But it was Kate who spoke first.

'What's wrong?' she asked quietly.

'She's bleeding. I am going to take her to St Piran's.' Even in her distress, Annie could hear he was having difficulty keeping his voice even.

'I'll come with you,' Kate said. 'I'll drive while you take care of Annie.'

'I'll come too.' Annie recognized Chloe's anxious voice.

'We can manage, Chloe,' Kate said gently. 'Hopefully it's nothing serious. I'll call you later.'

And then Annie felt herself being lifted into the back of the car. Raphael covered her with his jacket before getting in beside her. He pulled her into his arms and stroked her head while her sobs turned to hiccups. Kate started the car and with a squeal of tyres headed towards St Piran's. They were the most dreadful minutes of Annie's life, but she was glad that Raphael was with her. He, more than anyone, would know what she was going through.

At the hospital, Raphael insisted on carrying her up to the maternity wing, Kate having to run alongside to keep up with him. Annie knew that come tomorrow, when all this was over, she would be mortified at all the attention. But right now she didn't care. If anyone could help her it was Raphael, and she trusted his medical skills absolutely.

He set her down on a couch in one of the examination rooms, calling for the ultrasound scanner in a voice that suggested that, if it wasn't brought to him this instant, there would be hell to pay. Fear closed Annie's throat and numbed her lips, but she answered Kate's questions as best she could. No, she hadn't bled before. She'd only had mild cramps tonight. Nothing until tonight. She had even felt the baby move earlier, but couldn't feel anything now.

Raphael, his eyes tight with concentration, was spreading cool gel on Annie's tummy. In any other circumstances she might have felt awkward as his hands lifted her dress, revealing her lacy underwear, but right now all she could think about was her baby.

Kate held her hand as Raphael scanned her abdomen, his attention fixed on the monitor. Suddenly his face creased into a smile and Annie felt the first small tug of hope since she had been to the bathroom.

'I can see the heartbeat,' Raphael said, relief in his voice. 'Look, Annie, there.' He turned the screen towards her and even through her swollen eyelids she could see the fluttering of a heartbeat. Her heart soared. She was still pregnant. For the time being, at any rate. She shook the thought away. She had to stay positive, for the baby's sake. There was no way she was going to give up on this baby, not until all hope was gone. And right now the baby was still there, inside her, needing her to be strong. She counted four limbs on the 3D image. Tiny legs folded and was it…? Yes, it was sucking its thumb. She felt a fresh wave of tears prick her eyes. But this time it was with relief and a wash of love. That was her baby, safe inside her womb.

It seemed as if Raphael was experiencing the same sea of emotions as he too stared at the tiny image. He muttered something in Spanish in a voice filled with awe. Kate was also smiling.

Through her relief, Annie was aware of Dr Gibson, her obstetrician, coming in to the room.

'The midwives told me our miracle mum was in,' she said. 'So I thought I'd pop in to see how you were.' She looked at Raphael, curiosity evident in her bright blue eyes. 'Although I can see Dr Castillo is already here.' She squinted at the monitor and nodded, looking satisfied.

'Baby looks fine, although I'm sure Dr Castillo has already told you that.'

'We should keep you in under observation, Annie. Just to be on the safe side,' Kate said.

'Will it make any difference if I stay?'

She saw Kate and Raphael exchange a look.

'No,' Raphael said gently. 'If you are going to miscarry, it will happen anyway.'

'Then I want to go home,' Annie said softly but firmly.

'I think you should stay,' Raphael responded. 'I will stay with you.'

Once again, Annie was aware of Dr Gibson's puzzled eyes on Raphael, before the older doctor looked at her.

'I know how much this pregnancy means to you, Annie. Particularly when you thought it could never happen. I don't think a night in hospital would do you any harm.' Dr Gibson turned to Raphael. 'I'm sure you'll be aware that Annie was thought to have ovarian failure.'

Raphael drew his brows together and Annie watched as realisation dawned that she had been telling him the truth. Emotions chased across his face. Delight followed by—could it be shame? Despite herself, she enjoyed watching him squirm.

Annie struggled into a sitting position and Kate came forward to help her.

'Look,' she said. 'We all know that it will make no difference whatsoever to the outcome if I stay in hospital. This pregnancy will either continue or...' Her voice broke. 'It won't. Staying here isn't going to change anything as you have just admitted. Am I right, Dr Gibson?'

'Yes. Bed rest won't make a difference. But you know that your medical history means you have to be extra-careful. So no vigorous exercise—and that includes penetrative sex. Just to be on the safe side.'

This time it was Annie's turn to squirm and she felt her face burn. Before she could help herself she slid a glance in Raphael's direction. Out of sight of Dr Gibson and Kate, he raised an eyebrow in her direction, a small smile tugging at the corner of his mouth. Her embarrassment deepened. Had the man no shame?

'I can't stay in hospital for the rest of my pregnancy,' Annie said, swinging her legs over the side of the bed. 'If I thought it would make the slightest difference, I would be happy to remain flat on my back and not move a muscle for the next few weeks or so. But it won't. So I'm going home where I feel more comfortable.'

'Okay, Annie,' Dr Gibson said, as her pager bleeped. 'You can go home if you wish, but remember what I said about taking it easy. I need to answer this, but come and see me at my clinic in about a week.'

'I'll stay at your house with you,' Kate offered after Dr Gibson had left the room. 'That way, you won't be alone if anything happens. We hope it won't, but we can't be sure. I can ask Rob if Jem could stay over at his house.'

But Raphael interrupted. 'No, I will. It is my responsibility.'

Kate narrowed her eyes and looked from Annie to Raphael. Annie could tell from the slow realisation dawning in her eyes that she was putting two and two together. What she made of Raphael being here in Penhally Bay was anyone's guess. But Annie knew that whatever her thoughts she would keep them to herself, and she was grateful for the older midwife's well-known discretion.

'I can stay on my own,' Annie protested. 'I have my phone. Kate only lives a short distance away. If I need her she can be with me in minutes.'

Irrationally Annie felt that if she stayed in the hospital, it would only make matters worse. At home she could pretend that everything was as it had been when she'd left the house earlier in the day.

'Either I stay with you at home, or you will stay here.' From the tone of Raphael's voice, Annie realised she wasn't going to win the battle. She didn't really have the strength for it. All she wanted now was to go home and climb into her own bed and sleep, comforted with the knowledge that her baby was okay.

'All right,' she agreed reluctantly. She would agree to anything as long as it got her out of the hospital. But she couldn't prevent a flicker of relief and happiness that Raphael would be coming home with her. If only for a night she could pretend it was for all the right reasons.

Kate dropped Annie and Raphael off at Annie's place with a final entreaty to Annie to call her any time, no matter what the hour, if she needed to. Once again, Raphael insisted on carrying her as if she was too fragile to stand on her own two feet, but for once she let him take care of her. She had looked after herself for so long, it felt strange but not unpleasant giving herself, even temporarily, into the care of someone else. In his arms she could believe that everything would turn out all right.

He laid her gently on her bed and insisted on removing her tights and her dress as if she were helpless. She felt every touch of his fingers burn into her skin. Then when she was left wearing only her bra and panties he looked down at her and she could hear his breath catch in his throat. But he shook his head and, muttering something in Spanish that sounded like a curse, he held the duvet up so she could crawl into bed. He surprised her even more by lying next to her, on top of the quilt, and pulling her into his arms so that her back rested against his chest. His hands were on her hair, soothing her, and she let herself drift away, secure in the knowledge that he was there if she needed him.

Raphael stroked Annie's dark brown hair, feeling the weight of it under his fingertips. He inhaled her perfume as her breathing deepened and became regular. He stole a glance at her sleeping face, the pale skin and tiny creases of worry at the corners of her eyes. He wondered if she had any idea how vulnerable she appeared despite that tough independent exterior. He was surprised by a rush of protectiveness she aroused in him. When he had come across her in the bathroom, one look at her had told him that she was almost destroyed at the thought of losing her baby. And he had been surprised at his own feelings, too. He wanted this baby, but the gut-wrenching sorrow he had felt when he had thought she had lost it had shaken him.

And then the realisation, back at the hospital, that she had been honest with him all along. He had misjudged her and felt acutely ashamed. Just because Ruth had lied to him, it didn't mean Annie was the same. He should have known she was telling the truth when she had been so adamant that she didn't want or need him in her life. He could only imagine what his reaction must have done to her. It would have taken courage to phone him, and then for him to doubt that the baby she was carrying was his. After everything she had gone through. Any other woman would have lashed out, but not Annie. She had done what she thought was right—for the baby.

There was no longer the slightest shred of doubt in his mind. She was carrying his baby. His child. And he hadn't been mistaken about Annie. She was the woman he had thought she was back in Spain. She had told him about the baby because she thought he had a right to know—not because she wanted anything from him. But was she as strong as she liked to make out? Somehow he doubted it. And as long as she was carrying his baby, he would stay and watch over them both—whatever she said.

CHAPTER SIX

WHEN Annie opened her eyes the next morning it was to the delicious aroma of fresh coffee. She stretched luxuriously beneath the sheets, unable to think at first who could be moving around in her cottage. But then the previous night's events came flooding back. She dropped her hands tentatively to her tummy, feeling the reassuring swell of her pregnancy, and then a tiny movement made her gasp. Her baby was still there, alive and kicking. She smiled to herself, feeling a bubble of happiness. One day at a time. She'd take one day at a time, just as she'd told so many of her patients.

Raphael appeared at the doorway, a tray balanced in his hands. Despite his rumpled appearance, Annie felt her breath catch in her throat. How could any man be so damned handsome? It just wasn't fair. As he walked towards her, she pulled the bedclothes up to her chin, suddenly self-conscious under his searching eyes. It was a bit late in the day, she thought ruefully, to be trying to hang onto her modesty. After all, this man had explored every inch of her already with his lips as well as his hands. She bit back a moan as a delicious heat flooded her body. She had to stop thinking about him in that way. No good could come of it. He was here because of his child. No other reason. And she'd do well to remember that.

'*Buenas días,*' he said evenly, but he couldn't quite hide the anxiety that darkened his eyes. If Annie had ever wondered how much he wanted this baby, any remaining doubts had disappeared when she'd sensed his anguish when he'd shared her fear that she might lose it. He propped the tray on her lap as she sat up.

'Morning,' she responded awkwardly. Then she added, 'I felt the baby kick just now.'

Knowing he would want to feel the reassuring movement as much as she did, she set the tray aside and took his hand, guiding it to her belly. As she felt his warm hand on her bare skin she felt goose-bumps prick her skin. Just then the baby moved and Annie was touched to see a look of relief and joy in his eyes. They smiled at each other and it was as if the air between them was alive. As if a cord bound them together. Or was it just their shared hope?

'My baby,' he said softly, before lowering his head and kissing her ever so gently on her small bump. Once more jolts of pleasure shot through her body. How was she going to cope having him around for the duration of her pregnancy if her body reacted like some wanton harpy every time he touched her?

As soon as he raised his head, she scrambled for the duvet again, snuggling under the protective folds. Not knowing what else to do to break the atmosphere that fizzled and sparked between them, she picked up her tray and almost laughed out loud. The coffee was fine, he had managed that, and the single rose clearly picked from outside her front door was a sweet touch, but the toast looked as if it had been dropped in water then wrung out and placed on her plate. What was he trying to do? Poison her?

He must have seen her look of incredulity as he looked hurt for a moment. '*Lo siento*—I am sorry about the toast,' he said. 'I didn't know what to do with it. I never eat my bread like that.'

'It's fine,' Annie said. 'I'm not particularly hungry, anyway. You needn't have bothered. I'm sure you'd rather be at home.'

'I am staying with you,' he said. 'I will go and change my clothes and then go to the shop and get us some proper breakfast. You stay where you are until I get back. Kate phoned to say she is coming to check on you, so she will be here with you while I am away.'

For a moment Annie was tempted to tell him to stop treating her as if she was a child, in fact, would everyone stop treating her like a child, but bit back the words. Right now she didn't have the energy nor the willpower to argue. As soon as he was gone she'd shower and dress. He would soon see that she wasn't the type of woman who he could order about. He might be used to getting his own way in Spain and at the hospital, but this was her house and she would do as she pleased.

'I didn't hear the phone,' she said.

'It has been ringing constantly, but I unplugged the extension in here so it wouldn't disturb you. So many people want to know that you are okay. So many people care about you.'

Annie sank back in the pillows. He was right, she knew that. But what about him? Did he care for her at all? And as for all these people who had phoned. What on earth had they thought when Raphael had answered? Hopefully, no more than one colleague looking out for another. Nevertheless,

Annie knew that the jungle drums of Penhally Bay would be beating furiously. It was really only a matter of time before everyone guessed that Raphael was the father of her child. But she no longer cared who knew. The only thing that really mattered was the health of her baby.

Before she could ask him who exactly had phoned, there was a knock at the front door and she heard Kate's voice calling out. Raphael looked down at her, his eyes darkening. For a moment she imagined he looked reluctant to leave her. He leaned over towards her, and her breath caught in her throat. Was he going to kiss her? Her lips parted involuntarily but instead he brushed his fingertips against her cheek.

'I will see you soon,' he said, and headed for the door.

She could hear him and Kate talking in low voices, followed by the bang of the door. Moments later her friend popped her head around the door.

'Okay if I come in?' she asked.

'I don't seem to be able to stop anyone,' Annie grumbled before immediately feeling contrite. 'I'm sorry, Kate, please ignore me. I'm just feeling a little rattled, that's all. I can't help but feel that if everyone fusses around me, there must be something wrong.'

'Raphael said he felt the baby move. That's a good sign.'

'I know.' Annie sighed. 'But I can't help but worry.'

Kate's eyes were warm with sympathy. 'We're all going to do everything we can to get you through this,' she said gently. 'Everyone's rooting for you. I had to forbid them all from coming down here to see you in person. Although I suspect you'll want to see Chloe later?'

'Does she know? About Raphael?' Annie asked, easing herself out of bed and slipping her dressing gown on.

'I think most people, Chloe included, will have guessed

who the father is,' Kate said. 'None of them are so stupid that
they can't put your holiday in Spain together with the sudden
arrival of Dr Castillo. According to Ben, Raphael used all his
connections to get the job at St Piran's so he could be near
you.' Kate smiled at Annie. 'Besides, people would have had
to have been blind not to see how torn up he was last night.
Most obstetricians don't go carrying patients around in their
arms, even if they are the most caring of doctors.'

'He certainly cares about the baby,' Annie said softly. 'I've
got the feeling he's going to be my personal physician for the
rest of my pregnancy.'

'Would that be so bad?' Kate said. 'God knows, we can
all do with support sometimes, no matter how strong we like
to think we are inside.'

Annie thought Kate looked sad for a moment, but before
she could say anything the smile was back.

'By the way, he said that your sister had phoned. Fiona,
isn't it? He told her you'd call her back. I'll just make us some
tea if you want to phone her now.'

Annie searched her house, eventually finding her phone
in the kitchen, which incidentally looked as if a bomb had hit
it. Whatever talents Raphael had, domesticity wasn't one of
them. Leaving Kate in the kitchen, she wandered into her
sitting room and dialled her sister's number.

After reassuring Fiona that, yes, she really was fine and,
no, there was no need for her to leave her family and come
to Penhally Bay and, yes, of course she would call if she
changed her mind, Fiona asked about Raphael, agog to find
he had come to work at St Piran's.

'I couldn't believe it when he answered the phone,' she
said. 'Then he told me what had happened, but that you and
the baby were fine. So, Annie, what's the deal? Why didn't

you tell me he had followed you? Are you two going to be together? I'm so excited for you.'

'I can't talk now,' Annie told her sister. 'I've visitors. I'll call later. But don't get too excited about Raphael being here. It's not what you think. And, Fi, don't tell Mum and Dad about last night. They'll only worry and insist on coming home early. And there's really nothing anyone can do.'

Annie hung up when she heard Chloe talking to Kate. She went into her kitchen and the young midwife handed her a cup of tea.

'How are you doing?' she asked. 'Kate says everything has settled down. She was good enough to phone me after she dropped you off, otherwise I wouldn't have slept a wink, worrying.'

Annie was grateful for the genuine concern in Chloe's eyes, but hurried to reassure her.

'And I understand our new doctor refused to leave your side.'

Annie didn't miss the teasing look she sent her way. She felt herself blush furiously.

'Does everyone know?' she asked.

'What about?' Chloe asked innocently.

Annie could feel her face get warmer. 'Do people know who the father is?'

'There is gossip. You must know there was bound to be, but most of it is just kindly interest. However, I'm afraid the way that our Dr Castillo carried you off and refused to budge from your side was a bit of a give-away.'

'I suppose it was inevitable that people put two and two together,' Annie said.

'Especially those who knew about your holiday in Spain. No one knew there was a vacancy at the hospital when, lo and behold, Dr Castillo turns up. Rumour has it that he called in every favour he was owed, to get the job. So, yes, I'm afraid the cat is well and truly out the bag. Do you mind very much?'

'No, I guess not,' Annie said quietly. 'People were bound to find out sooner or later. He's an experienced doctor, too. Anyway, St Piran's is lucky to have someone with his experience.'

'And what about you, Annie? How do you feel about him being here?' Chloe asked quietly.

How could she answer Chloe's question when she didn't know the answer herself? Annie knew she felt the same way about him as she had from the moment they had met. And that wasn't good. He would never feel the same way about her. And what if he carried out his threat to claim his rights as a father and demanded shared access? She didn't want her child to spend half its life away from her in Spain.

'I'm not sure. I don't really know that much about him,' Annie said evasively. 'I know he comes from a big extended Spanish family but that's about it.' She felt herself grow warm under their scrutiny. She wished she could at least say that they had been together the whole two weeks while she'd been in Spain, that their child had been conceived after spending time together, instead of it being obvious that she had spent very little time in the man's company before jumping into bed with him. She just knew she couldn't explain the instant, overwhelming attraction she had felt for Raphael.

'But anyway,' she continued, 'that is neither here nor there. As far as he is concerned, the baby is his and he is determined to stick around. Or so he says.' Annie hesitated then decided to confide in Chloe and Kate, knowing that neither woman would ever break a confidence.

'He tells me he intends to apply for legal access. What if he takes my baby to Spain for a visit and never brings him back?'

Two pairs of eyes studied her sympathetically.

'I don't think he could do that,' Kate said reassuringly. 'Anyway, the mother usually wins—what do they call it now—rights of residence.'

'But these days fathers have equal rights, don't they?' Annie tried to keep the panic out of her voice.

'Why don't you speak to him about it, Annie?' Kate suggested. 'It could be that you're worried about nothing. Maybe he'll put your mind at rest.'

Kate was right, of course. Annie needed to face up to the situation like the grown woman she was. But she couldn't help wondering whether she had done the right thing in letting Raphael know he was the father of her child. How much less complicated it would have been had she said nothing at all.

Kate and Chloe left shortly after Raphael arrived back. He had showered, and dressed in a thin cashmere pullover with a pair of jeans, looking, Annie thought, sexy as hell. Every time Annie saw him she remembered how he had made her feel that first night. How the atmosphere between them had seemed charged with electricity. But so far he was still an enigma to her. One thing was for sure, though, if the baby inherited its father's dark good looks it would be beautiful.

'What are you doing out of bed?' he growled at her. 'I thought we agreed you were going to stay in bed for the weekend and let me look after you?'

Once again Annie felt exasperated. While she welcomed his support, there was no way he was going to tell her how to live her life. Didn't he know that she would do whatever she could to protect the life growing inside her?

'Actually, no,' Annie said firmly. 'I agreed to nothing. As I said before, you and I both know that me staying in bed won't change a thing.'

'I had no idea you were so stubborn,' he said, his mouth twitching. 'But you will find out I am stubborn, too.' Before she had a chance to protest he had crossed the room and scooped her up in his arms. Annie had no choice but to wrap her arms around his neck and cling on for dear life while he marched into the bedroom and laid her, as if she could break in two, gently on the bed.

As he looked down at her, his eyes glowing, Annie felt her breath catch in her throat. For a second the world stood still and her treacherous body yearned to feel his hands on her once more. He bent over her and brushed a stray curl away from her face with a gentle finger. *'Dios,'* he said hoarsely, 'why do you have to look at me like that?' And then, almost as if he couldn't bear the sight of her, he straightened and moved to the other side of the room, apparently determined to put as much space as possible between them.

'I have brought supplies from the shop as well as newspapers and magazines. I had no idea what you like, so I bought the lot. I will bring them to you.'

By this time Annie had had enough. Raphael had to understand that she didn't need him fussing over her like a mother hen. If he wanted to stick around she had to make him realise that she needed to do things her way. For all she knew, he could disappear back to Spain at any time, leaving her to get on with it on her own, and the last thing she wanted was to become reliant on somebody who might not stick around. She knew he was enamoured with the idea of becoming a father, any idiot could see that, but what about when the harsh realities of being a parent struck home? Would he be so keen then? She had fought so hard for her independence, she was damned if she was going to give it all up now. Just because it suited him.

'I'm going for a shower,' she said. 'Then I'm going to get dressed. You,' she said crossly, 'can do what you like.' She felt a moment of pleasure as she saw the look of surprise on his face. Then she hopped out of bed and, wrapping the sheet around her as well as much of her dignity as she could salvage, she stalked off to the bathroom without a backward glance.

By the time Annie came out of her deliberately long shower, Raphael was nowhere to be seen. She ignored the flash of disappointment and, selecting a dress that was loose around the waist, finished dressing. She dried her hair, taking her time over the ritual until her brown hair was tamed into a neat bob. Now she felt almost human again and ready to face the world. There was no more spotting and no cramping. Everything seemed to have settled down.

'Hey, you,' she said softly laying a hand on her belly, 'you just keep fighting in there. You have a mummy who wants you more than anything in the world and who already loves you more than she can say.' As if in response to her encouragement the baby moved and Annie felt a surge of relief. It was a fighter, this little one. It was a miracle it was here in the first place.

She padded through to her sitting room. As he'd promised, Raphael had left enough magazines and newspapers to keep her occupied for the rest of her pregnancy, never mind the weekend. She frowned in confusion as she leafed through the pile. He had even included a copy of *Biker's Weekly*! She smiled, imagining him in the newsagent's, grabbing the first magazines that came to hand, unsure what she liked to read and in too much of a hurry to get back to check up on her to think about it. Her smile faded as another thought hit her—or did it show how little they knew of about one another? And yet they were going to parent the same child. She picked up a well-known travel magazine with a four-page spread on the part of Spain he came from. Now, was that deliberate? she wondered. Was he determined to persuade her to bring their baby to Spain? She couldn't make up her mind whether to be amused or angry. In fact, everything about Raphael confused her. She had been content on her own, and as soon as she'd known she was going to have a baby, her life had been complete. But now that he was back in her life again, all testosterone, making her go weak at the knees every time she saw him, he had gone and upset everything all over again. In many ways it would have been better if he had stayed out of her life.

Looking out the window, she saw that the sun was shining. It was a perfect early summer day and Annie felt restless. Maybe she should practise some yoga? That always calmed her and no one could say it counted as vigorous exercise. She felt her cheeks grow warm as she remembered what else Dr Gibson had said. No penetrative sex. As if! There was no worry on that score! It was clear that any desire Raphael might have had for her had long since vanished. Although when he had raised an eyebrow at her, back there in the hospital room, she had seen from his eyes that he had been thinking of the night they'd conceived the baby. She crossed over to the window and opened it, letting the gentle breeze cool her cheeks. It was a lovely day. Perhaps she would go for the walk she had threatened, but she didn't feel confident enough to go on her own. Whatever she had told Raphael, she was still scared—no, terrified—that she could yet lose her baby.

CHAPTER SEVEN

ANNIE was beginning to feel hungry when there was a tap on the door. She opened it to find Raphael standing there, holding another bunch of flowers. For a moment she was taken aback. It was almost as if he was wooing her. Despite everything she had told herself, she couldn't help a tiny spurt of pleasure at the gesture. But she needed to remember that this man would do anything to make sure he was kept in her baby's life. She mustn't let his little-boy grin get to her.

In addition to the flowers, Raphael was laden with cardboard boxes that smelled delicious.

'I had a look in your fridge earlier,' he said, 'but there was nothing. Don't you know you have to eat? To stay strong?'

'I know. For the baby,' Annie retorted.

'Isn't that what we both want?' He looked puzzled.

'Yes. Of course.' Annie was suddenly aghast. What was she thinking? That she wanted him to see her as more than the mother of his child? That she wanted him to see her as a woman? But she didn't. She would never have a relationship with a man who threatened her with lawyers. But he still hadn't actually told her what he was planning to do when the baby arrived. She should take Kate's advice and talk to him about it.

'We need to talk,' he said, as if he'd read her mind. 'But

first we need to eat. I for one cannot think on an empty stomach. I was going to cook for us, but I don't know what you like—except seafood. But best not to chance that while you're pregnant. So I got a selection of other things I thought you might like from the restaurant on the main street.'

He emptied the contents of the boxes onto plates he had fetched from the kitchen.

'Remembering the way you cook,' Annie said, smiling, 'I think you did the right thing.'

Raphael pretended to look hurt for a moment. Then he grinned and Annie's heart somersaulted.

'I thought about going for a walk later,' Annie said. 'I hate being cooped up inside. Especially when the weather is so perfect.'

Raphael's smile was replaced by a frown. 'I thought we agreed you were going to rest—at least for a day or two.'

Annie replied, not even attempting to hide her frustration, 'Dr Gibson said no vigorous exercise. I hardly think a stroll falls into that category.' She blushed, remembering what else Dr Gibson had said. 'You can hardly stand guard over me for the rest of the pregnancy, Raphael!'

Raphael put his fork down and, reaching across the table, took Annie's hand.

'*Cariño,*' he said softly. 'If I thought standing guard over you would help, I wouldn't leave your side, but as you are determined to go for a walk, there is nothing for it except that I go too!'

Before Annie could protest, he dropped her hand and touched her lips with his finger. Annie swallowed a moan as her body thrilled to his touch.

'No more arguments,' he continued, tracing the line of her lips. 'You will find I can be as stubborn as you. Now—' he looked at her with mock severity, thankfully unaware of Annie's furiously beating heart '—let's finish eating. Or make no mistake—you won't be leaving this house.'

After they had eaten, they followed the road down towards the shore. The early evening was warm and the scent of flowers and sea filled the air. Annie loved this time of year in Penhally Bay. Soon she would need to make a start on converting the spare room into a nursery and had already decided she would paint it buttercup yellow.

They followed the road until they came to the lighthouse.

They stood in companionable silence for a moment, watching as the sun turned the sky to strips of red, gold and lilac. Eventually Raphael turned molten brown eyes on her.

'I owe you an apology and an explanation,' he said. 'I should never have doubted you and I cannot have you worrying about me taking the baby from you. You must understand I would never do that. It is not easy for me to tell you why I went to a lawyer, but I feel I must. Can I ask you not to tell anyone else—do I have your word?'

'I can keep a confidence,' Annie said.

Raphael took a deep breath before speaking. 'I was married. Until last year.'

Annie felt her heart thump. Was he going to tell her he was still in love with his wife?

'My wife and I had a child. Sebastian. He is three now.' Raphael smiled grimly before continuing, 'I love that little boy. He is my life.'

Annie drew in a breath. The pain in his voice was evident. She hadn't known he had a child. Where was he? And what was Raphael doing so far away from his him? If he loved him, and it was evident he did, how could he bear to be away from him?

She waited quietly for him to continue. It was obvious he was having difficulty keeping his emotions in check. His eyes were dark and Annie had to sit on her hands to prevent herself leaning towards him and brushing the stray lock of hair from his eyes.

'My wife left me,' he said baldly. 'And she took my son with her. Only it turned out that Sebastian wasn't my son after all. He belonged to the man she ran off with.'

Annie was appalled. But in that instant she knew more about Raphael than she had thought possible. His hurt was written all over his face.

'I'm sorry,' she said. 'That must have been hard.' She longed to reach out and comfort him, but something in the way he held himself, in his forbidding expression, warned her that he wouldn't welcome her touch.

'She wouldn't let me see him. So I went to the court and asked for access. But it was denied. They said that I wasn't the biological father, so I had no rights.'

The bitterness and pain in his voice shook Annie. No wonder he was so determined to have some legal rights to their child.

'It didn't matter that I was the only father he had ever known, that he loved me and I loved him. None of that counted when it came to access. She took him away to another part of Spain. I don't know how he is, if he is missing me. I know nothing about my child's life. And he *is* my child. Even if I am not the biological father.'

'I'm so sorry, Raphael. I can only imagine what that must be like for you. Not to be able to see him. Not to have any contact whatsoever.'

He stood up and turned away as if he couldn't bear to look at her. 'I don't want your sympathy,' he said roughly. 'I just need to be certain that the same thing won't happen again.'

Annie's blood chilled. But it must be difficult for this proud man to admit that he had been deceived.

'Did you love her very much?' she said quietly. 'Your ex-wife?'

'Ruth? I told myself I loved her. When she told me she was pregnant with my child, I asked her to marry me. I thought we could make it work. For the sake of the child. But we were never really happy, and eventually she met with the real father again.' His voice was bitter with the memory. 'She started seeing him again while she was still married to me. I was such a fool.'

This time Annie couldn't help herself. She got up and went to stand beside him, touching his arm. He flinched almost as if she had burnt him.

'And Sebastian? What about him?'

His voice was raw when he spoke. 'Whatever she says, he *is* my son. I was the one who looked after him in the night when he couldn't sleep. The one who kissed his knee when he scraped it. Whatever the court says, he is still my son.'

'Do you see him at all?'

'No. That is why I am speaking to the lawyers about this baby.' He smiled grimly, still looking into the distance. 'I can't lose this child too. You must see that.'

Annie *could* see it. Just by looking at him she could tell how badly he had been hurt. More than hurt, betrayed. It was the sadness she had seen inside him the night they had first met. And it was still there. But that didn't mean she could risk losing control over her child's future to appease a hurt Raphael had experienced at the hands of another woman. No matter how sympathetic she felt.

'I wouldn't stop you seeing your child. Not unless I thought it was harmful in some way. Can't you trust me to do the right thing? After all, I needn't have told you I was pregnant.'

'I know. I misjudged you. And for that I am sorry. Can we start over again? Please?' He smiled his killer smile which never failed to make Annie go weak at the knees.

She felt a shiver of excitement, and her heart beat faster. Did he mean start over from where they had left off in Spain? Did he still feel that same connection she did?

'Can we be friends for the sake of our child? Work something out between us?' Raphael continued.

Annie's heart plummeted. Of course, she should have known. All he was interested in was the child. But he had a point—no matter how disappointed she felt that he didn't want anything more than friendship from her, they needed to reach an agreement about what was going to happen once the baby was born.

'You can come and see him any time you like,' Annie said through stiff lips.

Raphael drew his brows together. 'But I would also want him to come to Spain. He must get to know his family, what it is to be Spanish. I would want him to visit often.'

Instinctively, Annie placed her hands protectively on her belly. Could she trust him? This man she barely knew, yet was the father of her child? How was she going to bring herself to let this precious little one out her sight for a second, never mind to another country.

'Don't you trust me?' he asked softly, as if he had guessed what she was thinking. 'What can I do to make you believe me that I only want to do what is right for my child?'

Raphael raised a finger to her cheek, tracing a line down

to her jaw. She couldn't have felt his touch more keenly if he was drawing a knife across her skin. 'What are you thinking? Please—tell me, *cariño.*'

This time it was Annie who drew away. She wrapped her arms around her body.

'A year ago, I was going to get married, to Robert. We had known each other almost all our lives and planned to have a large family,' Annie said slowly after a few moments. 'But my periods had been irregular for years and somebody at the clinic I worked in, back in Edinburgh, suggested I have a fertility test.' She looked into the distance, remembering. 'I took it more out of curiosity than anything else. It never really occurred to me that there could be a problem.'

'What was this test?' Raphael asked.

'It's called an AMH. It's fairly new but deemed to be very reliable.'

Raphael nodded. 'I have read about it in the medical journals.'

'Apparently my ovarian reserve was so low that even IVF would be out of the question.'

Raphael looked at her steadily.

'Go on,' he said.

'It hadn't even crossed my mind that there wasn't plenty of time to think about having a child. You don't think when you're twenty-seven that it's already too late do you? At least, I didn't.' She remembered only too well her feeling of shock and disbelief. 'When I told Robert he was dismayed. And once he realised that even IVF was out of the question, he began to change. I told him that we could always adopt, but he said that he could never bring up another man's child. After that we drifted apart. There was no more talk of weddings. I realised he couldn't love me the way I thought he did, so I called the whole thing off. I think he was relieved. That's when I decided to come to Penhally Bay. To start afresh. But the pain follows you, you know. It's ironic, being a midwife. Every day you're confronted with what you can't have. Don't get me wrong, I love my job and I love bringing happiness to all these couples, but it used to hurt.'

'He couldn't be much of a man, this Robert,' Raphael said, frowning.

'I can't blame him. He wanted something I couldn't give him. It was unfair to expect him to give up the chance of a family for me.'

'If you were my woman, I wouldn't have let you go. You should be with someone because you have to be. Not because you want children.' His eyes were warm with sympathy. 'But now I understand. Our baby will be very special for you. But for me, also.'

Annie nodded, relieved that he seemed to understand. 'Raphael, this baby is like a miracle to me. I can't believe how lucky I am. It's unlikely, though, that I will ever fall pregnant again. This is my one chance to have a child.' Annie struggled to keep her voice even. She knew there was no way that she could convey properly how devastated she had been when she had thought having a child of her own was an impossibility. And anyway, did she want to reveal anything more of herself to this man? She had already shown him too much of her soul. He was the father of her child, that was all, and she'd do well to remember that. Even if it almost broke her heart.

CHAPTER EIGHT

A FEW weeks later, Annie was back at work, feeling much more rested. She was surprised to find Claire and Roy waiting to see her. Claire wasn't due to come in for another couple of weeks and Annie was immediately concerned to see her back so soon. She was even more worried when she saw the look of anxiety on the couple's faces.

'What is it Claire?' Annie asked gently. 'What's bothering you? Is it the babies?'

'I've had a little spotting,' Claire said anxiously. 'I know it can happen sometimes, but—'

'We just wanted to make sure everything was all right,' Roy finished for her.

Annie's heart went out to the couple. She knew they'd be terrified. Claire had seemed so fragile the last time Annie had seen her that she was worried that if she lost the babies she would sink so far into depression that she might not come out the other side. Claire was already in her late thirties and the chance of another pregnancy was diminishing with every passing year.

'I'm going to page Dr Castillo. His special interest is high-risk pregnancies and I'm sure he'll want to scan you, Claire, to see what exactly is going on. I'll ask him to come as soon as he's free. In the meantime, could you try and drink as much as possible so your bladder is nice and full for the scan?'

Claire's eyes filled with tears and she reached for Roy's hand. 'I'm so scared, Annie,' she said shakily. 'I don't know if it's better not knowing, if you see what I mean? As long as I don't know I—we—still have hope.'

Annie stood up and went over to Claire and wrapped her in her arms. 'You're way ahead of yourself. I know how scary all this can be. Believe me. Let's just take one step at a time, okay?'

When Claire nodded, Annie picked up the phone and asked switchboard to page Dr Castillo. While she waited for him to answer she filled a glass of water from the jug on her desk and handed it to Claire.

'Dr Castillo.' Annie heard his deep voice on the other end of the phone. 'You were paging me?'

'Dr Castillo,' she said formally. 'It's Annie. I have someone I'd like you to scan. Could you come down to the antenatal clinic?'

'I'm due in theatre in fifteen minutes. Can it wait until later?'

Annie looked over at Claire, who was drinking the water as if her life depended on it. 'No,' she said, 'it can't.'

'Are you all right?' Immediately the concern was back in his voice.

'Of course,' Annie said. 'It's a couple with a twin IVF pregnancy. She's had some bleeding and is feeling anxious.'

'I'll be right there,' Raphael said, and disconnected.

Annie only had enough time to prepare Claire for the scan before Raphael arrived. He was wearing his theatre scrubs, which framed his muscular body perfectly. Once more, despite herself, Annie felt a thrill when he came into the room. Must be the pregnancy sending her hormones into overdrive, she told herself.

Raphael introduced himself to the worried couple and his easy and relaxed manner soon put them at ease.

While he set up the scanning machine Annie gave him an overview of Claire's history to date. 'This is their third attempt at IVF. Neither of the first two goes resulted in a pregnancy, but this time both the embryos put back implanted successfully. Claire had a scan around seven weeks and two heartbeats were clearly visible at that stage. She's been well up until now, but had some spotting last night. They thought it best to have it checked out.'

Raphael caught Annie's eye. It was obvious from the sympathetic look in his eyes that he knew how close to the bone seeing Claire was for her.

'How many weeks into the pregnancy are you?' he asked Claire, bringing her into the conversation.

'Twenty-four,' Claire replied.

Roy held his wife's hand as Annie covered her stomach in ultrasound gel. They all watched the screen as Raphael scanned. As the image came up on the monitor, Annie could immediately make out two heartbeats. She felt a surge of relief, but almost as quickly it was replaced with concern. While two babies were clearly visible, neither of the babies were the size they should be for the dates. To make matters worse, one was significantly bigger than the other. As Raphael turned to look at her, she could see he shared her concern.

'I have some good news for you and some not-so-good news,' he said gently. 'As you can see from the monitor—' he indicated the two beating hearts with his finger '—there are two heart beats—there and there.' Claire and Roy craned their heads to see what he was showing them. 'The problem, however, is that one baby—' he pointed to one of the tiny forms '—is significantly smaller than the other. This suggests that the bigger baby is taking more than its fair share of the nutrients from the placenta, meaning that the smaller baby is struggling to get enough to grow.'

'What does it mean?' Roy asked.

'It means,' Raphael said, 'that both your babies are still alive. That's the good news. However, we will have to monitor both of them carefully over the next couple of weeks. If it looks like the second baby isn't getting enough nutrients, we will have to think about what to do.'

'What might those options be?' Although Roy's voice was calm, Annie knew he was only keeping it together for Claire's sake.

Raphael looked at him sympathetically.

'It's too soon to know. As I said, we will monitor your babies very closely over the next couple of weeks. Keep an eye on their growth.'

'And if the second baby doesn't grow? What then?' Roy insisted. 'Look—' he turned to his wife and gripped her hand tightly '—we'd both prefer to know, so please tell us. What is the worst that can happen?'

'We might have to deliver the twins much earlier than we would like. I know this a lot for you to take in, and I believe it is important for patients to have all the facts so they can be fully involved in the decision making process, but I am not ready to make that decision yet. As I say, we should wait and see how they get on.'

Claire turned terrified eyes to Annie.

'I don't understand,' she said. 'Annie, is there a chance my babies could die?'

Annie put her arms around the distraught woman's shoulders. 'There's nothing to suggest that right now, Claire. I know all this is difficult for you to take in. But you are lucky to have Dr Castillo to look after you. He is one of the leading experts in his field. We have to trust him.'

Raphael looked at Annie, seeming surprised at her warm endorsement, but then he turned to the couple.

'I want you to go home and try not to worry, even though I know that will be difficult. I will scan you again in two weeks' time. We will have another look at your babies then, and think about what to do. In the meantime, all we can do is wait.'

And pray, Annie thought. Pray that this couple weren't going to have their dreams dashed. But Raphael was right, there was nothing more that could be done right now.

She made another appointment for Claire and Roy to come back to see her and Raphael before seeing them out of the department. When she returned to the room, Raphael was still there, writing in Claire's notes.

'What do you really think?' she asked him.

He looked up at her, surprised. 'Exactly what I told them. We'll know more in a couple of weeks. In the meantime, all we can do is wait.'

'Couldn't we have waited until the next scan? Now they'll have days of worry to live through when it might not be necessary.'

Raphael narrowed his eyes at her. 'I believe that parents have the right to know all the details. The days when doctors decided to hold back information from their patients for their own good are gone. No?'

'But if it means putting them through unnecessary worry? Can't you see how terrified they are?'

Raphael leaned back in his chair and looked at Annie thoughtfully. 'Tell me,' he said softly, 'if you were in her shoes, would you want to know the truth?'

Annie knew she was being unreasonable but she couldn't help herself. Having experienced the terror of thinking she was about to lose a desperately wanted child, she knew exactly what Claire was going through. Raphael leaned across the desk and touched her arm gently.

'They asked me for the truth, Annie. I couldn't do anything else but tell them. Can't you see that?' He dropped his hand. 'Maybe you are getting too close to your patients. We need to keep some professional distance, otherwise we can't help them.'

Suddenly all the anger went out of Annie. Raphael was right. Roy had asked and he had deserved an honest answer. And Raphael was right too about her letting her personal feelings get in the way. If she were to help the couple, she needed to keep her perspective.

Later that day Annie saw Mrs Duncan, a smiling mother of four young children.

'Nurse Kate sent me here for a scan,' she said, settling herself into the chair. 'I'm pregnant again. Number five! I know it's a bit unexpected—for me, too—but the more the merrier, I say.'

Annie looked at Mrs Duncan's notes. Her last pregnancies had been straightforward and Kate had looked after her at the surgery. The first two had been born at St Piran's and the last two at home, with Kate in attendance.

Instantly she was concerned. Mrs Duncan had been in her mid-thirties when her first child had been conceived and almost forty when her youngest, now four and a half, had been born. At almost forty-five Annie knew that the chances of the baby having some sort of abnormality were significantly raised. No doubt the same thought had occurred to Kate and that was why she had sent the woman to Annie's clinic for a nuchal scan. But it seemed as if the reason for the scan hadn't really sunk in with the happy woman in front of her.

'It's not the best timing,' Mrs Duncan continued. 'Not with the six of us still living in the caravan while our house is being rebuilt. Although we should be back in our own house by the time this one is ready to be born.'

Annie shivered as she remembered the storm that had devasted a large part of Penhally Bay months earlier. The buildings that had been damaged were almost repaired but two people had lost their lives and no amount of rebuilding would ever completely undo the trauma of that day in people's minds. She couldn't help but admire her patient's cheerfulness in the face of what must be very demanding circumstances.

'I'm sure Kate told you why she was sending you here for a scan, Mrs Duncan?' Annie asked. Of course, the senior midwife at Penhally Bay Surgery would have explained it all to her patient, but from Mrs Duncan's cheerful attitude, Annie sensed that she didn't seem to realise that she had a significantly higher chance of a chromosomal abnormality in this pregnancy.

'Oh, please call me Mary,' the older woman said. 'And, yes, Nurse Kate said that everyone was offered a scan when they were twelve weeks now. So that's why I'm here. I'll have my scan and then if you could give me the picture, I'll be on my way.'

Annie suppressed a smile, before inviting Mary up onto

the couch. News of the brand-new scanner they had at St Piran's had spread quickly. The 3D images were clear enough to see even minute details and patients loved taking home photographs of the images. But almost as soon as she started to scan Mary, she could see that her instincts had been right. The nuchal fold, indicating an increased chance of Down's syndrome, was obviously thicker than normal. Her heart sank.

Mary quickly sensed that something was wrong. She squinted at the screen and then turned to look at Annie.

'What is it?' she asked. 'There's something wrong, isn't there? I can tell from the look on your face.'

'I'll need to do a blood test to confirm it, but I have to tell you that there are signs that your baby has a higher risk of Down's syndrome. If the blood test comes back positive, you may wish to think about amniocentesis.'

'What's that when it's at home? Anyway, I thought that was why I was having this scan.'

'This scan and blood test only tells us whether you have an increased risk. We need to do another test to confirm the result.'

'I think Nurse Kate suggested I might want that test with my last one,' Mary said slowly, 'but I decided against it. And my baby was fine. All my babies have been fine. So surely I don't need to worry about that?'

'The older a mother gets, the greater the risk of a Down's syndrome baby. The test does carry a small risk of miscarriage with it. You'll need to weigh up the pros and cons. You don't have to have the test, but you should consider it.'

'If you think I should then I will.' Mrs Duncan replied cautiously. 'I'm not sure I could cope with a disabled child, not when I have four of them and we're all crammed into the tiny caravan up in the park.'

Annie could see how deflated she was. Mrs Duncan had come in full of hope and excitement and all Annie had done was burst her bubble. But, as Raphael had just pointed out, she wouldn't be doing her job if she didn't give her patients all the facts and let them make up their own minds.

'I think you should have a word with the doctor before you go. If you can wait a few minutes, I'll give him a shout.'

Mary nodded. Annie left the room and went in search of Raphael. Fortunately she caught him just as he was seeing a patient out.

'I have someone in with me I'd like you to see,' Annie said. 'When I did her booking scan I could see a larger than normal nuchal fold. I'm not sure whether to arrange for her to come back for amniocentesis in three weeks or whether we should be doing a CVS today. I suspect that depends on what you think and whether you have time.'

Raphael took Mary's notes and the picture of the scan Annie had taken. 'You're absolutely right about the nuchal fold,' he agreed. 'The hospital is lucky to have a midwife who can scan. It is much more efficient this way.' He held his hands up and grinned as Annie started to speak. 'I know you are highly trained. I recognise that. Shall we see Mrs Duncan?'

Mrs Duncan had finished dressing by the time Annie and Raphael returned. Although pale, she seemed composed.

'I gather Annie here has explained things to you?' Raphael said gently. 'I realise it's probably a bit of a shock, but we are going to do everything we can to help you make the right decision for you. Okay?'

Mary nodded.

'There are three options here. One—we do nothing. Two—we bring you back for an amniocentesis. That's where we take a sample of the fluid surrounding the baby in the

womb. We can only do that when you are a little further on.'
He glanced at the notes. 'In about three weeks' time. The third
option is that we can do a test today where we take a sample
of the placenta. I have to warn you that both the tests carry a
risk of miscarriage. So we have to weigh up whether the
risks outweigh the benefits. Do you understand all this?'

'I think so.' Mary turned frightened eyes on Annie. 'What
do you think?'

'I think you should go home and speak to your husband
about it before you decide anything.'

'But Bill's away fishing. He won't be back for another
three days—at least.'

'Another few days won't make much difference either
way, and it's something you should speak to him about. We
can, of course, do the CVS today, but I really feel you should
take some time to think about it. I can also ask Kate to pop
around and see you, if that helps. I know you saw her through
your last pregnancies and sometimes it helps to talk things
over with someone else before coming to a decision.'

'Doctor?' Mary turned to Raphael.

'I think it's good advice. Some women decide not to have
the test at all, but I'm afraid it has to be your decision.
Whatever you decide, whenever you decide, we will be here
to help.'

'I think I will wait, then. Can I let you know when I make
up my mind?'

'Of course, Mary. The important thing is not to leave it
beyond sixteen weeks. Having a termination after that can be
very hard, if that's what you eventually decide to do.'

'And I think it would be useful if I gave you some stuff
explaining about Down's syndrome to take away with you,'
Annie interrupted. 'Many women find that these children

can bring a lot of joy to the family. It may not be right for you, but think about it.'

As soon as Annie had seen Mary out, armed with all the literature she could find for her, as well as a few useful Internet sites that she might want to look at, Annie went in search of Raphael. She found him talking to one of the junior doctors at the reception desk. As soon as he noticed her he came towards her and, taking her by the arm, took her to one side out of the hearing of his colleague.

'What is it?' he said. 'You are pale. There's nothing wrong with the baby, is there?'

'No, everything's fine. It's just…' She tailed off, uncertain why she had sought Raphael out but knowing she needed to speak to him. Maybe it was the threatened miscarriage and the knowledge that she had an increased chance of going into early labour. She was so scared for her baby.

'Seeing these patients makes you worry about your own pregnancy. Is that it?' His warm brown eyes searched hers. He raised a hand to her face and brushed her cheek with a fingertip. 'It must be hard for you.'

'I'm just so frightened,' she admitted. 'I know the chances of me going into early labour are increased and, well, we both know what that could mean.'

Raphael put his hands on her shoulders, and ignoring the presence of his junior, pulled her close.

'I know you are frightened. Try not to be. I am here with you.'

Annie let herself relax against his chest. He was here with her. For now. But would he stay?

CHAPTER NINE

THREE weeks later, Raphael tapped the front door of Annie's house before walking in. They had slipped into a comfortable pattern and there had been no more scares with the pregnancy, much to Annie's delight. As the door led straight into the small sitting room, Raphael found himself confronted with the sight of an inverted Annie. *Dios.* What was she doing?

Her upside-down face peered at him from the gap between her legs. She had tied her hair in a ponytail and it hung almost to the floor. She was wearing tight-fitting trousers that emphasised the shape of her bottom and her crop top revealed the taut mound of her belly and just the merest glimpse of the mound of her breasts. He felt something primeval stir in his belly.

'Oh, hello,' she said. 'I'm just doing a few rounds of The Salute to the Sun. I'll be finished in a few moments.'

In a fluid movement she changed position, curving her sweet body through a series of movements. One minute he'd be staring at her delicious rear, the next he'd be watching as her toned arms took the weight of her body and she moved into a series of lunges. Eventually she stood upright and brought her hands together as if she were praying. He took in the tiny droplets of moisture on her skin, her face glowing with her exertions, the gentle rise and fall of her breasts. The swell of her pregnancy was outlined by her Lycra trousers. She had never looked so beautiful or so womanly to him before, and it took every ounce of his willpower not to pull her into his arms and run his tongue over her skin.

'Yoga,' she said, a small smile tugging at her lips. 'In case you are wondering. I've been doing it for years. And since it seems as if I am forbidden—' she looked at him with mock anger '—to do anything more strenuous, I've been practising every day.' She picked up a towel from her sofa and wiped the moisture from her skin. 'I find it helps me stay calm,' she added. 'And I'm hoping it will help me stay focused in labour.'

Raphael tore his eyes away. He loved the way her eyes sparkled with amusement. He hadn't seen Annie smile as often as he would have liked. More than anything, he wished he could be the one to bring the light to her face.

'I have come to ask you if you would like to come for a picnic. Catalina and Maria arrived last night and as it's a beautiful day, we thought Maria would like a trip to the beach. I know she would like it if you came too. Catalina also. She wants to meet the mother of her niece or nephew again.'

Dios, why had he said it in that way? Why couldn't he admit that he wanted to spend time with her, too? Because he couldn't, that was why. He had to remember that it didn't matter how much he wanted this woman back in his arms, an affair was out of the question. No woman was ever going to rip his heart out again. Not even this one. Especially not this one.

'Maria? Catalina?' She was frowning. A tiny pucker of her eyebrows. 'They are here? In Penhally Bay? To see me?'

Annie wrapped the towel around her shoulders, hiding the exquisite swell of her breast from him.

'To see you, yes, but also because my mother had to go to the north of Spain to see her sister and she didn't want to take Maria with her. So she asked Catalina to take her for the weekend. My sister thought it was a chance to come here for a couple of days and get to know you a little. And Maria still talks about you. It would be a good chance to kill a bird with a stone, as you say in English.'

'Kill two birds with one stone,' Annie corrected him automatically. She wasn't looking as pleased as he'd thought she'd be. 'I don't know, Raphael. I'd like to see them both again, especially little Maria, but…' She tailed off.

Raphael could guess what she was thinking. He wondered if she had any idea how easily he was able to read her. She'd be worrying whether this was another attempt to persuade her to come and live in Spain.

'Please,' he said. 'I know I have no right to ask you. Your time is your own, but Maria would be so happy to see you again.'

He knew it was unfair of him to play the Maria card. Annie might be able to resist a plea from him, but from the little girl? He doubted it. As soon as he saw the acceptance in her eyes he knew he had been right.

'Where are they?'

'I dropped them off at the beach. I told them I couldn't promise that you would come.'

'But you knew I would.' Annie quirked an eyebrow in his direction. She was right. He had been certain that she wouldn't be able to resist seeing Maria again.

'I'll just have a quick shower then change. You go on if you like. I'll walk down when I'm ready. It won't take long and I could do with the exercise.'

'I'll wait for you,' Raphael said, picking up one of the magazines he had brought over a few weeks ago, noting that they hadn't been read. What was wrong with Annie? Didn't she like motorbikes?

By the time they arrived at the beach, the sun was beating down and the beach was busy with locals making the most of the first really hot summer's day.

'In a couple of weeks the beach will be crowded with tourists,' Annie told Raphael. 'We'll feel the impact at the hospital, too.'

'It is like Spain. In the winter everywhere is peaceful. Then the summer arrives and suddenly it doesn't feel like home any more.'

'I don't mind, though,' Annie protested. 'We're all tourists somewhere at some time. And I quite like the buzz when the visitors arrive.'

'Buzz?' Raphael repeated, looking perplexed.

Annie laughed. 'It's an expression. It means, an energy— an atmosphere.'

Raphael pointed to a couple of figures sitting on a blanket near the shelter of a wall.

'There they are. You go on while I find somewhere to change.'

Annie tiptoed across the hot sand, her sandals in her hand. As soon as Catalina saw her she jumped to her feet and hugged Annie.

'It is good to see you again.' She smiled. 'And looking so well. I trust my brother has been looking after you? Is everything all right now? He told us…' She tailed off.

'Everything's okay,' Annie said softly. 'I got a fright, but I'm okay now.'

Annie looked past Catalina's shoulder. Maria, wearing

her swimming costume, was standing watching Annie carefully, her thumb in her mouth.

'Hello, little one,' Annie said in Spanish. She had been swotting up some basic Spanish. As her child would almost certainly be bilingual, it seemed sensible.

The little girl broke into a shy smile and, stepping forward, wrapped her arms around Annie. Annie's heart squeezed as she ruffled Maria's thick dark curls.

'Where is my brother?' Catalina asked glancing over Annie's shoulder. 'Don't tell me he decided that he was needed at the hospital?'

'No. He's just getting changed.'

Suddenly Catalina grinned. 'Here he comes!'

Annie swung round. Raphael was striding towards them, wearing a wetsuit and carrying a surfboard. His bronzed chest was bare, the top half of his suit gathered around his lean hips. Annie could see the muscles in his upper arms bunch with the effort of carrying the board and she let her eyes slide down his body, taking in the toned six pack of his abdomen. The skin-tight fabric of his wetsuit clung to his thighs and across his hips. Annie's skin tingled.

As Maria ran towards him, short legs sending puffs of sand in her wake, he dropped the board and opened his arms. Maria careered into him and he pretended to be knocked over.

Annie watched them, regret vying with the feeling of lust. She was glad about the baby—more than glad. Why, then, did she feel this aching sense of loss?

Annie paddled with Maria while Raphael took his board to an area a little further along, which was cordoned off from bathers. Out of the corner of her eye she watched him as he rode the waves, his body bending and curving as he balanced.

Every so often she would catch her breath as he disappeared from view, but seconds later he would reappear from under the wave still upright. He had surfed before, that much was obvious.

'I want to make a sandcastle,' Maria said after she had finished splashing about, so they left Raphael to make most of the waves and returned to where Catalina was setting out the picnic. Keeping a watchful eye on Maria as she played, the two women stretched out on the blanket.

'It is good to see my brother happy again,' Catalina said softly. 'It has been too long since I saw him laugh. I think being here, as well as you and the baby, has been good for him.'

'He told me about Sebastian, and Ruth,' Annie said softly. 'It must have been hard on him.'

'I have never seen him so…' Catalina paused. 'So distraught. He loved that little boy. You know, he left his room exactly how it was the day she took him. His toys on the bed, his football, everything, as if he expected him to come back. And he did expect him to come back, right up until the court case. When he knew he had lost Sebastian for ever, it was as though Raphael had lost part of himself.'

'What kind of woman was she, his ex-wife? I can't imagine anyone being so deceitful and then so cruel.'

'Ruth? I never liked her.' Catalina shrugged. 'She always seemed to me as if she thought herself above everyone. You know, before Raphael became a doctor he was a very good football player. He could have played professionally, but he decided to study medicine instead. I think she would have stayed if he had chosen a different profession. She wanted more money, a better lifestyle than a doctor could offer her. Raphael told her that he would never go back to football, that, apart from everything else, he was too old, but she never

stopped trying to change his mind. Then she met Sebastian's
father again. He is now a very important and rich man in
Spain. She decided he could give her a better life. So she
went, and took Sebastian with her.'

Maria had left her sandcastle and had come to sit next to
Annie. She pressed her body into Annie's and Annie put her
arm around the child, drawing her closer.

'He tried everything to get access, even just once a month,
but he couldn't. I think it broke his heart. When he met you, he
had just been at the lawyer to try one more appeal, but that failed,
too.' Catalina looked at Annie thoughtfully. 'He was a good
father. He will be a good father to your child. If you will let him.'

'I won't stop him seeing our child, Catalina. I wouldn't do
that, not unless he gave me cause. But I worry sometimes that
he will try and take our baby away from me. And I could
never let that happen.'

Catalina looked Annie directly in the eyes. 'You are wrong
to think like that. He would never do to you what has been
done to him. Never. He knows a child needs a mother and a
father. You have to believe me. Just be patient with him.'

Annie did believe her. She knew that she had been worried
all along for nothing. Raphael wasn't the kind of man to
remove a child from its mother. And if she hadn't been so
scared she would have seen that before now.

Maria shifted in her arms and, putting a small hand up to
Annie's face, turned it towards her.

'You are not sad any more?' she said

'No,' Annie replied, and included Catalina in her smile. 'I
am not sad any more.'

The rest of the weekend sped past in a happy blur. Annie
couldn't resist the entreaty in Maria's big brown eyes when

Catalina suggested that Annie go with them to explore some of the hidden coves along the coast. As the four of them tramped along the beach, searching rock pools and underneath rocks for crabs, Annie let herself imagine what it would be like if this were *her* family. She saw the way Raphael was with Maria, the way he rolled up his jeans to paddle in the sea with her, the way he made the sad little girl giggle, and Annie's heart ached. If only he felt about her the way she felt about him. If only *they* could be a family.

She could no longer pretend that the way her heart hammered every time she saw him was simple lust. She loved him. With all her heart and soul. She had loved him from the moment she had met him and she would love him to the day she died. But, she reminded herself, even though the realisation almost cracked her heart in two, friendship was all he had to offer, and for the sake of their child it would have to be enough.

The following Monday, Annie was down at the Penhally Bay Surgery for a check-up with Kate when Nick popped his head around the door.

'Oh, I'm sorry. I didn't realise Kate still had someone with her. I'll come back in a few minutes.'

'No, come in,' Annie said. 'We're finished here. I was just chatting to Kate before getting back to St Piran's for the clinic.'

'Actually, it's useful that you're here, Annie. The patient I wanted to talk to Kate about involves you too.'

He sat down opposite Kate and stretched his legs out in front of him. Annie didn't really know him that well. The older GP was always friendly and helpful, but there was a reticence about him that didn't really invite confidences. All

Annie knew about him was that he was a widower with grown-up children and that he and Kate had worked together for a long time.

'I gather you saw Tilly Treliving a while back at the family planning clinic?' Nick said to Kate without preamble.

'Yes,' Kate replied. 'Is there a problem?'

'You could say that,' Nick said grimly. 'She's come to see me this morning. She's around thirty weeks pregnant, I think. If her dates are right.'

Kate looked shocked. 'She came to see me, let me see, almost a year ago about wanting to start a family, but I thought I'd agreed with her that we were going to get her diabetes stabilised first and that she would continue to use contraception until it settled down. I think Gemma has been following her up,' Kate said, referring to the practice nurse.

'Obviously she decided to go ahead anyway. It was only when Gemma became concerned that she hadn't been attending the surgery and went to visit her that we discovered the reason she'd been staying away.'

'Oh, poor Tilly. She must have been scared we'd tell her off,' Kate said.

'She'll need to be followed up at the hospital, of course,' Nick continued. 'I'm referring her to Dr Castillo. I'm just waiting for him to call me back. I gather he's in surgery, but if he isn't free to see her could you fit her in to one of your clinics, Annie?'

'Of course I'll see her,' Annie said. 'I'm down to do the afternoon clinic with Raphael. It would be no problem to add her on. But if she's still here, I could have a chat with her now, if you like. Unless you'd prefer to see her, Kate?'

'It sounds as if you'll be following her up, so it's probably best for you to see her,' Kate said. 'Besides, I'm due to visit a couple of my new mothers this afternoon. But let me know if there is anything I can do.'

A few moments after Kate and Nick had left, there was a soft tap at the door and a frightened-looking Tilly came into the room.

'It's all right, Tilly,' Annie said gently. 'I just need to do a few tests so we can see what's going on. Where's John? Couldn't he get time off work to come with you?'

'He's really angry with me.' The young woman burst into tears. 'We're barely speaking. He didn't want me to get pregnant. Not after what Kate told us.'

Annie handed Tilly a tissue and waited until the sobs tailed off. It wasn't great that Tilly had gone ahead and fallen pregnant, but she couldn't find it in her heart to blame her. She knew only too well how much the desperate desire to have a child could take over everything. But Tilly was taking a risk. Her diabetes could bring all sorts of complications for the baby as well as the mother.

'I'm sure John will come round. He's probably frightened for you, but we're going to take good care of you,' Annie said. 'Dr Tremayne is going to speak to the obstetrician, Dr Castillo, at St Piran's. He specialises in pregnancies such as yours and will want to see you. He and I will follow you up at the hospital.'

'Won't Dr Castillo be angry with me too?' Tilly said. She had dried her eyes and was looking calmer. 'You promise you'll be with me when I see him?'

'Of course. But you mustn't worry about him being annoyed with you. He'll simply be concerned that we get you and the baby safely through the pregnancy. He's very kind, actually.'

Annie stood and went to fetch some more tissues. As she did, Tilly looked at her in surprise. 'Are you…?' she asked.

'Pregnant?' Annie finished for her. 'Yes, I am.'

'Oh, I didn't know you were married.'

'I'm not,' Annie said quietly.

Tilly looked embarrassed.

'Hey, it's okay,' Annie said.

'I don't care that I've put *my* health at risk,' the young woman said fiercely. 'I'm glad I'm going to have a baby. It's going to be loved.'

There was a tap on the door and Nick popped his head in. 'I've spoken to Dr Castillo,' he said. 'He's agreed to see Tilly at his clinic this afternoon, if she can manage that?'

'You can come with me in the car. I'm heading there myself. That way I can be with you when you see Dr Castillo. How does that sound?' There was no way Annie was going to give Tilly any opportunity to miss the appointment. Not when there was so much at risk.

Annie and Raphael saw Tilly together before the main clinic started. Raphael examined the young woman thoroughly before asking her to wait while he and Annie had a chat.

'I am not happy with her glucose levels, and the baby is already bigger than I would have expected for her dates. We are going to have to keep a close eye on her.'

Annie knew why he was concerned. Diabetic mothers often had problems in pregnancy and when the diabetes wasn't well controlled there was an increased risk of stillbirth. They would have to monitor her carefully and intervene just at the right time. It would be a tricky balancing act.

'Don't worry,' Annie said. 'I intend to. Luckily she stays in Penhally Bay, so I can pop in and see her from time to time.'

Raphael smiled broadly. 'Are you always so determined to get your patients safely through their pregnancies? Anyone would think you care about their babies almost as much as you do your own.'

Annie's heart flipped. Why did he have to be so gorgeous? Why did her hormonally loaded body react to him the way it did? But it wasn't her hormones. She had reacted this way to him from the moment she had met him, and she couldn't blame pregnancy hormones then. And the way he had been with Tilly. Kind, reassuring, not judgemental at all. It was a different, softer side to Raphael. And it just made her love him more.

'Speaking of your pregnancy, why don't we check your BP while we are waiting for the next patient to arrive?'

Before she could react he was wrapping a blood-pressure cuff around her arm.

'Hey, wait a minute,' Annie protested, alarmed to feel goose-bumps all along her arm where his fingers brushed her skin. 'Kate checked my blood pressure earlier. And it's fine. She's looking after me perfectly well. I wish you would stop treating me as if I were some walking incubator.'

Raphael narrowed his eyes at her. 'Is that what you think?' he said, amusement threading his voice.

'What else am I to think?' Annie said crossly. 'All you're interested in is the health and welfare of this baby.'

'Don't you think I'm interested in the health and welfare of the mother as well?' His eyes were unfathomable, but a smile tugged at the corner of his mouth. It was enough to make Annie's heart beat faster.

But before either of them could say more, the receptionist popped her head around the door to tell them that Claire and Roy had arrived to see them.

Annie watched as Raphael scanned Claire, who happily had no further bleeding. But as Raphael replaced the probe he had been using and Annie wiped away the lubricating gel from Claire's abdomen, Annie could tell that he was concerned.

He waited until Claire was dressed. As always Roy was there by her side. So far he hadn't missed a single appointment, even though Annie knew he had a demanding job that often took him away from home.

'The babies have grown since the last time I saw you,' Raphael said. 'But not as much as I would have liked.'

Claire's face paled and she clutched her husband's hand. The couple sat in silence, waiting for Raphael to continue.

'It's good that we have got the babies to over twenty-five weeks,' he continued. 'But now, I'm afraid, we have to make a decision.'

The couple nodded and waited for him to continue.

'We can continue to monitor the babies, and see how they progress, or we can deliver them now by Caesarean section. Both options carry a risk.' His voice was gentle. 'If we wait, it is possible that the smaller baby will die. If, on the other hand, we deliver them now, the smaller baby has an increased risk of not pulling through. The bigger baby also has greater risk of complications as all pre-term babies do.'

Claire and Roy absorbed the information silently, but Annie could see the fear etched on their faces.

'What would you do?' Roy asked Raphael. 'If it were your babies we were talking about?'

'I'm afraid this has to be your decision,' Raphael replied softly.

'Which option carries more risk for Claire? However much we want these babies, it is her that matters most.'

'Neither option is more or less risky for your wife,' Raphael said. 'Whatever you decide, it is more than likely that Claire will require a C-section. Any operation carries a small risk, but many, many women have this procedure every day without harm.'

Roy looked at Annie. She could see the tension in his face. The love he felt for his wife was written there plain for the world to see. 'What would you do, Annie?'

Annie shook her head. She didn't know what she would do if she were in their shoes. It wasn't a question she could answer.

'Both options carry a risk,' she replied. 'If we leave Claire, there is a chance the second, smaller twin could die suddenly in utero. The bigger twin would continue to grow and every day spent inside Claire's tummy increases its chances of being born healthy. If we chose to deliver both twins now, the bigger one will probably do okay, though there is still the chance of complications, but the second, smaller twin is more likely to struggle, because they are twins they are already smaller than they would be for their gestation. I'm guessing—' Annie turned to Raphael for confirmation '—from what we can see on the scan that the smaller baby is closer to twenty weeks' size.'

'So essentially you are saying that, whatever we do, we could lose either one or both of our children.' Although Roy's voice was calm, Annie could see that he was finding it difficult not to break down in front of his wife. Once again she marvelled at the very real love between this couple. Beside him, Claire was crying quietly. 'How are we supposed to decide what to do?' Roy continued.

'If I were you,' Raphael said, 'I would wait another week or two.' Annie looked at him, surprised. After everything he had said about not wanting to make a decision for the couple, here he was doing just that. But as she caught his eye, she knew what he was thinking. Waiting gave the couple a better chance of one healthy child.

'Essentially, what Dr Castillo is saying is that if you do nothing right now, you have a better chance of having one normal child. But there is a greater risk of the second twin dying in utero. If you go ahead and have a section today then the second twin could still die, and the bigger one still has a chance of complications. But there is a chance both could survive.'

'I don't want either of my babies to die,' Claire cried. 'I love them both. I can't sacrifice one for the other.'

'We will go along with whatever you decide, of course,' Raphael said. 'I just wanted to make sure you understand the options.'

'Thank you for your frankness, Dr Castillo,' Roy said quietly. 'I wonder if my wife and I could have a moment to discuss it?'

'You don't have to make up your minds right now,' Annie interjected. 'Go home. Have a think about it. Then let us know.'

'From what you tell us, every day we delay is a day that one of our babies could die. No, I think we need to decide now, today. We just need some time.' He looked up at Annie and she recoiled from the naked pain in his eyes. She had grown fond of the couple and she would have given anything in her power to make everything all right for them. But it wasn't in her power, she admitted sadly as she followed Raphael out of the room, leaving Claire in Roy's arms. They had done everything they could.

In the staff room Raphael turned to face Annie.

'Are you okay?' he asked gently.

Annie nodded glumly. 'I just wish we could wave a magic wand and make everything all right for them. They want this so much.' Her voice broke and before she knew it Raphael had pulled her into his arms. She leaned her head against his chest as he stroked her hair.

'You shouldn't take every case so much to heart, *cariño*.'

She let herself relax in his arms. Here it felt as if nothing bad could ever happen to her, or to anyone else. In his arms she felt as if she'd come home. Reluctantly, she eased herself away from him. She had to remember that all he was offering her was friendship. Even if her beating heart reminded her that she wanted so much more.

Raphael looked down at her, his dark eyes glowing, and Annie caught her breath. She knew she must be mistaken, but he was looking at her as if…as if he wanted to kiss her. The air fizzled and crackled between them, just as it had the night they'd met, and Annie felt her world tilt.

Before either of them could move, Roy appeared at the door, mercifully oblivious to the atmosphere in the room.

'We've made our decision,' he said.

Back inside the consulting room, Claire had dried her tears and was sitting pale-faced but composed.

'We are going to take Dr Castillo's advice and wait,' she said calmly, looking Annie directly in the eyes. 'I know we might lose one this way, but we have waited so long to have children we just can't take the chance of losing them both. It's not about whether they'll have problems, I will love my children regardless and with Roy and his family's support we would cope. No, it's the thought that if I have a section now, I could lose both my children. I cannot risk that.'

'For what it's worth,' Raphael said, 'I think it's the right decision. But I'm going to suggest you attend day-care clinic twice a week so we can monitor you. I know it will be difficult for you, but it means if there is a sudden change we can act quickly.'

'I think you're being very brave,' Annie added. 'It's an impossible decision, but we are going to do everything we can to see you through it.' Glancing up, she caught the gleam of approval in Raphael's eyes. Almost imperceptibly he nodded at her. But it wasn't that she necessarily agreed with him, it was simply that the couple having made up their minds needed her full support. She just hoped for all their sakes that they had made the right choice.

CHAPTER TEN

ALMOST imperceptibly, Annie and Raphael developed a routine. Every evening, when he wasn't on call, Raphael would call at the cottage and after he had interrogated her about her health they would go for a walk down to the harbour. They would talk about Spain and Penhally Bay and places they had been on holiday. Everything, it seemed, except what was going to happen once the baby was born. But Annie didn't want to spoil the fragile peace between them. They discovered a shared love of opera and Annie admitted she loved country and western music and Raphael teased her about it. He told her that he played the guitar sometimes for the flamenco dancers for which his home town was famous.

'You must come back to Spain,' he said. 'There is so much I want to show you.'

Whenever he suggested it, which was often, Annie would smile. 'Of course I'll want to bring him or her to Spain. I want my child to grow up knowing about all their family.'

The evenings were getting lighter every day as her bump grew larger. Annie saw Kate at the surgery for her check-ups and the senior midwife declared herself happy with Annie's progress. Her baby was due at the end of September and towards the end of June, Annie decided that it was time to prepare the nursery. If she waited much longer she'd never be able to balance on the stepladder.

And that was where Raphael found her one evening when she was up the ladder, painting the wall of the soon-to-be nursery.

'Come down at once,' he said crossly. He had stopped waiting for Annie to open the door to him and would just come in after a brief warning knock.

'Whatever for? I've still a good half of the wall to do.' She carried on painting. 'If you want to help, grab a brush from over there.' As she indicated the brushes and paint for the wall, the ladder wobbled and Annie almost lost her balance. But in a flash Raphael was up the ladder, steadying her against him.

'Be careful, *cariño*,' he said. 'Please come down.'

'Hey, I'm okay. I just lost my balance for a moment. I wouldn't have fallen.' But Raphael clearly wasn't in the mood for an argument. He picked her up and lifted her down from the ladder. He held her tight against him and she could feel the thudding of his heart through the thin cotton of his T-shirt. Her body melted into his, at least as far as her abdomen would let her, and his arms moved down her body, pressing her closer. Annie felt dizzy with desire. Before she could help herself her arms snaked around his neck and she was lifting her face to his.

Gently he disentangled her arms from around his neck and stood back.

'I don't think it would be a good idea,' he said.

Annie was mortified. What on earth had got into her? Given the slightest bit of encouragement, she would have kissed him. It was what she longed to do. It was what she had been longing to do for weeks now, she realised with a thud of her heart. It didn't matter what she told herself, she found him as devastatingly gorgeous and sexy as the day she had first met him. She had tried to pretend that she didn't but she could no longer hide it from herself. Or from him, she thought ruefully. There was no mistaking her intent—at least not for a man as experienced as Raphael.

'No,' she said shortly. 'I can see that a heavily pregnant woman might not be everyone's cup of tea.'

'*Mierda*,' he groaned under his breath. 'You should see yourself. I doubt there is a woman in the world who looks more beautiful than you do right now. But it is not right. We have to be sensible. What is the point in having sex—no matter how much I would like to—when we are just becoming friends?'

Regardless of what he said, Annie felt rejected. Did he think she was trying to seduce him, to force him into a deeper relationship?

'I'm sorry,' she said stiffly. 'I don't know what I was thinking.' Then she tried a smile to ease some of the tension. 'They do say some women react like that to pregnancy hormones. I'm clearly one of them.'

Raphael looked at her quizzically then opened his mouth as if he were about to say something. But then he seemed to change his mind and picked up a paintbrush.

'I will finish this,' he said. 'You put your feet up and rest.'

'I'm not tired! In fact, I feel great. I'll make us something to eat,' she said.

By the time she returned from the kitchen to tell him the meal was ready, Raphael had finished the room. He stood back and surveyed his work, looking decidedly pleased with himself.

'I wonder what it will be. A boy or a girl.'

'We'll just have to wait to find out,' Annie teased.

Raphael wiped his hand across his forehead, leaving a yellow streak of paint behind. Impulsively, Annie stood on tiptoe to wipe away the smear.

Raphael reached up and trapped her hand in his. He brought her hand to his lips and kissed her fingers, sending a jolt of electricity all the way to her toes. Before she knew it, he was kissing her. Deep, searching kisses as if he wanted to possess her very soul. But even as she felt herself melt in his arms, Annie knew it was a mistake. Breathlessly she pulled away. They stood looking at each other. Before either of them could speak, Raphael's pager bleeped. He looked at the number and frowned. 'It's the hospital. Can I use your phone?'

As soon as he replaced the phone a little later, Annie knew something was up.

'It's Claire,' he said. 'She's gone into labour. I need to go to the hospital. I promised her I would do her section.'

'I'm coming with you,' Annie said, picking up her jacket.

'Of course. I know they both want you there.'

As they drove, they discussed Claire.

'At least she's made it to twenty-eight weeks,' Annie said as Raphael negotiated the narrow lanes to the hospital. Annie had been present when Raphael had scanned Claire the day before. Everyone had been relieved to see the second twin's heart was still beating strongly.

'Yes. It's better than I hoped or expected.'

'The twins will need to spend a few weeks in Special Care. But let's just hope the second twin survives.'

Too busy concentrating on the road, Raphael didn't reply.

As soon as they arrived at the hospital they rushed down

to theatre and were ready and waiting by the time Claire was wheeled in with an apprehensive Roy at her side.

Annie bent over the mother to be and smiled reassuringly. 'You'll be a mum soon,' she whispered.

Claire looked up at her with frightened eyes. 'I'm scared, Annie. So scared.'

'Everything will be okay,' Annie said. 'You've done really well to have managed this far. And both hearts are beating strongly. We'll need to take your babies up to Special Care as soon as they are delivered. But we'll let you see them as soon as we can. Okay?'

As soon as Claire's spinal block was working, Raphael made his first incision. It wasn't the first time Annie had seen him operate, but she never tired of the way his brow furrowed as he concentrated. He operated quickly, without wasting any time. Within minutes he was removing the bigger of the twins. As Annie stepped forward to take the girl from Raphael she was pleased to note that the first baby was a good size and, as it gave a loud cry, with a good set of lungs. The second twin was a little boy, and was more of a concern. He was very small and Annie knew that his parents were in for weeks of worry while his lungs developed fully. Very briefly, as promised, Annie showed Claire and Roy their babies before handing them over to the paediatrician.

'They're both so tiny,' Claire whispered.

'They both have a good chance, Claire,' Annie said. 'They'll look after them upstairs. I'll take you up to see them as soon as possible.'

Claire looked from Annie to Raphael, tears glistening in her eyes.

'Thank you,' she whispered.

Annie smiled back. She had a good feeling about the twins.

* * *

Later, after they had left Claire and Roy, Raphael drove them both back to Annie's house. Neither of them spoke, each too preoccupied with their thoughts. Annie thought back to the kiss they had shared. She had known that she loved him, had known from the day she had met him that she loved him, she just hadn't been able to admit it to herself. Whatever she had felt for Robert, it had come no where near the feelings she had for Raphael. Whenever he was near every atom in her body seemed to come alive, and when he wasn't there she missed him desperately.

She sneaked a glance at him from under her lashes. He was like the missing piece of the jigsaw that was her life. But it was no use. Although he was attracted to her, he didn't love her. And Annie would never again be with someone who didn't feel about her the way she felt about them. Whatever pain lay in store for her, she would have to deal with it. Even though it would be torture to see him, share her child with him, stand by while he married someone else, she had no choice. As long as he wanted to be part of their child's life, she would have to let him. She just had to make sure he never guessed how she felt about him.

The days passed and Annie felt well and continued to revel in feeling the life growing inside her. Although she still had a few weeks to go, she was happy that everything was ready for the baby. Raphael had finished painting the nursery and he had assembled the cot, with her passing him the tools, much in the same way as she passed him instruments in theatre. At the hospital they worked together often and had developed an easy understanding of how each other worked. Raphael's reputation was spreading and more and more patients, especially those with high-risk pregnancies, were asking to see him.

After her clinic one morning, Annie went in search of Raphael and she found him in the doctors' lounge, chatting with Ben Carter.

As soon as Raphael spotted her he stood and went across to her. He touched her hand. 'What is it, Annie? Are you okay?' His concern never ceased to touch her, although she knew it was mainly for his unborn child. They still hadn't spoken about what would happen after the birth. For the time being, Annie was content to let things ride.

'I've just seen Tilly down at the clinic. I wanted her to see you, but she wouldn't stay.'

'What's going on with her?' Raphael asked. 'Her blood-glucose control was terrible the last time we saw her. I had hoped she would have managed to bring it under control with changes to her diet and increasing her insulin.'

'That's just it. Her glucose profile was even worse today and the baby is much bigger than it should be for her dates.'

Raphael chewed his lip, looking thoughtful. 'Does her partner come with her?'

'He wasn't here today.'

'It would be useful to know what he thinks,' Raphael said. 'Tell you what, why don't I call in on them on my way home tonight? Would that help, do you think?'

Annie was relieved. She couldn't explain it but she felt really uneasy about Tilly. The young woman wasn't looking after herself and Annie knew she would be devastated if she lost her baby. Why wasn't she looking after herself better? Was it simply that Annie and Raphael hadn't managed to get across how crucial this was for the health of her baby?

'We should both go,' Annie said. 'I'll meet you there after work. Say about sixish. Would that be okay?'

'I have an elective section this afternoon after my main list is finished. But I should be able to make it, if everything goes according to plan. Which it will do.' He grinned down at her.

Her heart flipped. There was something so supremely confident about Raphael. In another man it might have come across as arrogance, but in him it was simple recognition of his own ability.

'But before theatre I have a postnatal ward round to do,' he continued. 'Are you joining me?'

Annie watched as Raphael went to see each of his patients. Each woman got the same attention, as if she were the most important person in the world to him right at that moment. If someone's baby was crying, Raphael would pick it up and rock it in his arms while he talked to the woman. He always managed to find some compliment for each baby that left the mother smiling with pride, believing her baby to have been singled out for particular praise. But it wasn't an act. Annie could see he was genuinely interested. It was a different side to Raphael, one she had seen countless times since he had come to work at St Piran's but it never ceased to surprise her. How much more tender he would be with his own child she could only guess at.

'I thought Spanish men were too macho to coo over babies,' she teased him as they made their way out of the ward.

'Coo?' He looked at her, puzzled. 'What is this coo? It doesn't sound very nice.'

'Fuss. That's what it means,' Annie replied.

'Spanish men love children,' he said. 'We don't see them as inconveniences to be hidden away, like some countries. I would like a whole brood of them one day. A football team—or at least a five-a-side.'

Annie felt her heart crack a little. It was another reason why she and Raphael would never be anything except co-parents. The baby she was carrying was enough of a miracle. There would never be any more for her.

Annie knocked on the door of Tilly's small cottage but there was no reply. It was strange. She had telephoned after speaking to Raphael to warn her that they would be calling in around six. Perhaps Tilly had popped out to the shops?

She knocked again and then tried the door, and was surprised to find it unlocked. She opened it and walked in. The residents sometimes left their doors unlocked in the winter, but with the influx of tourist at this time of year, people tended to be more careful. The house didn't feel empty. Music was playing on the radio and there was a bag of unpacked shopping at the door, as if it had been abandoned. Immediately Annie felt alarm bells ringing. She stepped further into the house, calling out Tilly's name. Perhaps she had gone for a bath? But then as soon as she entered the sitting room she saw her. Tilly was lying on the floor, unmoving, and Annie rushed to her side, dropping to her knees. The young woman was unconscious and Annie made sure Tilly was breathing before pushing her over on her side into the recovery position. She smelt for the distinctive odour of ketones, but it wasn't there. Tilly must be having a hypo. So she needed to get sugar in to her system. Quickly, she rummaged in her bag. Did she still have the glucose gel she kept for emergencies? Thankfully, she discovered it hidden under a glucose test kit—she'd need that too. Taking a generous dollop from the container she spread the gel inside Tilly's lips, hoping the sugar would be absorbed rapidly.

She wondered how long Tilly had been lying unconscious. Where was John? Shouldn't he be home by now? And where was Raphael? She could do with his help. She bent over Tilly, pricking her finger with the stylet from the testing kit. Her glucose was dangerously low, no wonder she was unconscious. She needed to get her to hospital. She was digging in her shoulder bag for her mobile when she heard Raphael's voice calling out her name.

He stood there, taking in the scene with a glance.

'I found her here like this just a couple of minutes ago. She's having a bad hypo. I've put some glucose gel on her lips, but so far it's having no effect and I haven't had a chance to check the baby yet. I was just about to call for an ambulance when you arrived.'

'What about glucagon?' he said, crouching beside Annie and checking Tilly's pulse. 'We teach all the diabetic mothers to use it an emergency. She must a keep a syringe of it somewhere handy.' He took the Sonicaid Annie held out to him. 'I'll check the foetal heart while you see if you can find it.'

'Shouldn't I phone for an ambulance first?'

'No, if we can get some glucagon into her that'll buy us the time we need. She could do with a drip, too.'

'Found it!' Annie exclaimed, taking the cover off the pre-filled syringe and plunging the needle into Tilly's leg. Thankfully she had left it in full view on the side table.

'She should come round quickly now,' Raphael said, and sure enough Tilly groaned. Over her stirring form Raphael and Annie smiled at each other. Their eyes locked and Annie felt her world spin on its axis. He was looking at her as if… Then his eyes seemed to lose their warmth—as if she was a professional he admired, she admonished herself. Nothing more.

'We still need to get her to hospital. The baby seems fine, but her diabetes is so badly controlled I'm not sure we should let the pregnancy continue much longer. She's thirty-five weeks. Maybe it's just as well to get her delivered.'

'I need to find out what's going on with her when we get her to hospital,' Annie said. 'I know how much she wants this baby so for her to be taking chances with her health like this seems out of character.'

'There will be time for that later. I agree it's important, but right now we have to make sure that the baby stays healthy long enough to be delivered. I suggest that once she comes round completely, we put her in the back of my car and take her there ourselves. If that's okay with you?'

Annie nodded. She'd feel happier once she knew that Tilly was in hospital where she could be properly looked after.

Tilly stirred and her eyes focused gradually on Annie. 'Where am I? What happened? Where's John?' She tried to sit up, her eyes frantically searching the room. As soon as she realised John wasn't there she sank back down and began to cry quietly. 'He didn't come back, did he? He's never coming back. What am I going to do?'

'Hush, Tilly,' Annie soothed. 'You slipped into a hypo, but you and your baby are all right now. Dr Castillo is here and we're going to take you to hospital. We can find John later. You can phone him from the ward.'

'You don't understand,' Tilly wailed. 'He's not coming back. He doesn't want me or the baby.' And then as Annie put her arms around the heaving shoulders of her distressed patient, Tilly sobbed as if her heart would break.

By the time they had Tilly settled in the ward it was almost eight. Annie was feeling tired and hungry. She and Raphael agreed that they would wait until the next day before making a decision whether or not to deliver Tilly's baby early.

'She's thirty-five weeks,' Raphael said as they made their way to his car. 'Obviously I'd prefer to wait another couple of weeks but I don't think we can afford to take the risk.'

'At least these days a thirty-five-weeker has an excellent chance of doing well. I agree with you, the longer we wait the riskier for Tilly's baby.'

Raphael opened the door of his car for Annie and helped her in. As she sat back in the leather seat Annie yawned. 'I think I'll go straight to bed,' she said. 'I'm too exhausted even to think about cooking.' Raphael looked at her sharply but slid the car into gear without saying anything.

'I wish Tilly had told me she and John were having problems,' Annie said. 'I would have kept a closer eye on her had I known.'

'What kind of man leaves his partner to cope with a pregnancy on her own?' Raphael said savagely. 'Especially when he knows there are difficulties.'

'From what she told us, they had been having problems for a while. That's why she got pregnant. She thought it would bring them back together. Poor girl.'

'Irresponsible, you mean,' Raphael said. 'Gambling with her own health as well as the health of her baby.'

'I don't think you can be too hard on her,' Annie said. 'She loves John and she really wants this baby. Sometimes we all do things that aren't completely rational. At least, I do. Can you say you've never done anything that wasn't logically thought out?'

He turned his head towards her and looked as if he were about to say something then thought better of it. 'I just wish people would realise that a baby isn't an accessory,' he said.

'That they are a commitment for life. Not just something you have on a whim.'

Annie heard the underlying bitterness to his words and knew he was thinking about Sebastian.

'It is not our job to be judgemental,' Annie insisted. 'Our job is to ensure a healthy baby at the end. Just that. And if that means getting involved with their lives to make sure of that outcome, it's all part of the job. At least, that's the way I see it.' Annie broke off, aware that she sounded heated. But to her, patients weren't just pregnant women, they were women with lives, women like Tilly with relationship problems, women like her who had to balance motherhood with a career, women who had financial worries, and all of that had to be taken into consideration.

Raphael pulled up outside her house and switched off the ignition. 'You really care about them all, don't you?' he said. 'They all matter.' He looked into the distance and Annie could see the lines of tiredness creasing his eyes—or was it sadness? 'But what about the fathers?' he continued softly. 'Don't they have rights too? Don't they play an important part?' He laughed mirthlessly. 'Or do we exist just to provide the sperm?'

Annie turned to Raphael. 'I know your wife hurt you badly,' she said, 'but not every woman is like her. Most of us just want…' She hesitated. 'Most of us want a loving relationship, someone to share the ups and downs of life. And if a baby is part of that…so much the better.' She had to force herself to look at him. 'I know we got it the wrong way round. In an ideal world, I would be having a baby with someone who loved me.' A muscle twitched in his jaw as he studied her intently. He looked as far away from Annie as she had ever seen him. 'But at least I know my baby will have a father who will cherish him. Who will, I know, be there for him. And when it comes down to it, that is the most important thing of all.'

Suddenly the clouds vanished from his eyes. 'What is important that you eat and then get some rest. Come on, let's see what you have in that fridge. I may not be any good at making toast but I can cook a great frittata.'

Annie thought about protesting. She didn't know whether she had the energy to deal with Raphael in her house. It was hard enough to hide the way she felt about him at work, but alone with him, with her guard down? The last thing she wanted was for him to guess, if, God forbid, he hadn't already done so. But Raphael was already out of the car and was holding her door open.

'I won't take no for an answer,' he said firmly. 'You're tired. Making you something to eat is the least I can do.'

He stretched out a hand and Annie had no choice but to take it. As she felt his hand wrap around hers she felt a warmth suffuse her body. It would be so good to have someone who cared about her. Someone who wanted this baby as much as she did, because they had deliberately made it out of love. But that wasn't going to happen. But just this once, just for tonight, even if it was only inside her head, couldn't she pretend that they were a normal couple looking forward to the birth of their baby, knowing they had the rest of their lives to look forward to?

'I want to do something for you.' He looked at her intently. 'Please?'

She couldn't refuse the look of entreaty in his deep brown eyes.

'Okay,' she said. 'I give in. Just as long as it is better than the breakfast you made me.'

Annie showered, leaving Raphael to rummage around in her kitchen for the ingredients for a meal. By the time she returned, delicious smells of bacon and garlic were wafting through the kitchen.

'What can I do?' she asked.

'Nothing. Just sit there and look beautiful,' Raphael replied, settling her into an armchair.

'I'm not ill, you know,' she protested, but she couldn't stop a smile from creeping across her face. He had called her beautiful. Did he really think so, or was it just part of the patter he gave every woman? The thought wiped the smile off her face. Don't think about that just now, she told herself. Just enjoy being here with him tonight.

After they had eaten—and Raphael was right, the frittata was delicious—Raphael made them some coffee. They sat in companionable silence for a while.

'What are you hoping for?' Raphael asked suddenly. 'A boy or a girl?'

'Oh, I don't mind. I'm just so happy to be having a baby at all. As long as it's healthy…' She laughed. 'You know, when mothers used to say that, I wasn't ever sure whether I believed them or not. Now I know that they meant it.' Suddenly she felt a kick just below her ribs. 'Oops,' she said. 'The way this one is kicking, I think we may have a footballer on our hands.'

In a flash, Raphael was off his chair and on his knees beside her. He looked up, searching her eyes. 'Can I feel?' he asked.

She nodded, suddenly breathless. He placed his hand gently on her stomach, just as the baby gave another vigorous kick. As she looked down on Raphael's bent head, she was tempted to place her hand on his thick curls and run her fingers through his hair. It took all her willpower to resist the impulse. Especially when he looked up at her and she saw the tenderness in his eyes.

'I would like a girl,' he said. 'One who looks just like you. A girl who is just like you.'

Her breath caught in her throat. He reached up and took her hand, kissing each finger in turn. The pressure of his lips was an exquisite pain and every bit of her cried out to be taken in his arms and kissed senseless.

Slowly he rose to her feet and pulled her upright. Then she was in his arms and he was kissing her. Unsure, she pulled away slightly but as he held her closer, dropping his hands to her hips, there was no mistaking his desire for her. She closed her eyes and gave in to the feelings shooting around her body. If he hadn't been holding her, she didn't think her legs could have kept her upright.

Suddenly he pulled away. He was breathing deeply, his eyes black with desire. She almost whimpered when she felt him release her.

'*Mierda,*' he said. 'It is not good to make love. Not now.'

But then she was back in his arms. His hands were on her breasts, his touch sending hot flashes of need to her groin. Slowly he pulled open her dressing gown, revealing her bra and panties and her swollen belly. She covered her belly with her hands, feeling shy.

'Let me see,' he demanded. 'Don't you know how beautiful you are to me, especially now, with my baby growing inside you?'

He eased the dressing gown off her shoulders and lowered her onto the rug beside the fire, the flickering light playing across his features. He dipped a hand under her bra and she felt her nipples tighten in response. Why was he doing this?

He had just said they couldn't make love. Then his hand reached behind her back and he undid the clip of her bra. Her breasts sprang free and he cupped them, his thumbs circling her nipples sending shock waves of pleasure through her.

'Ah,' he said, a smile on his lips 'But I didn't say there weren't other ways of making love that would be safe for the baby.' He trailed a hand down over her stomach. His hand rested there for a moment, then he lowered his head and took one of her nipples into his mouth. Annie was lost. She could no more have stopped him than she could have carried an elephant on her back. Every touch of his fingers made her want more. The sensations in her body were overpowering. She knew it wouldn't be long before she had to give in, but at the same time she never ever wanted him to stop doing what he was doing.

His hand resting on her belly slid lower until it was resting just at the top of her panties. He pulled his head away and looked into her eyes. 'Do you want me to stop?' he asked. She shook her head, unable to speak. She had just enough time to see the triumph in his eyes before he was slipping his hand under the silk and between her legs. Then she was moving against him, unable to prevent her body's response to his touch. Then slowly, as he touched her gently at first, then with increasing pressure and pace, she felt her body explode with pleasure and she cried his name.

Eventually the world steadied around them and Raphael held her in his arms as her breathing returned to normal. She wondered at his self-control, that he could have the restraint to love her without asking anything in return. All of a sudden she felt shy again. She reached over and undid his belt and he groaned as she touched him lightly with her fingers and pulled her closer.

'You don't have to,' he said, as if the words physically hurt him.

'But I want to,' Annie said quietly. She knelt over him and undid the buttons of his jeans, then they were off and he was lying naked beside her. Remembering from the night they had met, she touched him the way he liked it, teasing him, slowing down, sometimes stopping when she sensed he was near then starting again. Then when she knew he couldn't take much more she used both her hands until he, holding her in a vice-like grip, gave in to his own climax.

Later they lay in each other's arms. Annie laid her head on the smoothness of Raphael's chest where she could hear the steady thump, thump of his heart. His hands stroked her hair, smoothing it away from her eyes.

'Will you marry me, Annie?' he said.

Annie sat bolt upright. She felt a zing of happiness course through her veins. He wanted to marry her. He must feel the same way she did. The connection they had felt that first night was still there; it hadn't gone away.

'Pardon?' she said, wanting to make sure she had heard him right. 'What did you say.'

He sat up, grinning at her. The light bounced off his bronzed skin. She had never thought him so sexy as she did right them. She knew she loved every inch of him. His thoughtfulness, his humour, even his old-fashioned masculinity, and he loved her! It was almost too much to take in. She had resigned herself to never finding someone who loved her the way she needed to be loved. Wholeheartedly, without reservation, and now, just when she had thought she couldn't be happier...

'We could live in Spain. You, me and the baby. Be a family,' he said. 'A real family.'

An icy shiver ran up Annie's spine. She couldn't help but notice that he hadn't said he loved her.

'Live in Spain? But my job is here, my parents, my friends,' she said quietly. If he loved her, surely he'd be prepared to be wherever she was?

'You would be part of my family. My mother would welcome you like her own daughter. She will love you. I am sure of it.'

But still he hadn't said *he* loved her.

'And as for your job, you don't need to work. I have plenty of money and besides a woman should be at home with her child, no?' He continued, seemingly oblivious to her silence, 'Of course, then there will be no need to go to the lawyers for access.'

She was furious. She stood, picking up her discarded dressing gown and pulling it on over her shoulders.

'So that is what this is about,' she said through clenched teeth. 'My God, Raphael, is there nothing you wouldn't do to get your own way? Had you planned this all along? Did you really think that after you made love to me, I'd be so grateful that I would go along with your plans? Was this the only way left to get your child with you in Spain? And if the price you have to pay for that is marriage to a woman you don't really love, then so be it.'

She picked up his jeans and T-shirt and flung them at him. 'But what about what I want? Did that cross your mind? Please don't imagine for one minute that I would enter into a loveless marriage, no matter how convenient.'

If she hadn't been so angry she might have laughed at the bewilderment on Raphael's face as he slipped on his T-shirt and jeans. But she was in no mood for laughing. How could she have let her guard down? She knew how much Raphael wanted this baby and she had completely underestimated the lengths he would go to to get what he wanted.

'Let yourself out,' she said. 'I'm going to bed.'

CHAPTER ELEVEN

AFTER leaving Annie's, Raphael decided to go for a walk on the beach. He was far too restless to go to sleep and he needed time to think. He always thought better when he was doing something. He had thought about following her into the bedroom and trying to explain, but something told him that Annie was in no mood to listen to him, let alone believe him. *Dios*, he thought ruefully, she is like a tiger when she is angry. He had never seen her other than quiet and calm, but he didn't find the new side to Annie off-putting. He was delighted that there was still lots more to find out about her. And whatever she thought right now, he fully intended that they would have time to discover each other.

The night sky was shot with lilac. Until recently he had wondered if he had done the right thing coming here. He thought back to the day he had met Annie. He had been hurting then, and the pain he had seen reflected in her eyes had drawn him to her. It hadn't just been her beauty, although with her pale skin and light green eyes and that luscious body, there was no denying he had been powerfully attracted to her. So attracted he hadn't been able to stop himself taking her to bed, even though he had known in his soul that it was dangerous. And he had been right. But she had turned out to be dangerous in a way he couldn't have possibly imagined.

When he'd found out she was pregnant he hadn't been sure she was telling him the truth. After all, he had been deceived before. But the more he learned about her, the more he knew that she didn't have a deceitful bone in her body. She was too transparent for a start. He wondered if she realised how every emotion showed on her face—he always knew what she was thinking. But the worst thing of all was he knew he was falling in love with her. He couldn't stop thinking about her, he couldn't stop himself remembering how she had felt in his arms. Her soft, silky skin, the smell of her perfume, the way the pulse beat at the base of her throat, the way her thick hair fell across his face when they were making love covering him in her scent. And it wasn't just a physical attraction he felt any longer. If it had been he knew he would have been able to deal with that. It was her innate kindness, her laugh, the way she smiled, her mouth curving at the corners, and the way her eyes sparkled when she was happy.

He groaned aloud and, picking up a pebble, he threw it into the sea where it skipped over the waves. It was too late. He wasn't *falling* in love with her. He already loved her. With a passion. All he had to do now was persuade her that he meant it.

After Raphael left, Annie made herself a cup of tea, still fuming. How could she have been so naïve? She rubbed her back. She'd had a dull ache all day and now it was getting worse. A flicker of fear shot through her as her abdomen cramped. Dear God, no! She couldn't be going into labour. It was far too early. She was only twenty-eight weeks.

'Okay,' she told herself. 'Keep calm.' It could be Braxton-

Hicks contractions, couldn't it? Or a tummy bug. It was one thing being a trained midwife and being able to reassure her patients, but quite another being the patient herself. She looked at her watch. Ten o'clock. It was late, but Kate or Chloe would probably still be awake. She could phone one of them, just for reassurance. She could also phone Raphael, of course, but she quickly dismissed the thought. Right now he was the last person she wanted to speak to. She had told him she could cope perfectly well without him so she could hardly call him every time she felt a twinge.

Making up her mind, she phoned Kate. Happily she hadn't gone to bed, but straight away Kate picked up on Annie's anxiety.

'What is it, Annie?' she said. 'Is something wrong?'

'It's probably nothing,' Annie said. 'But I've been having some lower back pain and some cramping. I'm probably being over-anxious, but I just wondered…' As she said the words a sharp tight pain squeezed her abdomen and she gasped.

'I'm coming,' Kate said. 'But first I'm going to call an ambulance. Only as a precaution. Just hold on, Annie, I'll be there in ten minutes.'

Now Annie was seriously frightened. If Kate was calling for an ambulance, she must be worried too. But they had to be wrong. She couldn't be going into labour. She just couldn't. It was far too early. But Annie knew that it was entirely possible. The chances of premature labour had slightly increased after she'd had the miscarriage scare. Kate would know that, too. It was probably why she had called the ambulance. She sat down as another wave of pain washed through her body. She wrapped her arms around her body, almost as if by doing so she could keep her baby safe inside her. If she was going into labour she needed to get to hospital, perhaps there they could give her something to stop it. Every day the baby stayed safe in her womb was crucial at this point.

Unaware of how much time had passed since she had called Kate, she was relieved when she heard a knock on the door. Thank God, she thought. Kate had arrived. Maybe everything would still be okay.

Raphael had decided to go back and see Annie. Whatever she said, they needed to talk. He had to tell her how he felt.

But one look at her, curled up in the armchair, her eyes wild with terror, was enough to send his heart crashing against his ribs.

Before he could breathe he was by her side.

'What is it, Annie?' he said, taking in her pale face and pinched lips.

She moaned and clutched her stomach. 'The baby,' she gasped. 'I think it's coming.'

She reached out a hand and gripped his arm. 'Make it stop, Raphael. It's too early, please make it stop. I can't lose my baby. You have to help me.'

Raphael forced his own fear away. He needed to be strong for Annie right now.

'Tell me,' he said gently.

'I've been having backache all day, but it was different from before. I just thought I had strained a muscle doing yoga. But now I've started cramping.' Her eyes shimmered with tears as she looked up at him. 'I phoned Kate. She's phoning for an ambulance and then she's coming.'

Raphael's heart contracted. She had gone to someone else—not him—when she had needed help. She must really hate him. But he couldn't let himself think of that right now.

All that mattered was making sure that Annie was all right. Even the baby…his heart twisted…wasn't as important as Annie.

In the distance he could hear the wail of the ambulance and the door opened and Kate burst in, carrying her medical bag.

'Dr Castillo. I didn't realise you were here. What's going on?'

'I haven't had time to make an assessment,' he said. 'But I'm afraid it sounds as if Annie has gone into labour.'

Hearing his words, Annie moaned again and folded in on herself. Raphael had never seen such anguish before. But she mustn't give up hope. Not yet.

He crouched down beside her and lifted her chin, forcing her to look into his eyes.

'Listen to me, Annie,' he said. 'I am going to do everything we can to save our baby. You have to believe that. Okay?' It took every bit of strength to keep his voice steady, but he couldn't let Annie see how terrified he was.

Annie looked back at him, her eyes wide with pain and fear. But he saw resolve in her eyes. His Annie was stronger than she realised.

Kate passed him the Sonicaid from her bag so he could listen to the foetal heart. He felt almost weak with relief when he heard a steady beat.

'Baby's heartbeat is strong, Annie. We can do a better assessment when we get you to hospital.' He could hear the wail of the ambulance getting closer. 'Perhaps we'll be able to give you steroids. There may still be a chance we can stop labour.'

He looked over at Kate.

'Can you gather a couple of things, please? I will go with Annie in the ambulance.'

'I'm coming, too,' Kate said firmly. 'Annie is my patient

as well as my friend. As far as this baby is concerned, you are the father and not in the best position to make clear-headed judgements. Rob is over at mine, so Jem will be fine.' She took Annie's hand. 'I'll stay with you as long as you need me.' Then she looked at Raphael. 'As long as you both need me.'

Raphael took one look at the determined set of the senior midwife's mouth. He was glad she would be around. Annie needed all the help she could get. She was all that mattered.

Annie was barely aware of being lifted into the ambulance. All she knew was that the pains were stronger and becoming more frequent. She searched Raphael's and Kate's eyes as they bent over her, looking for any sign of optimism, but their expressions were guarded. However she felt about Raphael, she was glad he was there with her. Between him and Kate, Annie knew her baby had the best possible chance, but, if they didn't manage to stop her labour, then her baby would be born at twenty-eight weeks. Annie knew only too well that even if it survived, the chances of complications were hugely increased.

Raphael must have read her mind. He gathered her in his arms, pulling her head against his chest. She felt safe, as if he could protect her from her worst fears.

'We will give you a tocolytic when we get you to hospital,' he said. 'We may still be in time to stop your labour. If we aren't, the baby still has a good chance. Many babies of that gestation do well. You need to remember that.'

'And many don't,' Annie mumbled into his chest. She couldn't even cry now, the fear was too intense. All she wanted was for her baby to live.

Then she was being lifted out of the ambulance. Raphael was shouting orders and Kate was holding her hand. There were lights and people and fear and pain. Then she was in one of the side rooms in the labour ward. Kate was examining her and Annie heard her tell everyone that she was five centimetres dilated. And there was another obstetrician and Julie. Where had she come from? And her obstetrician, Dr Gibson, was talking to Raphael. She couldn't hear what they were saying, but she heard the word *paediatrician* and *too late* and she was more frightened than ever. But Raphael was by her side again.

'It's too late to stop labour,' he said gently. She looked up and she could see the concern and sympathy in Julie and Kate's eyes.

'Look at me,' Raphael commanded. So she forced herself to look at him, not wanting to, knowing that whatever she saw there would be the truth and she wasn't ready for the truth—she'd never be ready.

Her eyes found his and she read the anguish there. He couldn't hide it from her, no matter how much he wanted to.

'You're going to have our baby—soon.' Annie looked away, but he eased her head around. 'Everyone is ready to help. The paediatrician is here and as soon as the baby is delivered he will be taken up to the special care nursery. They will do everything they can up there to keep our baby alive. Right now, you have to listen to Julie and Kate. And I'll be right here.'

'Don't leave me,' she whispered through lips frozen with fear.

'I'll never leave you, *cariño*. I'm staying right here. Where I belong.'

Two hours later Annie gave a final push and felt her child slip into the world and into Kate's waiting arms. Desperately she listened, waiting for a sound to let her know her baby lived. She watched as Julie rushed the baby over to the waiting incubator as she and the paediatrician started working over the tiny form.

'You have a little girl,' Kate said. 'Well done.'

'Can I see her?' Annie asked. More than anything else she wanted to hold her baby in her arms. It could well be the last chance she had.

'We need to let Julie and the paediatrician do what they have to, Annie. Let them take care of our daughter,' Raphael said, but she could see his eyes were shining with unshed tears.

Tentatively she reached out her hand and brushed a lock of hair away from his eyes. 'Is she breathing? Please, Raphael, go to her.'

Raphael left her side, to be replaced by Kate.

'She is breathing, Annie,' she said. 'And although she's very small, she has a good chance. They'll be taking her away to Special Care as soon as they have her stabilised. They'll take you up to see her in a little while. Try and rest now. I promise you, one of us will let you know the second we have news.'

Annie looked past her to the incubator, but there were too many bodies in the way for her to see properly. She struggled to sit up. She needed to see her baby. Her daughter needed to feel her mother's presence. But Kate pressed her back down.

'Annie, we still need to deliver the placenta. And you'll only get in the way. I know it's horrible, but you need to let us do our job.'

Kate was right, of course. But it was so damned hard not being able to see her child. But just then a tiny cry filtered into the room. Her baby was crying. That was a good sign. There was a flurry of activity around the cot and Raphael came back to stand next to Annie.

'They are taking her upstairs just now,' he said. 'But she is breathing. She is beautiful. The most beautiful baby I have ever seen.' His voice cracked.

Hope flared as she saw the look of wonder in his eyes. He wouldn't look like that if her baby wasn't all right, would he? If she couldn't be with their daughter, at least Raphael could. Her baby wouldn't be alone.

'Go with them,' she whispered. 'Stay with her. She needs you.'

Suddenly the atmosphere in the room changed. 'She's haemorrhaging,' Dr Gibson called out. 'Get me some hemabate stat.' There was a flurry of activity and Annie felt panic clench her throat. Who was bleeding? What was happening?

Then Raphael's face swam into view. 'You have a bit of retained placenta,' he said quietly. 'They are giving you something to stop the bleeding.'

'We need to get her to theatre.' It was Dr Gibson. 'Julie, ring down and tell theatre to get ready for us. Then page the anaesthetist. C'mon, everyone, let's get moving.'

Raphael brushed a lock of hair from Annie's eyes. 'Don't be frightened, cariño. Everything's going to be okay. You'll be back on the ward before you know it.'

Annie clutched at his hand, amazed at her own strength. 'I need to see my baby before I go. Please. Just in case…' Her voice caught on a sob. She willed Raphael to understand. If anything went wrong, she might never see her baby.

'There isn't time,' he said. 'We can't afford to wait. We have to take you now.'

'Please, Raphael. Do this for me?'

She could see the hesitation in his eyes. But then he straightened.

'Let her see our baby,' he said urgently.

'There's no time,' Dr Gibson said. 'We have to operate on her *now*. She could bleed out.'

But Raphael moved towards the incubator. 'It will only take a second,' he said, and, picking up the tightly swaddled infant, he brought her over to Annie.

Annie gazed down at her child. She was barely the size of Raphael's hands and she could see every vein in her translucent skin. As she looked at her Annie knew that she would never again experience the powerful emotions that swept through her body. This was her child, and she would fight tooth and nail for her for the rest of her life.

There was a hush in the room as everyone stopped for a second to watch Annie meet her child.

'You fight,' Annie said to her daughter. 'Don't you dare leave me.'

'We need to take you down to theatre now,' Raphael said gently, and Annie knew that her brief moment with her baby was over. 'I'll be there with you.'

'No, Raphael,' Annie said, mustering the last of her strength. 'You go with our daughter. Please. I'll be all right.'

'I don't want to leave you on your own.' He looked after his departing child, obviously torn.

'She needs you more than I do. Besides, Kate is here. Come and tell me as soon as there is any news. Promise?'

He leaned over and brushed the top of her head with his lips. 'Everything is going to be all right. I'll be back as soon as I can.'

When Annie next opened her eyes, it was to find Raphael looking down at her. Fear clutched her chest but before she could speak, Raphael smiled.

'They stopped the bleeding. They had to put an intra-uterine balloon in but it will be removed shortly. You are going to be OK.'

Dazed, Annie looked around. She had a drip in her arm, but apart from feeling a little groggy she was fine. She licked dry lips and, without asking, Raphael poured a glass of water and, slipping his arm behind her shoulders, lifted her slightly so that she could drink. The water was enough to ease Annie's throat sufficiently to speak.

'Where is she? Is she all right? I want to see her.'

'Hey, take it easy, Annie. She's upstairs in Intensive Care. They have her on a respirator, but she's doing well. Our daughter is beautiful.' Annie saw the wonder in his deep brown eyes. But she needed to see her child for herself. That was the only way she could believe that she was all right. She pushed the sheets aside just as Julie entered the room. Annie had worked with Julie many times before and knew the experienced midwife well.

'And just what do you think you are doing?' Julie said, lifting Annie's legs and popping her back into bed.

'I want to see my child, Julie,' Annie said. 'Then I'll come back to bed. I promise.'

'No way,' Julie said firmly. It was a different side to the midwife, one that Annie hadn't seen before, but, then, she hadn't been a patient before. 'You are not leaving this bed. Not until I say so.'

Annie looked across at Raphael. She had to see their daughter. She just had to.

'Raphael, please. Tell them I can go upstairs. Only for a moment. I'll do as I'm told after that.'

Raphael looked at Annie. His eyes softened. 'I'll take responsibility,' he said. 'We'll take the drip with us and put her in a wheelchair. She's so stubborn, if we don't take her she'll be up there as soon as we aren't looking, anyway.'

Julie looked indecisive, but before she could protest further, Raphael was helping Annie out of bed.

'I don't need a wheelchair,' Annie protested, but then as her legs buckled she had to lean on Raphael for support.

'It's a wheelchair or nothing,' Julie said. 'Just give me a mo' to fetch one.'

Annie didn't have the strength to argue. Besides, she didn't want to wait a moment longer to see her baby. Only when she saw her for herself would she truly believe what Raphael had told her.

But it was almost more than she could bear when she finally saw her tiny baby. She was almost hidden from view by wires, her face covered by the ventilator that was breathing for her, and Annie felt cold with dread. More than anything in the world she wanted to hold her daughter. Transfer the strength from her own body to that of her child. Let her know that she was there.

'Remember, it looks worse than it is,' Raphael said, resting his hands on her shoulders. 'The lines and wires are there to monitor her as much as anything.'

Annie nodded. She knew all that, of course she did. Plenty of her mothers over the years had had babies that required time in Special Care. But it was one thing telling a mother not to be frightened by the paraphernalia of Special Care and quite another when it was your baby lying there. So small and so helpless.

She slipped a hand through the hole in the incubator and slipped a finger into her daughter's minuscule hand. Her heart filled with wonder as she felt the small fingers close around hers.

'Hello, darling,' she whispered. 'This is your mummy.

Everything is going to be okay. But you have to fight.' Turning to Raphael, she could see his anguish in eyes. 'I want you to tell me everything the paediatrician has told you. I don't want to be protected, so keep nothing back from me.' She meant every word. Whatever terror gripped her, she was going to stay strong. Her baby needed her and until she was out of danger… She pushed the thought away. One step at a time.

'As you can see, she is being ventilated. Her lungs aren't fully developed yet, so she'll probably stay on it for a few days at least. They are also giving her surfactant to help her breathing.'

'What about…?' She could hardly bare to say the words, but Raphael guessed what she wanted to know.

'We won't know whether there are any complications— if she's suffered any—until later, Annie. She has to get through the next few days first.' He laid a hand on her shoulder and squeezed. 'Come on, let's get you back to bed. I'll come back up here and stay with her while you sleep.'

'I can't leave her,' Annie whispered.

'You are going to need all your strength in the next few days. And she is going to need her mother fit and healthy.'

'How can I sleep when she is fighting for her life?' But even as she said the words Annie felt a wave of fatigue wash over her. She was so tired.

'You can't stay here, Annie. The nurses need to work on her. But you can come back later, when you have had a rest. You lost a great deal of blood earlier.' He looked at his watch. 'It will be morning soon.'

Reluctantly Annie let Raphael take her back to her room and help her back into bed. 'You will wake me if there is any change, no matter how small?'

'Of course.'

'And you won't leave her?' She clutched his hand. 'I know you must be tired, too.'

'I won't leave her,' he promised. 'I'll watch over her while you sleep.'

Knowing he would be true to his word, Annie closed her eyes and gave in to sleep.

It was getting light when Annie next opened her eyes. As the memory of the night before came flooding back, she panicked.

Her baby. She needed to see her baby. Where was Raphael? Why wasn't he here to let her know what was happening? If he was still in Special Care, did that mean something had happened? Knowing that if she called for a nurse they would try and prevent her from getting out of bed, she pushed the bed covers aside and reached for the dressing gown Kate had packed for her. Then on legs that felt like rubber she slipped upstairs and into the special care nursery.

She found Raphael in a chair by the side of the incubator. He was leaning forward, gazing into the incubator and talking quietly in Spanish. Annie stood silently listening. Although she couldn't understand the words, she knew by the timbre of his voice that he was suffering too.

He must have felt her standing behind him because he turned. Annie drew a sharp breath when she saw his face. He looked gaunt with fatigue, his eyes were shadowed and there were lines on his face that Annie had never seen before. Clearly he hadn't left their baby's side, not even to change or shave. He had told her that he would watch over their baby and he had. There was no doubt he cared about his daughter, but would he feel the same way if she turned out to be less than perfect?

'There's no change. I was going to come and see you,' he

said. 'The nurses were supposed to ring up as soon as you were awake.'

'They didn't know. I slipped out when no one was looking. I know the night sister well and she would have tried to stop me. I didn't want to take that risk.' She bent over the cot. Her daughter was still on the respirator and there were wires everywhere. But she was alive. That was all that mattered.

Raphael stood next to her.

'Have you thought of a name? We should name her.'

Annie felt fear claw her throat again. Why was he so keen? Was he about to suggest that they had her baptized—just in case? She shook her head.

'I would like to call her Angela, after my mother.' She took a deep steadying breath and clenched her hands so hard that the nails dug into her palms.

Raphael put his arms around her and held her close. For a moment she resisted, then as he whispered her name she couldn't help herself. She clung to him as she gave in to her grief and fear.

'Angela. Little Angelica. It is a good name,' he murmured into her hair.

And then she was only vaguely aware of Raphael leading her away from the cot and into the staff room. The nurses, seeing her distress, quietly stood up and left them alone. Raphael sat in one of the easy chairs and, still holding her, pulled her onto his lap as if she were a child. She wound her arms around his neck and cried until eventually her tears subsided to hiccups.

She hid her face in his chest. She felt safe there, as if nothing bad could ever happen as long as this man held her. He slid a handkerchief under her bowed head and she took it gratefully, using it to dry her face then blow her nose noisily.

Eventually she sneaked a glance at his face, knowing, but not caring, that she must look a mess.

'I'm sorry,' she said. 'I don't usually cry like that, at least not in front of people.'

As he looked down at her with warm brown eyes she suddenly realised she was still curled up in his lap. Embarrassed, she struggled to her feet, but he put a restraining arm around her waist.

'You must not apologise. Not everyone can be strong all the time, and this is a terrible time for you. But you are not alone. Not any longer. I am here with you.'

He sounded more Spanish, almost as if emotion had robbed him of his hitherto perfect English. But he was suffering too. This was a child he had also longed for. But what if Angela didn't pull through? There was nothing to stop Raphael walking away—and she wouldn't try to stop him. Once again she realised how little she actually knew about this man. She loved him, there was no doubt about that, but if he chose to walk away, she would let him.

She rested her head back on his chest and felt him rest his chin on top of her head. They sat there for a while longer, not saying anything, each one alone with their thoughts.

Eventually Annie eased herself out of his arms. 'I'm going to have a shower and get dressed so I can spend the rest of the day with Angela. Then you could go home and get some rest yourself. You must be exhausted.'

'I'm used to not sleeping.' He smiled up at her.

'No argument,' Annie said firmly. 'I want you back here later this afternoon awake and alert. Neither of us will be any use to Angela if we are falling asleep on our feet.'

Raphael looked surprised. He raised an eyebrow at her and a small smile tugged at the corner of his mouth.

'You must be feeling better, *cariño*, to be wanting to boss me about.'

Annie's heart melted at the look in his eyes. How she wished everything could be different. If only Raphael could love her, nothing would be impossible.

'Go,' he said, tipping her gently off his lap. 'There is something I need to tell you. But now is not the right time. Soon, I hope. When our child is safe, we will talk. But for now let us do what we have to.'

CHAPTER TWELVE

KATE finished packing the box of fruit, home-made jam and crusty rolls she had bought down at the farmers' market earlier that morning. Although she knew Annie wouldn't feel hungry, she hoped she'd be tempted by the snacks. Chloe was due to pick her up shortly so that the two women could go and see Annie together. They wouldn't stay long, just long enough to let Annie know that they were there if she needed them.

Poor Annie. The next few days, even weeks would be awful for her. But all they could do now was hope.

She thought about what she had found that morning when she'd been showering, and wondered what to do. See a doctor, obviously, although the lump was bound to be nothing. If only Rob wasn't away, she could have discussed it with him. Put it in perspective. She'd told herself a hundred times already that it was probably only a cyst, but the small voice in her head wouldn't go away. What if it wasn't? What then?

The slamming of a car door announced Chloe's arrival.

'Are you ready?' Chloe asked as she came into the kitchen. 'Yum, is that some of the Trevellyans' fab cheese?' she said, pinching a piece and popping it into her mouth. Then she looked at Kate sharply and frowned.

'There hasn't been bad news from the hospital, has there?' she asked anxiously.

'No, the baby's doing okay. If she had taken a turn for the worse, someone would have phoned us.'

'What is it, then? You're looking a bit tired.'

Kate laid her hands on the worktop. She didn't want to burden Chloe with her worries, but she hadn't counted on her friend's intuition.

Chloe came across and laid an arm across her shoulder. 'Kate, I can see something's wrong. You know you can talk to me about anything. Is it Rob? Are you two having problems? Or Jem?'

'No, Jem's fine. He's at football practice. And Rob and I are getting on fine. More than fine, in fact. He's so good to me, and fun to be with. I'd forgotten what that was like.'

'Mmm. He is lovely. And Jem seems to get on with him—unless there are problems there? Or is it Nick? Has he said something to upset you?'

Kate realised that Chloe wasn't going to give up. She knew something was wrong and was clearly determined to get to the bottom of it. The young midwife was the closest thing she had to a best friend. One of the few people who knew the truth about Jem. And Nick.

'I felt a lump in my breast this morning when I was showering,' Kate finally admitted. 'I know it's probably nothing but...'

'But you're going to get it checked out,' Chloe finished for her. 'God, Kate, you must be scared stupid. So the sooner you see someone the better. Have you spoken to any of the doctors? What about Rob? Does he know?'

'Rob's away and it's Saturday so, no, I haven't seen anyone. I only discovered it this morning and I had to go to the farmers' market and I want to see Annie. I'll make an appointment to see Oliver next week.'

'Just like you, Kate, to put the needs of others before your own. You're always taking care of other people and forgetting about yourself. But for once I'm not going to let that happen,' Chloe said firmly. 'Oliver is doing the Saturday morning surgery. I'm positive he'll see you today.'

Chloe ignored Kate's protests about not wanting to bother anyone. She was right, of course, it wasn't an emergency and another day or two wasn't going to make any difference, but she dialled the number of the surgery anyway and asked to be put through to Oliver.

'Hello, darling. Yes, everything's fine. It's Kate. She needs to see someone. Straight away. I mean not in front of any life-and-death emergencies, but today, nevertheless.'

Kate couldn't hear the response on the other end of the line.

'She'll be there,' Chloe said firmly, before disconnecting the call and turning to Kate. 'He can see you at the end of surgery. About twelve? That way we can still go and see Annie if you want.'

Kate gave in, knowing it was useless to argue. 'I promised her I would. So if it's okay with you, I'd like to go as planned. But I had no idea you could be so bossy.' She smiled to show there was no malice in the words. 'You're always so mild-mannered with your patients.'

Chloe smiled back. 'I suspect it's the only way I'll get you to do as you're told.'

Suddenly Kate felt frightened.

'God, Chloe. What if it is cancer? What about Jem? I couldn't bear to leave my son alone. And Polly, the new GP. I persuaded her to come back to Penhally and said I'd be here to support her. She'll be here any day now. Now all this…'

Chloe hugged her fiercely. 'Slow down, Kate. Everything's going to be all right. Remember we have some of the best doctors in the world between here and St Piran's. And as you said, it could be nothing. Maybe just a cyst. Let's just wait and see what Oliver has to say.'

Kate knew that Chloe was right. There was no point in worrying until she had to. And right now she had a patient to see. Annie needed her support.

After checking on Angela, Annie returned to her room for a shower. She kept it short, anxious not to be away from the special care nursery too long.

When she emerged feeling almost human, it was to find Chloe and Kate sitting on her freshly made bed, waiting for her. The sight of her two friends broke the control Annie had been so desperately clinging to. Kate opened her arms and Annie let her hold her as she gave in to the anguish and fear of the last few days. It seemed that Kate was always there whenever Annie needed someone. In the absence of her mother, who was desperately trying to get a flight back to the UK, Kate was the next best thing.

Annie wiped her eyes and managed a shaky laugh. 'For someone who hardly ever cries, that's all I seem to have been doing lately.'

'Hey,' Chloe said gently. 'We all need to let go sometimes. And these are exceptional circumstances. How is she, anyway?'

Annie brought them up to date. There wasn't really that much to tell. The next few days would be critical. 'If Angela survives…' Annie choked on the word but took a steadying breath before continuing, 'Then the next hurdle will be whether her brain has been damaged.'

Kate reached out a soothing hand. 'Everyone is rooting for you both,' she said softly. 'How is Raphael holding up?'

'He's been wonderful,' Annie admitted. 'He's hardly left her side. But he's agreed to go home for a bit as soon as I get back up.' She tried a smile. It was weak, but the best she could manage. 'I don't suppose anyone could bring me some clothes from home? I could ask Raphael, I suppose…'

'Tra-la.' Kate smiled, holding up a small case. 'We called by your house on our way in—I held onto your key last night. I think you'll find everything there. I don't think you can trust a man in these circumstances. He might remember the top, but forget the trousers!'

'You're a love,' said Annie gratefully, and, taking the bag from Kate, rummaged around. 'Bless you, you remembered everything—even my deodorant.'

Kate whipped out another carrier bag. 'I brought you something to eat as well. I popped down to the farmers' market this morning and selected some goodies to tempt you. It's my guess you haven't had anything for some time.'

Annie felt her throat close at the gesture. It was so typical of Kate and Chloe and she really appreciated her friends' support.

'I'm sorry, sweetheart, but I'm going to have to get back. I have a patient who is due to deliver very soon and I promised I'd go and see her,' Chloe said apologetically. 'But I'll pop in later if I get the chance.'

Chloe looked at Kate. 'Call me later?'

Kate nodded. Annie thought she looked tired. There were lines of tension around her mouth she hadn't noticed before.

'Thank you both so much for coming. I know you both have your own lives to be getting on with. And I want to get back upstairs, anyway,' Annie said.

'Hey,' Kate said. 'What are friends for? You know you can call me any time.' She kissed Annie on the cheek. 'Take care. I'll see you soon.'

Annie returned to the special care ward to be given the welcome news that Angela had been taken off the respirator. Instead, two tubes had been inserted into Angela's nostrils and she could see her baby's face clearly for the first time. Her breath caught as she gazed down on the beloved features of her child. Angela's lips were like seashells washed in the ocean, her miniature nose perfect. She has Raphael's hair, Annie thought, taking in the dark hair that covered her head. Carefully she inserted a hand into the incubator and stroked the downy skin of her baby.

She knew then that she would stand between her child and a tank or a tidal wave or a stalking tiger. She would lay down her life without a moment's hesitation over and over again if she had to, but right now she could do nothing for her child. Nothing except wait and watch over her. She became aware of a presence behind her and she didn't have to turn to know it was Raphael.

'If I lose her…' Her voice cracked and she had to take a deep breath before she could continue. 'If I lose her, I don't know what I'll do. I can't imagine wanting to go on.'

She felt his hand on her shoulder and then he turned her so that she was facing him. Placing a finger under her chin, he tilted her head, forcing her to meet his gaze.

'Don't say that. Never say that. You are stronger than you think. And anyway, I told you I will not let anything happen to her.' His voice was low and urgent, his need to convince her evident in every syllable. Annie desperately wanted to believe him. She dropped her eyes to his achingly tender mouth before slowly raising her eyes to his. Through her fear she could see her pain reflected in his eyes. He too needed comfort, but Annie couldn't offer him any.

'*Cariño*,' he said, his voice a river of anguish. '*Te quiero con toda mi alma.* I love you with all my soul. You and our daughter are my heart, my soul, my future. All I ever want and all I will ever need.' Annie's heart thumped lurched.

Had he really said he loved her? Could he mean it?

He took her hand and placed it on his chest. She could feel the pounding of his heart through the thin fabric.

'Do you feel that?' he demanded.

Despite her grief, Annie felt a small smile tug at the corner of her mouth. It was such a Latin gesture. She nodded, the emotion welling up inside her preventing her from speaking.

'As long as my heart keeps beating, I will not let anything happen to you or our child.'

But however much she wanted to believe him, she couldn't. It wasn't in his power to promise anything. Least of all that their child would live.

Kate slipped off the examination couch and picked up her blouse, sliding her arms into the sleeves. Oliver waited until she had finished and was settled in the chair opposite him before he spoke.

'There is a lump there. I can feel it the upper left quadrant. As you said, it could be nothing, a cyst perhaps, but I think we should get it checked out all the same.'

Kate could read the concern in his brown eyes. He was being matter-of-fact, but she could read him like a book. He didn't believe it was a cyst and neither did she.

'Does Rob know?' Oliver continued. 'Can he go with you to the hospital? It's Saturday but I might be able to get one of the surgeons to come in and see you. They'll probably want to do a fine needle biopsy and a mammogram.'

'Rob's away this weekend. He's gone up north to see his mother. I would have gone with him if it hadn't been for Jem.' She stood up and went to look out the window. The day, which had started off dull and threatening to rain, had turned into one of those perfect days. In the distance she could see the tips of the waves as they rolled to shore. There were quite a few boats out as well, a mixture of fishing trawlers and yachts. Kate wished she were out there with them, far away from talk of lumps and biopsies and far away from the terror of what it would mean for her son if she turned out to have cancer. She thought about Annie. Her hopes and fears tied up with the tiny life she had given birth to, and all the other people, not just in Penhally Bay but all over the world who would be facing the same uncertainties and fears as she was.

'I can wait my turn like everyone else,' Kate said. 'A day or two isn't going to make much difference.'

'Are you sure you don't want me to phone Ben? He'll know who you should see.'

'No,' Kate said heavily. 'I don't want to jump the queue. It's not fair to every other frightened woman out there. Besides, by the time my appointment comes through, Rob will be back.'

'There's only a week waiting time for urgent appointments,' Oliver said. 'And I'm going to grade yours as urgent.'

Kate smiled wanly. 'Okay,' she said. Just then there was a knock on the door and Nick stuck his head around it.

'Oh, Oliver. I'm sorry. I thought you had finished seeing patients.' Then he noticed Kate and he looked surprised. 'Kate! I didn't think you were in today. Is there something up with one of your patients?' His eyes narrowed. Something in her and Oliver's expression seemed to alert him that Kate's presence was unusual.

'I just had something I wanted to talk over with Oliver,' she said hastily. Well, it was true. But let think Nick it was about a patient.

'There's nothing wrong, is there?' he asked. He walked over to the desk and crouched down next to Kate. 'You would tell me if there was something wrong, wouldn't you?' Kate felt her heart tighten at the obvious concern in his eyes. Whatever problems they might have had, were *still* having, she knew that somewhere deep down inside Nick cared about her, even if it was as just a friend. But that didn't mean she was ready to share her worries with him. He had made it clear often enough that he wasn't prepared to offer her more than the professional support of a colleague. And one thing Kate couldn't bear was for him to feel sorry for her.

She laughed, but the sound was hollow even to her own ears.

'What possibly could be wrong, Nick, that I couldn't cope with on my own?' She didn't mean the words to have such a bitter quality to them, but she couldn't help herself. The one thing she truly wanted from Nick, acceptance of the child they shared, he wasn't able to give her.

'If you're sure?' Nick said, straightening. He sounded less than convinced but Kate knew him well enough to know that he wouldn't probe. One thing you could say about him was that he respected her privacy. He turned back to Oliver, who was watching the exchange quietly. Kate wondered if he had picked up on the tension that seemed to be a permanent feature between her and Nick these days. 'I wondered if you fancied a round of golf this afternoon?' he asked. 'Dragan and Ben are up for it if you are.'

'Sure,' Oliver said. 'I think Chloe has plans for this afternoon, so I'm free.'

'How is Annie?' Nick asked. 'Has anyone spoken to her?'

'I saw her this morning,' Kate said. 'She's okay. Raphael is with her.'

'Raphael? Dr Castillo?' Nick said, looking puzzled.

Oliver and Kate exchanged a smile. Good grief, Kate thought, Nick could be so dense sometimes, completely failing to see what was right underneath his nose.

CHAPTER THIRTEEN

A WEEK after their baby had been born Annie and Raphael sat in the easy chairs the staff had provided and watched over their child. The lights had been turned low, although the nurses and doctors still tended their tiny charges with the same dedication and attentiveness that they did during the day.

Annie rested her eyes, thinking back to what Raphael had said. He had called her his heart and his soul. But surely these were just the words of a man in emotional turmoil to the woman who was locked there with him? She still couldn't believe that he meant them.

'Maybe she'll be a piano player,' he said suddenly into the silence. 'She has your long fingers.' He picked up Annie's hand in one of his. 'Such beautiful hands.' Annie looked down at her hands in surprise. She had never thought of her hands as being beautiful before, but perhaps he was right. Her fingers were long and shapely.

'Why did you come back?' she asked. 'You know, the night Angela was born after we…' She tailed off, blushing furiously, but she wanted to know. Everything had happened so fast it was only now that she had begun to wonder.

He turned towards her, his eyes glowing in the semi

darkness. 'I came back because…because I realised something important. When this is over, I'm going to do everything to win you properly. Make you believe me when I tell you that I want to marry you. Because I love you.'

Annie started to say something but he stopped her words with his fingertip.

'I want us to start over. Do everything as it should have been. How it was meant to be.'

Annie felt something deep down inside her blossom at his words. Could she dare to believe that he meant what he was saying? And did he truly understand what he was saying?

'Don't. Please, Raphael. Don't say any more.' She flinched at the naked pain in his eyes, but forced herself to go on.

'I can't have any more children. You must know that. Angela was miraculous enough. If we marry, you will be signing yourself up to a lifetime of childlessness.' Her voice broke on the words. 'If…' she faltered, but forced herself to go on. 'God forbid, but if Angela doesn't pull through, there will be no more children.'

'I would be signing myself up for a lifetime with the woman I love,' Raphael said firmly. 'The woman without whom life has no meaning—a dark and empty place. Don't you know that when I am with you my life is full of light? I told you before and I will tell you again and keep on telling you until you believe me—you are all I need.'

'You would give up everything for me?' Annie whispered, hardly daring to believe he meant what he was saying.

'I would give my life for you if I had to.' He crouched by her side. 'I have been so foolish. Can you ever forgive me? How could I have ever believed even for the smallest second—' he held out two fingers millimetres apart '—that you were anything except the strong, loving, honest woman you are?'

'Because you believed it once before and she betrayed you,' Annie said, unable to bear the self-reproach in his eyes. 'I can understand.'

'I know I don't deserve you. I am full of mistakes...' Annie hid a smile. His English only ever suffered when his feelings ran high. 'But if you marry me, I will spend the rest of my life proving I am worthy of you. If you want to adopt a little brother or sister for our sweet daughter, I would be happy too.'

Annie still wasn't sure. He might mean it now, but later, in years to come, he might come to regret having married her and that was one thing she would never allow. She would rather let him go—even if it broke her heart—than see him become resentful of her. But before she could formulate the words there was the sound of an alarm going off at Angela's cot. Within seconds the incubator was surrounded. Annie looked at Raphael, terrified.

Quickly the paediatrician attached Angela to a machine again and after a few agonising minutes the monitor stopped bleeping as Angela's breathing returned to normal.

After listening to Angela's chest, the paediatrician turned to Annie and Raphael.

'I think your daughter has patent ductus arteriosus, or PDA as we call it. As you both are probably aware, the blood circulating in the foetus doesn't go through the lungs but bypasses the lungs via an artery. Normally this artery closes itself soon after birth, but in pre-term babies such as yours it sometimes fails to close.'

Raphael nodded. 'I've seen it before.'

'We've been giving her drugs for a day or two to try and close it that way, but that doesn't seem to have worked...'

'So you'll need to do it surgically,' Raphael finished for him.

'But she's so small,' Annie interjected.

Raphael turned to Annie and took both of her hands in his. He looked at her steadily, his brown eyes calm.

'It's her best chance,' he said. 'The surgeons are used to operating on babies of Angela's size. We have to trust them to do what's best for her.'

Annie looked at her daughter. Lying in her cot, all alone attached to tubes and wires. Her child was totally dependent on her parents making the right decision. Annie felt so helpless. What if they made the wrong one? 'But what if...?' Annie couldn't bring herself to finish the sentence.

'Look at me, Annie,' Raphael demanded. Annie dragged her eyes away from her baby. Raphael's eyes burned with his need to convince her. 'Only you have the right to make the decision. I can't. But I love her, too. You have to trust me about this. Please.'

There was no doubting his pain. There was no doubting his love for their daughter. And she did trust him. They were together in this and would always be. Annie realised that never again would she be alone. She would always have Raphael to share impossible decisions with.

'Okay,' she whispered, 'I'll sign the consents.'

Annie and Raphael passed what seemed like hours while their daughter was in surgery, in almost complete silence. Annie laid her head on Raphael's lap and he gently stroked her hair. They waited in the relatives' room just along the corridor from theatre. Every now and again Raphael would ask Annie if he could get her anything. Water? Coffee? But she always shook her head. She knew she couldn't possibly swallow anything until she knew Angela was out of surgery. Eventually they heard footsteps coming down the corridor.

Annie sat up, her heart in her throat, knowing that the moment of truth had arrived.

Raphael got to his feet and pulled Annie up and into his embrace. 'Whatever it is, be strong, my love. I am with you.'

The surgeon stepped into the family waiting room, a broad grin lighting up his face. It was the news they had both been desperately longing for. The paediatric surgeon explained that Angela had come through the surgery well and he expected her to make a full recovery. She was currently in Intensive Care but they could see her if they wanted. If they wanted!

Dr Nick Tremayne sat deep in thought. Something was up with Kate. He couldn't quite put his finger on it, but something was worrying her, he would bet his life on it. He crossed over to his consulting-room window and looked out. The perfect weather had turned again. The rain was falling in thick slabs, perfectly matching his gloomy mood. He didn't know why, but seeing Kate with her new partner made him feel uncomfortable. Not that it was any of his business. He should be glad she had found someone who could offer her a life free of complications. But, damn it, he hated seeing the way Jem responded to Rob. The way the growing boy seemed to look up to him, almost as if he had accepted that Rob was the father he had never known. And why should that bother him? Shouldn't he be glad that his son had a good man as role model in his life? Rob was a decent man. Nick knew that. And it wasn't as if he could offer the child anything, no matter how much Kate had tried to convince him. Perhaps if he'd known that Jem was his son much much earlier. Perhaps then he could have found a way to be a father to him. But it was too late now. Every time he looked at the child he remembered that he had been unfaithful to his beloved wife, Annabel. What kind of man was he?

He sighed with exasperation. How had he managed to make such a mess of it all? He couldn't see a way to make things right.

A soft tap on the door and then Kate popped her head around. She was still beautiful, he thought. The years had been kind to her. Why couldn't he let her go and make a proper life for herself? Why did the thought of her being with someone else drive him crazy? It wasn't as if he had anything to offer her.

'Just to let you know that Chloe is doing the antenatal clinic on her own this afternoon and I'm taking the afternoon off. So she might need some help from you.'

Nick was surprised. It was unlike Kate to take time off, especially when she knew it would leave her colleagues short-handed.

'Is everything all right, Kate? There's nothing up with Jem, is there?'

'No, Jem's fine. He's at school. It's just I have something I need to do this afternoon.'

'Can't it wait?'

He could see the exasperation in Kate's eyes.

'It's not as if I ever ask for time off, Nick,' she said frostily.

Of course, she was right. If anything, she had put the patients' needs before her own for years. He knew that. It was just that he sensed she was keeping something from him. And he wanted to know what it was. But one look at the determined set of her mouth told him it would be useless to pry. He had given up all rights to Kate's personal life and they both knew it.

'Of course,' he said. 'Forgive me.' He thought he saw a flicker of disappointment in her eyes, but just as quickly it was gone. It seemed that he was forever destined to disappoint this woman.

'I'll see you tomorrow, then,' she said before closing the door behind her.

Kate perched on her chair, trying not to show how nervous she was. In the seat next to her, Rob looked as ill at ease as Kate felt. He had insisted on coming with her to St Piran's. At first Kate had tried to dissuade him, she was so used to doing everything on her own, but then relented. Rob cared about her. Why face something so difficult on her own when he so clearly wanted to be there to support her? He had waited outside while Dr Bower had performed a fine needle biopsy and then waited some more while Kate had a mammogram. The hour they had waited to be called into see the surgeon for the results was the one of the longest in Kate's life.

The surgeon, Dr Bower, an older woman Kate had met before through work, seemed to take her time looking through Kate's notes before removing her glasses and placing them carefully on the table. Kate was dimly aware of Rob reaching across and taking her hand. He gave it a reassuring squeeze and she was thankful she had let him come with her.

'I'm sorry, Kate,' Dr Bower was saying, 'but the tests have come back positive. The lump is cancerous. The good news is that the mammogram suggests that we have caught it at a very early stage. I'm fairly confident that we can get away with removing the lump without having to resort to a mastectomy, but I won't be sure until we have you on the table. If there is any sign that the cancer has invaded the lymph nodes then we might be facing a different scenario. In that case, a mastectomy may still be an option, followed by chemotherapy and radiotherapy. As I said, I don't think that's what we are facing here, but I think it's best that you know the worst possible outcome. One way or another, I suggest we get you in for the procedure as soon as possible.'

Kate felt her world tip and slide. Of course she had known that it could be cancer, but she hadn't allowed herself to believe it. The pressure of Rob's hand on hers grew stronger but she was barely aware of it. She had cancer. She could die. Her son could be left motherless, and—a sick feeling washed over her—fatherless. How could life be so unfair?

'Are you sure?' she managed through a mouth that felt as if it was stuffed with pebbles, it was so dry. 'I mean—I'm sorry, of course you're sure. We wouldn't be having this conversation if you weren't.'

'I know it's a shock,' Dr Bower said sympathetically. 'But as I said before, it's good news that we caught it so early. You'll want some time to take it all in, but I really want to schedule you in for theatre, possibly the week after next.' She consulted her diary. 'I have a slot in my diary for a week on Monday. Would that suit you?'

Kate could only manage a nod. Her mouth was still too dry to speak. What was she going to tell Jem?

Kate managed to hold it together until she and Rob were back in his car. But when Rob silently put his arms around her and held her close, the tears came. Rob let her cry while he stroked her hair and murmured soothing words of comfort. He waited until her sobs subsided.

Kate removed herself from his arms, miserably aware of her tear-stained cheeks and swollen eyes. She blew furiously on the handkerchief Rob held out for her.

'I'm sorry, Rob, to land you in all this. I don't think it's what you expected when you took up with me.'

'I took up with you, as you put it—' Rob smiled '—because you are the most wonderful woman I have ever met. I would rather be with you than anywhere else in the world. But I want you to listen to me.' He swivelled around in his seat and took Kate's hands in his. She felt the warmth of his touch ease away some of the chill that had been seeping through her body since Dr Bower had given her the diagnosis.

'Dr Bower said that they caught it very early and survival rates from breast cancer have improved enormously over the last few years. That is what you need to remember.'

Kate looked at his dear, kind face. He always made her feel so protected and loved. Why couldn't she feel about him the way he so obviously felt about her?

'I know,' she said. 'But all I can think about is Jem. There is a chance when they do the biopsy at the time of surgery that they'll find it's more advanced. What will happen to him if…?' She took an uneven breath. 'If the worse comes to the worst? I have to think about that. I'm all he has…I can't imagine what it would do to him to be left alone. He's still so young.' Her voice broke and she couldn't help the tears from falling once more.

Rob pulled her back into his arms. 'It's all right. You'll see. Everything will work out fine.'

But Kate knew it wasn't all right. Bad things happened. And even Rob couldn't promise her that everything would be all right. No matter how much she wanted to believe him.

In the following days, as their daughter got gradually stronger, Annie let herself think about what Raphael had said. In the days after Angela's surgery they hadn't spoken much. When Raphael wasn't with them he was back at work, putting in a full day before returning to the ward to sit with them both.

Annie wondered if, now that their child was out of danger, he regretted his words the night of Angela's surgery. But she wouldn't be the one to speak of it. If he had changed his mind, or in the cold light of day realised he didn't love her, she would accept that. In time the pain would ease and whatever happened she would always have her beloved daughter. It would be a few weeks yet before they would be able to take Angela home, but the nursery, with its sunshine-yellow walls and crib stuffed with soft toys, was ready and waiting for her.

Kate had been to see Annie often, as had the other members of Penhally Bay Surgery, and Annie had been overwhelmed by their love and support.

She leaned back in her chair as her child suckled. It had been a great joy to find that it was still possible and Annie revelled in the feel of her baby's skin close against hers.

Annie looked up to find Raphael standing looking down, his face filled with wonder. Her heart started racing. She knew without a shadow of a doubt that she would never love anyone the way she loved him. When she had met him she had felt as if she had found the other half of her soul. And she still felt that way. She couldn't imagine a life without him. Not seeing him. Perhaps one day hearing that he had met someone else? But she also knew that she loved him too much to wish anything for him except happiness. Even if that life didn't include her. She loved him so much that she knew she could let him go. Even if it broke her heart.

'You look beautiful,' he said. 'How can I ever thank you for giving me the most precious gift in the world?'

He knelt by her side and touched her face with a gentle finger, before dropping his head and kissing the top of their child's head.

Annie felt her throat tighten. She wanted to imprint everything about him into her heart. Every facial feature, every expression, so in the months or years to come she would have her memories even if she didn't have him.

She replaced Angela in the incubator. She was only allowed to hold her for short periods, but she savoured every opportunity.

Raphael remained kneeling and reached a hand up and pulled her back down into the chair. Annie was uncomfortably aware of curious heads turning in their direction as the nurses stopped what they were doing to watch.

'I have something I want to ask you,' he said hoarsely. 'I was going to wait until we brought our baby home for good. But I can't sleep for not knowing what your answer would be.'

Annie studied him. He looked exhausted. The last few days of working while spending every moment with their child had taken their toll. There were dark shadows under his eyes and lines around his eyes that Annie hadn't seen before.

'I must know,' he said his voice tense. 'Do you think you could ever love me?'

Annie looked at him in wonder. Didn't he know? Hadn't he guessed how she felt? Without waiting for a reply, Raphael continued. 'From the moment I met you, I knew you were different. But I tried to tell myself it was impossible to fall in love with a woman I had only known so briefly. I couldn't let myself believe it. I wanted to contact you. I thought about it often, but I didn't. I thought it was better to keep my image of you alive and not risk having it smashed. And I still hoped there was a chance that I would win the court case for access to Sebastian on appeal. So I didn't listen to my heart. I let you go.'

Annie opened her mouth to speak, but he stopped her

words with his finger. 'Please. I have to say this. Whatever happens, I have to tell you.'

Annie waited for him to continue, acutely aware of the tiny shivers of delight and hope darting through her.

'Then when you told me you were pregnant, I thought that it was fate, but I couldn't let myself hope. I needed to know that it was my child and if it was, I needed to know that I couldn't lose her. The thought of losing another child drove me crazy. But when I saw you again, as I got to know you, I realised that I hadn't made a mistake about you. You were everything I ever thought you were. Everything I had ever hoped to find in a woman. Kind, caring, beautiful and loyal.' He looked a bit sheepish for a moment as he realised that the staff as well as most of the patients were riveted to every word he was saying. Annie felt a smile spread over her face.

'I love you. I love you more than I thought it was possible to love a woman. I want to marry you. I want to spend the rest of my life making you happy, making you smile. I want us, you me and Angela, to be a family. It doesn't matter where. Here or Spain. All that matters is that I am with you.'

'Can I speak now?' Annie asked when he came to a halt. Her heart was singing. She couldn't wait to put him out of his misery.

'I love you too, Raphael Castillo. I have loved you since the moment I saw you. And there is nothing that would make me happier than to marry you.' She could see the triumph in his eyes as he took in her words. She let him pull her to her feet, dimly aware of the sound of clapping and cheering. But as she tilted her face to his she knew that finally she had everything she had ever dreamed of.

EPILOGUE

ANNIE walked down the aisle her hand on her father's arm. The church where she had first met Raphael had seemed to them both to be the logical place for their wedding. She passed Raphael's mother, who was holding Angela in her arms. Little Maria was pressed close to the older woman's side. From the moment she and Raphael had returned to Spain with their daughter, Maria had become Angela's self-appointed guardian. She and Raphael had decided to look into the possibility of adopting Maria. Although it was early days yet, the young girl's father had raised no objections and it looked as if in time they would have two daughters. And maybe in a couple of years they would investigate the possibility of adopting another child. But all that was in the future, Annie thought as Raphael turned to watch her approach. His eyes darkened as he looked at her and Annie blushed, knowing that he was thinking of their wedding night.

Since he had proposed they had taken it slowly, getting to know the little things about each other and falling deeper in love every day. They hadn't made love, even though it had almost driven them both crazy. They had agreed to wait until they were married and Annie felt a heat low in her abdomen as she thought about the night to come. They had also agreed that they would live in Spain for the time being. It made sense. Annie had no plans to go back to work until Angela was a little older and the last thing little Maria needed was more disruption. They would go back to the UK often on holiday to see her parents and friends and, of course, they would come to Spain to see them too. She heard a little cry as Angela stirred from her nap. Annie caught Raphael's eye as she stood beside him and prepared to make the vows that would bind them together for the rest of their lives. In his eyes she found just what she was looking for. Right now she had everything she had ever wanted. Right here in this church.

THE SURGEON'S
DOORSTEP BABY

MARION LENNOX

To Cobrico. To Mayfield. To my beloved family
who form the bedrock of who I am.

CHAPTER ONE

As CHIEF orthopaedic surgeon for one of Sydney's most prestigious teaching hospitals, Blake Samford was used to being woken in the middle of the night for emergencies.

Right now, however, he was recuperating at his father's farm, two hundred miles from Sydney.

He wasn't expecting an emergency.

He wasn't expecting a baby.

Maggie Tilden loved lying in the dark, listening to rain on the corrugated-iron roof. She especially liked lying alone to listen.

She had a whole king-sized bed to herself. Hers, all hers. She'd been renting this apartment—a section of the grandest homestead in Corella Valley—for six months now, and she was savouring every silent moment of it.

Oh, she loved being free. She loved being here. The elements could throw what they liked at her; she was gloriously happy. She wriggled her toes luxuriously against her cotton sheets and thought, Bring it on, let it rain.

She wasn't even worried about the floods.

This afternoon the bridge had been deemed unsafe. Debris from the flooded country to the north was being slammed against the ancient timbers, and the authorities were worried the whole thing would go. As of that afternoon, the bridge was roped off and the entire valley was isolated.

Residents had been advised to evacuate and many had, but a lot of the old-time farmers wouldn't move if you put a bulldozer under them. They'd seen floods before. They'd stocked up with provisions, they'd made sure their stock was on high ground and they were sitting it out.

Maggie was doing the same.

A clap of thunder split the night and Tip, the younger Border collie, whined and edged closer to the bed.

'It's okay, guys,' she told them, as the ancient Blackie moved in for comfort as well. 'We're safe and dry, and we have a whole month's supply of dog food. What else could we want?'

And then she paused.

Over the sound of the driving rain she could hear a car. Gunned, fast. Driving over the bridge?

It must have gone right around the roadblock.

Were they crazy? The volume of water powering down the valley was a risk all by itself. There were huge warning signs saying the bridge was unsafe.

But the bridge was still intact, and the car made it without mishap. She heard the change in noise as it reached the bitumen on this side, and she relaxed, expecting the car's noise to fade as it headed inland.

But it didn't. She heard it turn into her driveway—okay, not hers, but the driveway of the Corella View Homestead.

If the car had come from this side of the river she'd be out of bed straight away, expecting drama. As district nurse, she was the only person with medical training on this side of the river—but the car had come from the other side, where there was a hospital and decent medical help.

She'd also be worrying about her brother. Pete was in the middle of teenage rebellion, and lately he'd been hanging out with some dubious mates. The way that car was being driven...danger didn't begin to describe it.

But this was someone from the other side. Not Pete. Not a medical emergency. Regardless, she swung her feet out of bed and reached for her robe.

And then she paused.

Maybe this was a visitor for her landlord.

A visitor at midnight?

Who knew? She hardly knew her landlord.

Blake Samford was the only son of the local squattocracy—squattocracies being the slang term for families who'd been granted huge tracts of land when Australia had first been opened to settlers and had steadily increased their fortunes since. The Corella Valley holding was impressive, but deserted. Blake had lived here as a baby but his mother had taken him away when he was six. The district had hardly seen him since.

This, however, was his longest visit for years. He'd arrived three days ago. He was getting over appendicitis, he'd told her, taking the opportunity to get the farm ready for sale. His father had been dead for six months. It was time to sell.

She'd warned him the river was rising. He'd shrugged.

'If I'm trapped, I might as well be truly trapped.'

If he was having visitors at midnight, they'd be trapped with him.

Maybe it's a woman, she thought, sinking back into bed as the car stopped and footsteps headed for Blake's side of the house—the grand entrance. Maybe he'd decided if he was to be trapped he needed company. Was this a woman ready to risk all to reach her lover?

Who knew? Who knew anything about Blake Samford?

Blake was a local yet not a local. She'd seen him sporadically as a kid—making compulsory access visits to his bully of a father, the locals thought—but as far as she knew he hadn't come near when his father had been ill. Given his father's reputation, no one blamed him. Finally she'd met him at the funeral.

She'd gone to the funeral because she'd been making daily medical checks on the old man for the last few months of his life. His reputation had been appalling, but he'd loved his dogs so she'd tried to convince herself he hadn't been all bad. Also, she'd needed to talk to his son about the dogs. And her idea.

She hadn't even been certain Blake would come but he'd been there— Blake Samford, all grown up. And stunning. The old ladies whispered that he'd inherited his mother's looks. Maggie had never known his mother, but she was definitely impressed by the guy's appearance—strong, dark, riveting. But not friendly. He'd stood aloof from the few locals present, expressionless, looking as if he was there simply to get things over with.

She could understand that. With Bob Samford as a father, it had been a wonder he'd been there at all.

But Maggie had an idea that needed his agreement. It had taken courage to approach him when the service had ended, to hand over her references and ask him about the housekeeper's apartment at the back of the homestead. To offer to keep an eye on the place as well as continuing caring for the dogs his dad had loved. Harold Stubbs, the next-door landowner, had been looking after Bob's cattle. The cattle still needed to be there to keep the grass down, but Harold was getting too old to take care of two herds plus the house and the dogs. Until Blake sold, would he like a caretaker?

Three days later a rental contract had arrived. She'd moved in but she hadn't heard from him since.

Until now. He was home to put the place on the market.

She'd expected nothing less. She knew it'd be sold eventually and she was trying to come up with alternative accommodation. She did *not* want to go home.

But right now her attention was all on the stupidity of his visitors driving over the bridge. Were they out of their minds?

She was tempted to pull back the drapes and look.

She heard heavy footsteps running across the veranda, and the knocker sounded so loudly it reverberated right through the house. The dogs went crazy. She hauled them back from the door, but as she did she heard the footsteps recede back across the veranda, back down the steps.

The car's motor hadn't been cut. A car door slammed, the engine was gunned—and it headed off the way it had come.

She held her breath as it rumbled back across the bridge. Reaching the other side. Safe.

Gone.

What on earth…?

Kids, playing the fool?

It was not her business. It was Blake's business, she told herself. He was home now and she was only caring for her little bit of the house.

Hers. Until Blake sold the house.

It didn't matter. For now it was hers, and she was soaking up every minute of it.

She snuggled back down under the covers—alone.

If there was one thing Maggie Tilden craved above everything else, it was being alone.

Bliss.

On the other side of the wall, Blake was listening, too. He heard the car roar over the bridge. He heard the thumps on his front door, the running footsteps of someone leaving in a hurry, and the car retreating back over the bridge.

He also thought whoever it was must be crazy.

He and his tenant—Maggie Tilden—had inspected the bridge yesterday. The storm water had been pounding the

aged timbers; things were being swept fast downstream—
logs, debris, some of it big. It was battering the piles.

'If you want to get out, you should go now,' Maggie had
said. 'The authorities are about to close it.'

Did it matter? He'd been ordered to take three weeks off
work to recuperate from appendicitis. He needed to sort his
father's possessions, so what difference did it make if he was
stranded while he did it?

'It's up to you,' Maggie had said, as if she didn't mind either way, and she'd headed back to her part of the house with
his father's dogs.

She kept to herself, for which he was profoundly grateful,
but now... A knock at midnight. A car going back and forth
over the bridge.

Was this some friend of hers, playing the fool? Leaving
something for her at the wrong door?

Whoever they were, they'd gone.

On Maggie's side of the house he'd heard the dogs go crazy.
He imagined her settling them. Part of him expected her to
come across to check what had just happened.

She didn't.

Forget it, he told himself. Go back to bed.

Or open the door and make sure nothing had been left?

The knock still resonated. It had been loud, urgent, demanding attention.

Okay, check.

He headed for the front door, stepped outside and came
close to falling over a bundle. Pink, soft...

He stooped and tugged back a fold of pink blanket.

A thick thatch of black hair. A tiny, rosebud mouth. Snub
nose. Huge dark eyes that stared upwards, struggling to focus.

A tiny baby. Three weeks at most, he thought, stunned.

Lying on his doorstep.

He scooped the infant up without thinking, staring out into

the night rather than down at the baby, willing the car to be still there, willing there to be some sort of answer.

The bundle was warm—and moist. And alive.

A baby…

He had nothing to do with babies. Yeah, okay, he'd treated babies during medical training. He'd done the basic paediatric stuff, but he'd been an orthopaedic surgeon for years now, and babies hardly came into his orbit.

A baby was in his orbit now. In his arms.

He stared down at the baby, and wide eyes stared back.

A memory stabbed back. A long time ago. Thirty or more years? Here, in this hall.

A woman with a baby, placing the baby by the door in its carry basket, pointing at Blake and saying, 'I've brought the kid his baby sister.'

After that, his memory blurred. He remembered his father yelling, and his mother screaming invective at his father and at the woman. He remembered the strange woman being almost hysterical.

He'd been six years old. While the grown-ups had yelled, he'd sidled over and looked at the baby it seemed everyone was yelling about. She'd been crying, but none of the grown-ups had noticed.

A baby sister?

He shook himself. That had been the night his mother had found out about his father's lover. He'd never seen either the woman or her baby again.

This baby was nothing to do with his history. Why was he thinking of it now?

He should call the police. He should report an abandoned baby.

Who looked like a baby he'd seen a long time ago?

And then he thought of Maggie, his tenant, and he remembered the references she'd given him.

She was the district nurse and she was also a midwife.

The relief that surged over him was almost overwhelming. This was nothing to do with him. Of course it wasn't. The whole valley knew Maggie's job. If a woman wanted to abandon an unwanted child, what better way than dump it on a woman you knew could look after it? Maybe Maggie had even cared for the mother during her pregnancy.

'Hey,' he said, relaxing, even holding the baby a little tighter now he knew what he was dealing with. The child seemed to be staring straight up at him now, dark eyes wondering. 'You've come to the wrong door. Okay, I know you're in trouble but you *have* come to the right place—just one door down. Hold on a minute and we'll take you to someone who knows babies. To someone who hopefully will take responsibility for getting you out of this mess.'

Maggie was snuggling back down under the duvet when someone knocked on *her* door and the dogs went nuts again.

What? What now?

She'd worked hard today. She'd set up the entire clinic, moving emergency gear from the hospital over the river, trying to get everything organised before the bridge closed. As well as that, she'd made prenatal checks of women on farms that were so wet right now that every able body was moving stock and if Maggie wanted her pregnant ladies to be checked then she went to them.

She was really tired.

Was this another evacuation warning? Leave now before the bridge is cut?

She'd gone to the community meeting. This house was high above the river. Short of a tsunami travelling two hundred miles inland, nothing worse was going to happen than the bridge would give way, the power would go and she'd have to rely on the old kerosene fridge for a few days.

What?

Another knock—and suddenly her irritation turned to fear. She had eight brothers and sisters. A couple of the boys were still young enough to be stupid. Pete… What if…?

What if the car had come with news?

Just open the door and get it over with.

Take a deep breath first.

She tucked her feet into fluffy slippers, wrapped her ancient bathrobe around her favourite pyjamas and padded out to the back porch.

She swung open the door—and Blake Samford was standing in the doorway, holding a baby.

'I think this one's for you,' he said, and handed it over.

She didn't drop it.

To her eternal credit—and thinking back later she was very, very proud of herself—she took the baby, just like the professional she was. Nurse receiving a baby at handover. She gathered the baby as she'd gather any infant she didn't know; any child when she didn't know its history. Taking care to handle it lightly with no pressure, anywhere that might hurt. Cradling it and holding it instinctively against her body, giving warmth as she'd give warmth to any tiny creature.

But for the moment her eyes were on Blake.

He looked almost forbidding. He was looming in her doorway, six feet two or three, wide shoulders, dark, dark eyes made even darker by the faint glow of moonlight, deep black hair, a shadowy figure.

Tall, dark and dangerous.

Heathcliff, she thought, suddenly feeling vaguely hysterical. Very hysterical. Here she was presented with a baby at midnight and she was thinking romance novels?

The dogs were growling behind her. They'd met this guy—he'd been here for three days and she'd seen him outside, talking to them—but he was still a stranger, it was midnight and they didn't know what to make of this bundle in their mistress's arms.

Neither did she, but a baby was more important than the dark, looming stranger on her doorstep.

'What do you mean, you think it's for me?' she managed, trying not to sound incredulous. Trying to sound like he'd just dropped by with a cup of sugar she'd asked to borrow earlier in the day. She didn't want to startle the dogs. She didn't want to startle the baby.

She didn't want to startle herself.

'Someone's obviously made a mistake,' he told her. 'You're the local midwife. I assume they've dumped the baby here to leave it with you.'

'Who dumped it?' She folded back the blanket and looked down into the baby's face. Wide eyes gazed back at her. Gorgeous.

She loved babies. She shouldn't—heaven knew, she'd had enough babies to last her a lifetime—but she had the perfect job now. She could love babies and hand them back.

'I don't know who dumped it,' he said, with exaggerated patience. 'Didn't you hear the car? It came, the baby was dumped, it left.'

She stared up at him, incredulous. He met her gaze, and didn't flinch.

An abandoned baby.

The stuff of fairy-tales. Or nightmares.

She switched her gaze to the little one in her arms.

'Who are you?' she whispered, but of course there was no answer. Instead it wrinkled its small nose, and opened its mouth—and wailed.

Only it wasn't a wail a baby this age should make. It was totally despairing, as if this baby had wailed before and nothing had been forthcoming. It was a wail that was desperation all by itself—a wail that went straight to the heart and stayed there. Maggie had heard hungry babies before, but none like this. Unbearable. Unimaginable that a little one could be so needful.

She looked down at the sunken fontanel, the dry, slightly wrinkled skin. These were classic signs of dehydration. IV? Fast?

But if the little one could still cry...

It could indeed still cry. It could scream.

'Can you grab the bag from the back of my car?' she snapped, and whirled and grabbed her car keys and tossed them to him. 'This little one's in trouble.'

'Trouble?'

She wheeled away, back to the settee. The fire was still glowing in the hearth. She could unwrap the baby without fear of losing warmth. 'Basket,' she snapped at the dogs, and they headed obediently for their baskets at each side of the fire. Then, as Blake hesitated, she fixed him with a look that had made lesser men quail. 'Bag. Now. Go.'

He headed for the car, feeling a bit...stunned. And also awed.

The only times he'd seen Maggie Tilden she'd seemed brisk, efficient and...plain? She dressed simply for work and she'd been working the whole time he'd been here. Plain black pants. White blouse with 'Corella Valley Medical Services' emblazoned on the pocket. She wore minimal make-up, and her soft brown curls were tied back in a bouncy ponytail. She was about five feet four or five, she had freckles, brown eyes and a snub nose, and until tonight he would have described her as nondescript.

What he'd just seen wasn't nondescript. It was something far from it.

What?

Cute, he thought, but then he thought no. It was something…deeper.

She'd been wearing faded pink pyjamas, fluffy slippers and an ancient powder-blue bathrobe. Her brown hair, once let loose, showed an auburn burnish. Her curls tumbled about her shoulders and she looked like she'd just woken from sleep. Standing with her dogs by her sides, the fire crackling in the background, she looked…

Adorable?

She looked everything the women in his life weren't. Cosy. Domestic. Welcoming.

And also strong. That glare said he'd better move his butt and get her bag back inside, stat.

She wouldn't know he was a doctor, he thought. When the baby had wailed he'd recognised, as she had, that the little creature was in trouble. The light-bulb over his door had blown long since, but once he'd been under the light of her porch he'd seen the tell-tale signs of dehydration, a baby who looked underweight; malnourished. He'd reached to find a pulse but her movement to defend the child was right. Until she knew what was wrong, the less handling the better.

She was reacting like a midwife at her best, he thought with something of relief. Even if she needed his help right now, this baby wasn't his problem. She was more than capable of taking responsibility.

She was a professional. She could get on with her job and he could move away.

Get the lady her bag. Now.

The bag was a huge case-cum-portable bureau, wedged into the back of an ancient family wagon. He grabbed it and grunted as he pulled it free—it weighed a ton. What was it—medical supplies for the entire valley? How on earth did a diminutive parcel like Maggie handle such a thing?

He was a week out from an appendectomy. He felt internal stitches pull and thought of consequences—and headed for the back door and grabbed the wheelbarrow.

Medical priorities.

If he broke his stitches he'd be no use to anyone. Worse, he'd need help himself.

One bag coming up. By barrow.

He pushed his way back into the living room and Maggie's eyes widened.

She'd expected landlord with a bag.

What she got was landlord, looking a bit sheepish, with her firewood-carting wheelbarrow, plus bag.

'Appendectomy,' he said before she could say a word. 'Stitches. You don't want two patients.'

Oh, heck. She hadn't thought. He'd told her he was here recovering from an appendectomy. She should have…

'It's fine,' he said, quickly, obviously seeing her remorse. 'As long as you don't mind tyre tracks on your rugs.'

'With my family I'm not used to house-proud. Thanks for getting it. Are you okay?'

'Yes.'

She cast him a sharp, assessing look, and he thought she was working out the truth for herself, and she figured he was telling it.

'If I tell you how, can you make up some formula? This little one's badly dehydrated.'

'Can I see?' he said, over the baby's cries.

The baby was still wailing, desperation personified.

He stooped beside her. He didn't try and touch the baby, just pushed back the coverings further from its face.

Maggie had obviously done a fast check and then re-wrapped the infant, leaving the nappy on, tugging open the stained grow suit to the nappy but leaving it on, rewrapping the baby in the same blanket but adding her own, a cashmere throw he'd seen at the end of the sofa.

With the blankets pulled aside and the grow suit unfastened, he could see signs of neglect. This was no rosy, bouncing baby. He could see the tell-tale signs of severe nappy rash, even above the nappy. He could see signs of malnourishment.

She was right about dehydration. They needed to get the little one clean and dry—but first they needed to get fluids in and if it was possible, the best way was by mouth.

'Tell me where, tell me how,' he said, and she shot him a grateful glance and proceeded to do just that. Five minutes later he had a sterilised bottle filled with formula, he offered it to Maggie, she offered it to one tiny baby—who latched on like a leech and proceeded to suck like there was no tomorrow.

The sudden silence was deafening. Even the dogs seemed to sigh in relief.

Maggie's wide, expressive mouth curved into a smile. 'Hey,' she said softly. 'You've just saved yourself from evacuation, hospital and IV drips. Now, let's see what we have here.' She glanced up at Blake. 'Are you man enough to cope with the nappy? I'd normally not try and change a baby in mid-feed but this one's practically walking on its own and I hate to imagine what it's doing to the skin. It needs to be off but I don't want to disturb the baby more than necessary. While the bottle's doing the comforting we might see what we're dealing with.'

He understood. Sort of. There was a medical imperative.

What he'd really like to do was offer to take over the holding and feeding while she coped with the other end, but he'd missed his opportunity. There was no way they should interrupt established feeding when it was so important. This baby needed fluids fast, and Maggie was the one providing them.

So...the other end.

He was a surgeon. He was used to stomach-churning sights.

He'd never actually changed a baby's nappy.

'You'll need a big bowl of warm, soapy water,' she told him. 'The bowl's in the left-hand cupboard by the stove. Get a couple of clean towels from the bathroom and fetch the blue bottle on the top of my bag with the picture of a baby's bottom on the front.'

'Right,' he said faintly, and went to get what he needed, with not nearly the enthusiasm he'd used to make the formula.

Baby changing. He had to learn some time, he supposed. At some stage in the far distant future he and Miriam might have babies. He thought about it as he filled the bucket with skin-temperature water. He and Miriam were professional colleagues having a somewhat tepid relationship on the side. Miriam was dubious about attachment. He was even more dubious.

He suspected what he was facing tonight might make him more so.

'Oi,' Maggie called from the living room. 'Water. Nappy. Stat.'

'Yes, Nurse,' he called back, and went to do her bidding.

CHAPTER TWO

BLAKE removed the nappy and under all that mess...'She doesn't look like she's been changed for days,' Maggie said, horrified...they found a little girl.

They also found something else. As he tugged her grow-suit free from her legs and unwrapped her fully, he drew in a deep breath.

Talipes equinovarus. Club feet. The little girl's feet were pointed inwards, almost at right angles to where they should be.

Severe.

He didn't comment but he felt ill, and it wasn't the contents of the nappy that was doing it. That someone could desert such a child... To neglect her and then just toss her on his doorstep...

How did they know Maggie would be home? Maggie had dogs. How did they know the dogs wouldn't be free to hurt her?

Seeing the extent of the nappy rash, the dehydration—and the dreadful angle of her feet—he had his answer.

Whoever had done this didn't care. This was an imperfect baby, something to be tossed aside, brought to the local midwife, but whether she was home or not didn't matter.

Returning damaged goods, like it or not.

He glanced up at Maggie and saw her face and saw what he

was thinking reflected straight back at him. Anger, disgust, horror—and not at the tiny twisted feet. At the moron who'd gunned the car across the bridge, so desperate to dump the baby that he'd take risks. Or *she'd* take risks.

'Surely it was a guy driving that car?' Maggie whispered.

Sexist statement or not? He let it drift as he cleaned the tiny body. The little girl was relaxed now, almost soporific, sucking gently and close to sleep. She wasn't responding to his touch—he could do anything he liked and it was a good opportunity to do a gentle, careful examination.

Maggie was letting him touch now. She was watching as he carefully manipulated the tiny feet, gently testing. As he felt her pulse. As he checked every inch of her and then suggested they lower her into the warm water.

She'd had enough of the bottle on board now to be safe. He doubted she'd respond—as some babies did—to immersion—and it was the easiest and fastest way to get her skin clean.

'You're a medic,' Maggie said, because from the way he was examining her he knew it was obvious. And he knew, instinctively, that this was one smart woman.

'Orthopaedic surgeon.'

She nodded as if he was confirming what she'd suspected. 'Not a lot of babies, then?'

'Um…no.'

'But a lot of feet?'

'I guess,' he agreed, and she smiled at him, an odd little smile that he kind of…liked.

Restful, he thought. She was a restful woman. And then he thought suddenly, strongly, that she was the kind of woman he'd want around in a crisis.

He was very glad she was there.

But the priority wasn't this woman's smile. The priority was one abandoned baby. While Maggie held the bottle—

the little girl was still peacefully sucking—he scooped her gently from her arms and lowered her into the warm water.

She hardly reacted, or if she did it was simply to relax even more. This little one had been fighting for survival, he thought. Fighting and losing. Now she was fed and the filth removed. She was in a warm bath in front of Maggie's fire and she was safe. He glanced at Maggie and saw that faint smile again, and he thought that if he was in trouble, he might think of this woman as safety.

If this baby was to be dumped, there was no better place to dump her. Maggie would take care of her. He knew it. This was not a woman who walked away from responsibility.

He glanced around at the dogs on either side of the fire. His father's dogs. When his father had gone into hospital for the last time he'd come down and seen them. They were cattle dogs, Border collies, born and raised on the farm. The last time he'd seen them—six months before his father had died—they'd been scrawny and neglected and he'd thought of the impossibility of taking them back to the city, of giving them any sort of life there.

His father hadn't wanted him here—he'd practically yelled at him to get out. And he'd told him the dogs were none of his business.

Despite the old man's opposition, he'd contacted the local hospital and asked for home visits by a district nurse.

Maggie had taken his father on, and the dogs, and when his father had died she'd suggested she take this place on as well. It had solved two problems—the dogs and an empty farmhouse.

This woman was a problem-solver. She'd solve this little one's problems, too.

The baby had fallen asleep. Maggie removed the bottle, then took over from him, expertly bathing, carefully checking every inch of the baby's skin, wincing at the extent of the nappy rash, checking arm and leg movement, frowning at a bruise on the baby's shoulder. A bruise at this age... Put down hard? Dropped?

Hit?

'There are basic baby clothes at the bottom of my bag,' she said absently, all her attention on the baby. 'And nappies. Will you fetch them?'

He did, thinking again that no matter who the lowlife was that had cared for the baby until now, at least they'd had the sense to bring her to the right place.

He brought the clothes back as Maggie scooped the baby out of the water, towelled her dry and anointed the sores. Looked again at her feet.

'They should be being realigned now,' he growled, watching as Maggie fingered the tiny toes. 'Three weeks after birth... We're missing the opportunity when the tissue is soft and malleable. The longer we leave it, the longer the treatment period.'

'I've only seen this once before,' Maggie said. 'And not as severe as this.'

'It's severe,' he said. 'But fixable.'

'We have basic X-ray facilities set up at my clinic—at the church hall,' she said tentatively. 'We've brought them in so I can see the difference between greenstick fractures and fractures where I need evacuation.'

'We don't need X-rays tonight. This is long-haul medical treatment.'

'I don't want to call out emergency services unless I have to.' Maggie was still looking worried. 'They have their hands full evacuating people who are being inundated, and in this rain there's no safe place for the chopper to land.'

'There's no urgency.'

'Then we'll worry about tomorrow tomorrow,' she said, her face clearing, and she dressed the little one so gently he thought the dressing was almost a caress in itself. The baby hardly stirred. It was like she'd fought every inch of the way to survive and now she knew she was safe. She knew she was with Maggie.

Maggie wrapped her in her soft cashmere rug—the one she'd tugged from her settee—and handed her over to Blake. He took her without thinking, then sat by the fire with the sleeping baby in his arms as Maggie cleared up the mess.

She was a restful woman, he thought again. Methodical. Calm. How many women would take a child like this and simply sort what was needed? Taking her from peril to safe in an hour?

She was a midwife, he told himself. This was what she did. This baby was her job.

She was gathering bottles, formula, nappies. Placing them in a basket.

A basket. He'd been drifting off in the warmth but suddenly he was wide awake. What the…?

'Are you thinking we should take her to hospital?' he asked. 'I'm not driving over that bridge.'

'Neither am I,' she said, and brought the basket back to him. 'She looks fine—okay, not fine, neglected, underweight, but nothing so urgent to warrant the risks of crossing the river again. I think she'll be fine with you. I'm just packing what you need.'

'Me?'

'You,' she said, gently but firmly. 'Your baby tonight.'

'I don't want a baby,' he said, stunned.

'You think I do?'

'She was brought to you.'

'No,' she said, still with that same gentleness, a gentleness with a rod of inflexibility straight through the centre. 'She was brought to you. If I didn't think you were capable of caring then I'd step in—of course I would—and I'm here for consulting at any time. But this little one is yours.'

'What are you talking about? You're the midwife.'

'It's got nothing to do about me being a midwife,' she said, and searched the settee until she found what she was looking for. 'I found this when you were making the formula. It was tucked under her blanket.'

It was a note, hastily scribbled on the back of a torn envelope. She handed it to him wordlessly, and then stayed silent as he read.

Dear Big Brother
The old man's dead. He never did anything for me in my life—nothing! You're the legitimate kid, the one that gets everything. You get the farm. You get the kid.

This kid's your father's grandkid. My father's grandkid. I don't want it—just take a look at its feet—they make Sam and me sick. I called it Ruby after my Mum's mum—my grandma—she was the only one ever did anything for me—but that was before I figured how awful the feet were. So it's deformed and we don't want it. Change the name if you like. Get it adopted. Do what you want. Sam and me are heading for Perth so if you need anything signed for adoption or anything stick an ad in the Margaret River paper. If I see it I'll get in touch. Maybe.
Wendy

Silence. A long, long silence.

'Wendy?' Maggie said gently at last.

'My...my half-sister.' He was struggling to take it in. 'Result of one of my father's affairs.'

'Surname?'

'I don't even know that.'

'Whew.' She looked at him, still with that calmness, sympathetic but implacable. 'That's a shock.'

'I… Yes.'

'I think she'll sleep,' Maggie said. 'I suspect she'll sleep for hours. She's not too heavy for you to carry. If you need help, I'm right through the door.'

'This baby isn't mine.' It was said with such vehemence that the little girl—Ruby?—opened her eyes and gazed up at him. And then she closed them again, settling. She was dry, warm and fed. She was in Blake's arms. All was right with her world.

'She's not mine,' Blake repeated, but even he heard the uselessness of his words. Someone had to take responsibility for this baby.

'I'm a nurse, Blake,' Maggie said, inexorably. 'I'm not a parent. Neither are you but you're an uncle. Your sister's left her baby with you. You're family. Let me know if you're in trouble.' She walked across to the porch and opened the door. 'But for now… You have everything you need for the night. I'll pop in in the morning and see how you're going.'

'But I know nothing about babies.'

'You're a doctor,' she said cordially. 'Of course you do.'

'Looking after them?'

'If fifteen-year-old girls can manage it, you can. It's not brain surgery.'

'I'm not a fifteen-year-old.' He was grasping at straws here. 'And I've just had my appendix out.'

'Fifteen-year-olds who've just had Caesareans manage it. How big are babies compared to an appendix? Toughen up.'

He stared at her and she stared right back. She smiled. He thought he sensed sympathy behind her smile, but her smile was still…implacable.

She'd given him his marching orders.

He was holding his niece. *His.*

Maggie was holding the door open; she was still smiling but she was giving him no choice.

With one more despairing glance at this hard-hearted nurse, at the crackling fire, at the sleeping dogs, at a domesticity he hardly recognised, he accepted he had no choice.

He walked out into the night.

With…his baby?

She shouldn't have done it.

The door closed behind him and Maggie stared at it like it was a prosecutor in a criminal court.

Maggie stands accused of abandoning one defenceless baby…

To her uncle. To a doctor. To her landlord.

To a guy recovering from an appendectomy.

To a guy who was capable of driving from Sydney to the valley, to someone who was well on the way to recovery, to someone who was more than capable of looking after his baby.

His baby. Not hers.

This was not her problem. She was a professional. She cared for babies when they needed her medical intervention, and she handed them right back.

She'd done enough of the personal caring to last a lifetime.

She gazed down into the glowing embers of the fire and thought, *My fire.*

It had taken so much courage, so much resolution, so much desperation to find a house of her own. Corella Valley had practically no rental properties. She had so little money. It had taken all the courage and hope she possessed to gird her loins, approach Blake at the funeral and say, 'I'm looking after your dad's dogs; why don't you let me take care of your house until you put it on the market? I'll live in the housekeeper's residence and I'll keep the place tidy so if you need to use it it'll be ready for you.'

The feeling she'd had when he'd said yes…

Her family still lived less than a mile away, on this side of the river. She was still here for them when they needed her—but she wasn't here for everyone when they needed her. She was not 'good old Maggie' for Blake. This baby was Blake's problem. Blake's niece. Blake's baby, to love or to organise another future for.

If she'd responded to the desperation in his eyes, she'd have a baby here, right now. A baby to twist her heart as it had been twisted all her life.

Eight brothers and sisters. Parents who couldn't give a toss. Maggie, who spent her life having her heart twisted.

'Of course you'll stay home today and look after your brother. Yes, he's ill, but your father and I are heading for Nimbin for a couple of days for the festival… You're a good girl, Maggie.'

Two guitar-toting layabouts with nine kids between them, and Maggie, the oldest, the one who had cared for them all.

She did not need any more responsibility, not in a million years. She had two dogs. She had her own apartment, even if it was only until Blake sold the property.

She was not taking Blake's baby.

And on the other side of the wall, Blake settled the sleeping baby into a cocoon of bedding he'd made in a tugged-out bureau drawer, then stood and stared down at her for a very long time.

Even in two hours she'd changed. Her face had filled out a little, and the signs of dehydration were fading. She'd been stressed since birth, he thought. She was sleeping as if she was intent on staying asleep, because being awake was frightening and lonely and hard.

He was reading too much into the expression of one sleeping baby. How did he know what she'd been through? How could he possibly guess?

This little one was nothing to do with him. As soon as the river went down he'd hand her over to the appropriate authorities and let them deal with her. But until then...

Maggie should take her, he thought. That was the reasonable plan. A trained midwife, accustomed to dealing with babies every day of her working life, was a far more suitable person to take care of a little one as young as this.

But there was something about Maggie that was implacable. *Not My Problem.* The sign was right up there, hanging over her head like a speech bubble. Said or not, it was what she meant and it was how she'd acted.

She'd sent him home with his niece.

His niece.

He watched her sleep for a while longer. Ruby, he thought.

His niece?

He didn't feel like he had a niece. He didn't feel like he had a sister. He'd only seen his sister that one appalling time, when she'd been little older than Ruby. The moment had been filled with sounds enough to terrify a six-year-old, two women screeching at each other, his father threatening, the baby crying and crying and crying.

He remembered thinking, *Why don't they stop yelling and cuddle her?* He'd even thought of doing it himself, but six was too young to be brave. He'd wanted a cuddle himself. He'd been scared by the yelling and far too young to cope with a baby.

Was he old enough now?

He didn't feel old enough.

He looked down at the tightly wrapped bundle and thought of the tiny feet, facing inwards, needing work to be aligned.

He could do that. He was an orthopaedic surgeon. Fixing twisted limbs was what he did.

Not the rest.

Maggie was just through the door. A trained midwife.

The phone rang and he picked it up with relief. It'd be Maggie, he thought, changing her mind, worrying about a baby who should rightly be in her charge.

It wasn't. It was Miriam, doing what she'd promised. 'I'll ring you when I've finished for the day,' she'd told him. 'You don't mind if it's late? You know I'd like to be with you but the board meets next week to appoint the head of ophthalmology and I need to be present to be in the running.'

Of course he'd agreed. They were two ambitious professionals, and a little thing like an appendectomy shouldn't be allowed to get in the way of what was needed for their careers.

A little thing like a baby?

Miriam didn't notice that he was preoccupied. She asked about the floods. He told her briefly that the bridge was blocked, that he was fine, that she needn't worry. Not that she'd have worried anyway. She knew he could take care of himself.

There was little she didn't know about him. They'd been colleagues for years now, in a casual relationship, maybe drifting toward marriage.

And now...

Now he was about to shock her.

'I have a baby,' he told her, and was met with stunned silence. He heard her think it through, regroup, decide he was joking.

'That was fast. You only left town on Friday. You've met a girl, got her pregnant, had a baby...' She chuckled—and then the chuckle died as she heard his continued silence. 'You're not serious?'

He outlined the night's events, the letter, Maggie, their

decision not to call for medical evacuation and Maggie's insistence that he do the caring. He heard her incredulity—and her anger towards a nurse she'd never met.

'She's dumped it on you?'

'I guess.' But it was hardly that.

'Then dump it right back,' she snapped. 'Fast. She has to take care of it. She's the local nurse. It's her job. This is like someone turning up in your office with a fractured leg and you refusing to help.'

'She did help. She bathed and fed her.'

'Her?'

'She's a little girl. Ruby.'

'Don't even think about getting attached.' Miriam's voice was almost a hiss. 'That's what she'll be counting on. You being soft.'

'I'm not soft.'

'I know that, but does she? The nurse? And this sister you've never told me about... Who is she?'

'I know nothing about her other than she's called Wendy. I can't be soft to someone I don't know.'

'So call in the authorities, now. If the bridge is properly cut...'

'It is.'

'How did they get over?'

'They went round the road block and risked their lives.'

'Okay,' she conceded. 'I don't want you risking your life. You'll probably have to wait till morning but then call for a medical evacuation.'

'She's not sick, Mim.'

'She's not your problem,' Miriam snapped. 'And don't call me Mim. You know I hate it. Call the police, say you have a baby you know nothing about on your doorstep and let them deal with it.'

'This is my father's grandchild. My...niece.'

There was a hiss of indrawn breath. 'So what are you saying? You want to keep it?'

'No!' He was watching the baby while he talked. She'd managed to wriggle a fist free from the bundle Maggie had wrapped her in, and her tiny knuckles were in her mouth. They were giving her comfort, he thought, and wondered how much she'd needed those knuckles in her few short weeks of life.

This was not his problem. Nothing to do with him.

She was his niece. His father's grandchild.

He'd loathed his father. He'd left this place when he'd been six years old and had had two short access visits since. Both had been misery from first to last.

His father had been a bully and a thug.

Maggie had known him better, he thought. Had there been anything under that brutish exterior?

He could ask.

'Just take the baby back to the midwife and insist,' Miriam was saying. 'It's her professional responsibility. You could…I don't know…threaten to have her struck off if she doesn't?'

'For handing a baby back to her family?'

'You're not her family.'

'I'm all she has.'

'Her parents are all she has. The police can find them tomorrow. Meanwhile, lean on the nurse. You're recovering, Blake. You do not need this hassle. Okay, misconduct mightn't fly but there are other ways. You're her landlord. Threaten to evict her.'

'Mim—'

'Just do whatever you need to do,' she snapped. 'Look, love, I rang to tell you about the paper I presented this afternoon. It went really well. Can I finally tell you about it?'

'Of course,' he said, and he thought that would settle him. He could stand here and listen to Miriam talk medicine and he could forget all about his little stranger who'd be gone to-morrow.

And he could also forget about the woman who'd refused to take her.

Maggie.

Why was he thinking about Maggie?

He was remembering her at the funeral. It had been pouring. She'd been dressed in a vast overcoat and gumboots, sensible garments in the tiny, country graveyard. She'd stomped across to him, half-hidden by her enormous umbrella, and she'd put it over him, enclosing him for the first time, giving him his only sense of inclusion in this bleak little ceremony.

'I took on your father's dogs because I couldn't bear them to be put down,' she'd said. 'But I'm sharing a too-small house with my too-big family. The dogs make the situation unworkable. I assume your dad's farm will be empty for a while. It has a housekeeper's residence at the back. If I pay a reasonable rent, how about you let me live there until you decide what to do with it?'

'Yes,' he'd said without any hesitation, and he'd watched something akin to joy flash across her face.

'Really?'

'Really.'

'You won't regret it,' she'd said gruffly. 'The dogs and I will love it.' Then she'd hesitated and looked across at the men filling in the open grave. 'He was a hard man, your father,' she'd said softly. 'I'm sorry.'

And he'd thought, uncomfortably, that she understood.

Did this whole district understand? That he and his father had had no relationship at all?

They weren't a family.

Family...

His mother had gone on to three or four more relationships, all disastrous. He'd never worked out the concept of family. Now...

He listened on to Miriam and he watched the sleeping baby. Would he and Miriam ever have babies? Family?

Now wasn't the time to ask, he thought, and he grimaced as he realised he hadn't heard a word she'd said for the last few minutes.

Focus, he told himself. Do what the lady says. Concentrate on medicine and not baby. Tomorrow give the baby back to Maggie or get rid of it some other way. Do whatever it takes. This was an aberration from the past.

One baby, with twisted feet and no one to care for her. An aberration?

He carried on listening to Miriam and he thought, Maggie's just through the wall. She might even be listening to half this conversation.

The thought was unnerving.

Forget it, he thought. Forget Maggie. And the baby?

Do whatever it takes.

If only she wasn't sucking her knuckles. If only she wasn't twisting his heart in a way that made him realise a pain he'd felt when he'd been six years old had never been resolved.

She was his father's grandchild. She was the child of his half-sister.

Family?

It was his health that was making him think like this, he told himself. He'd had his appendix out barely a week before, and it had been messy. He was tired and weaker than he cared to admit, and he was staying in a house that held nothing but bad memories.

He had a sudden, overwhelming urge to thump a hole in the wall in the sitting room. Let his father's dogs through.

See Maggie.

Heaven knew what Miriam was saying. He'd given up trying to listen. It had been an important paper she'd presented. Normally he'd listen and be impressed. Tonight, though, he looked at one tiny baby, sleeping cocooned in Maggie's cashmere blanket, and suddenly he felt tired and weak—and faintly jealous of the deep sleep, the total oblivion.

And he also felt…alone.

If the bridge was safe, maybe he'd suggest Miriam come down.

Don't be nuts, he told himself. She'd never come, and even if she did there'd be nothing for her to do.

She wouldn't care for a baby.

He had to.

Baby. Floods. Maggie. The images were drifting around his head in a swirl of exhausted confusion.

Baby. Floods. Maggie.

'I need to go,' he told Miriam, cutting her off in mid-sentence. 'Sorry, love, but I'll ring you back tomorrow. The baby needs me.'

'The midwife—'

'She's gone to sleep,' he said. 'That's where I'm heading, too. Hours and hours of sleep. I just have to get one baby called Ruby to agree.'

CHAPTER THREE

MAGGIE fed the hens at six the next morning and she heard Ruby crying.

She sorted feed, cut and chopped a bit of green stuff and threw it into the chookpen—there'd been a fox sniffing around and she wasn't game to let them out. She collected the eggs.

Ruby was still crying.

It wasn't her business, she told herself. Not yet. What district nurse dropped in at this hour? She'd make a professional visit a little later. Meanwhile, she should make breakfast and head to the makeshift clinic she'd set up in the back of the local hall, to do last-minute preparations and sort equipment.

That could wait, though, she conceded. The authorities had only put the roadblock up yesterday. Everyone who'd needed anything medical had had two days' warning. The weather forecast had been implacable. *The water's coming. Get your stock to high ground. Evacuate or get in any supplies you need because it may be a week or more before the river goes down.*

The pharmacy over the river and the doctors at the Valley Hospital had worked tirelessly over the last few days, checking every small complaint, filling prescriptions to last a month. The Valley people had seen floods before. There'd be no last-minute panic.

There would, however, be no doctor on this side of the river for a while.

Except Blake. The thought was strangely comforting.

Floods often meant trauma as people did stupid things trying to save stock, trying to fix roof leaks, heaving sandbags. Knowing she had a doctor on this side of the river, even one recovering from an appendectomy, was a blessing. If he'd help.

And if she expected him to help…maybe she could help him with his baby?

She'd made it clear she wasn't taking responsibility. That was what he wanted her to do, but even if she agreed, she couldn't care for a newborn as well as for the medical needs of everyone on this side of the river.

So she'd been firm, which wasn't actually like her. But firmness was her new resolve.

Right now, though, she was figuring that firm didn't mean cruel. The guy really didn't know anything about babies. If she had a teenage mum floundering, she'd move in to help.

Hold that thought, she decided, and she almost grinned at the thought of one hunky Blake Samford in the role of teen mum.

She'd help—even at six a.m.

So she knocked on his back door and waited. No answer. The wailing got louder.

She pushed the door tentatively inwards and went to investigate.

Blake was standing in the living room, in front of the vast, stone fireplace that was the centre of this huge, old homestead. The room was as it always was when she did her weekly check on the whole house, huge and faded and comfortable. A vast Persian rug lay on the worn, timber floor. The room was furnished with squishy leather settees, faded cushions and once opulent drapes, now badly in need of repair. The fire in the vast fireplace made it warm and home-like. The house was a grand old lady, past her prime but still graciously decorous.

Not so the guy in front of the fire. He was wearing boxer shorts and nothing else. He looked big, tanned, ripped—and not decorous at all.

Maggie was a nurse. She was used to seeing human bodies in all shapes and sizes.

She wasn't used to seeing this one.

Tall, dark and dangerous. Where had that phrase come from? She wasn't sure, but she knew where it was now. It was flashing in her head. Danger, danger, danger. A girl should turn round and walk right out of there.

Except he was holding a baby—all the wrong way—and his look spoke of desperation.

She put down her bucket of eggs, headed wordlessly to the kitchen to wash her hands, then came back and took the little one into her arms.

Blake practically sagged with relief.

'You need to wrap her,' she said, brisk and efficient because brisk and efficient seemed the way to go. 'She's exhausted.'

She cradled the little one tightly against her and felt an almost imperceptible relaxation. Babies seemed to respond instinctively to those who knew the ropes. To their mothers, who learned from birth how to handle them. To midwives, who'd delivered too many babies to count.

'She's been safely in utero for nine months,' she told him. 'She's been totally confined, and now her legs and arms are all over the place. It feels weird and frightening. She can handle it if she's relaxed, but not if she's tired and hungry.'

'But she won't feed,' he said helplessly, motioning to the bottle on the table. 'I can't—'

'She's gone past it. She needs to be settled first.' She sat on the settee and almost disappeared. These settees must be older than Blake, she thought. Old and faded and stuffed loosely with goosedown. She'd never seen such huge settees.

In truth she was finding it hard to thinking about settees. Not with that body...

Get a grip. Settees. Baby.

Not Blake.

She set about rewrapping Ruby, bundling her tightly so those flailing little legs and arms could relax, and the baby attached to them would feel secure. But she was a midwife. Bundling babies was second nature. She had more than enough time to think about settees and baby—and Blake Samford's body.

Which was truly awesome. Which was enough to make a girl...make a girl...

Think unwisely. Think stupid, in fact. This was her land-lord—a guy who wanted to get rid of a baby.

You show one hint of weakness and you'll have a baby on your hands, she told herself. And if you fall for this baby...

She'd fallen for two dogs. That was more than enough.

She lived in this man's house as a tenant, and that was all. If babies came with the territory then she moved out.

This was dumb. She was thinking dramatic when the situation simply needed practical. This guy had a problem and she could help him, the same way she'd help any new parent. She'd help and then she'd leave.

Ruby was still wailing, not with the desperation of a moment ago but with an I-want-something-and-I-want-it-now wail.

She lifted the bottle and flicked a little milk on her wrist. Perfect temperature. She offered it, one little mouth opened and accepted—and suddenly the noise stopped.

The silence was magical.

She smiled. Despite very real qualms in this case, Maggie Tilden did love babies. They sucked you in.

Her mother had used that to her advantage. Maggie's mother loved having babies, she just didn't like caring for them.

Over to Maggie.

And that was what Blake wanted. Over to Maggie.

Do not get sucked in, she told herself desperately. Do not become emotionally involved.

Anything but that. Even looking at Blake.

At his chest. At the angry red line she could see emerging from the top of his shorts.

Appendix. Stitches. Even if the external ones had been removed, it'd take weeks for the internal ones to dissolve.

'So no keyhole surgery for you?' she asked, trying to make her voice casual, like this was a normal neighbourly chat. 'You didn't choose the right surgeon?'

'I chose the wrong appendix,' he said, glancing down at his bare abs. 'Sorry. I'll cover up.'

'I'm not squeamish about an appendix scar,' she told him. 'I'm a nurse. So things were messy, huh?

'Yes.'

'No peritonitis?'

'I'm on decent antibiotics.'

Her frown deepened. 'Are you sure you're okay to stay on this side of the river?'

'Of course.'

But she was looking at problems she hadn't foreseen. Problems she hadn't thought about. 'If there's the least chance of infection... I assumed you'd had keyhole surgery. If I'd known...'

'You would have ordered me to leave?'

'I'd have advised you to leave.'

'You're in charge?'

'That's just the problem,' she said ruefully. 'I am. Until the water goes down there's no way I can get anyone to medical help. There's just me.'

'And me.'

She nodded, grateful that he was acknowledging he could help in a crisis—having a doctor on this side was wonderful but one who'd so recently had surgery? 'That's fine,' she told him. 'Unless you're the patient.'

'I don't intend to be the patient.' He was looking down at the blissfully sucking baby with bemusement. 'Why couldn't I do that?'

'You could. You can.' She rose and handed the bundle over, bottle and all, and Blake was left standing with an armload of baby. 'Sit,' she told him. 'Settle. Bond.'

'Bond?'

'You're her uncle. I suspect this little one needs all the family she can get.'

'It's she who needs medical help,' he said, almost savagely, and Ruby startled in his arms.

'Sit,' Maggie said again. 'Settle.'

He sat. He settled, as far as a man with an armload of baby could settle.

He looked…stunning, Maggie thought. Bare chested, wearing only boxer shorts, his dark hair raked and rumpled, his five o'clock shadow a few hours past five o'clock. Yep, stunning was the word for it.

It'd be wise if she failed to be stunned. She needed to remember she was here for a postnatal visit. Maternal health nurse visiting brand-new parent…

Who happened to be her landlord.

Who happened to be a surgeon—who was telling her the baby had medical needs.

She needed to pay attention to something other than

how sexy he looked, one big man, almost naked, cradling a tiny baby.

With medical needs. Get serious.

'If you think her legs are bad enough to require immediate medical intervention I can organise helicopter evacuation,' she said. She knelt and unwrapped the blanket from around the tiny feet and winced.

'I can't believe her mother rejected her because of her feet,' she whispered, and Blake shook his head.

'No mother rejects her baby because of crooked feet.'

'Some fathers might. Some do. A daughter and an imperfect one at that. If the mother's weak…'

'Or if the mother's on drugs…'

'There doesn't seem any sign of withdrawal,' Maggie said, touching the tiny cheek, feeling the way the baby's face was filling out already. 'If her mother's a drug addict, this little one will be suffering withdrawal herself.'

'She's three weeks old,' Blake said. 'She may well be over it. But if she was addicted, those first couple of weeks will have been hell. That and the talipes may well have been enough for her to be rejected.'

'That and the knowledge that you've come home,' Maggie said thoughtfully. 'If your sister knows you're here, and thinks you're in a position to care for her, then she might see you as a way out.'

'She's not my sister.'

'Your father is her father.'

'I don't even know her surname.'

'No, but I do,' she said smoothly. 'She's Wendy Runtland, twenty-nine years old, and she lives on a farmlet six miles on the far side of the base hospital. Ruby was born on the twenty-first of last month. Wendy only stayed overnight and refused further assistance. The staff were worried. They'd organised a paediatrician to see the baby to assess her feet but Wendy discharged herself—and Ruby—before he got there.'

'How the—?'

'I'm a midwife employed by the Valley Health Service,' she told him. 'If I'm worried about babies, I can access files. I rang the hospital last night and asked for a search for a local baby born with talipes. Ruby's the only fit. The file's scanty. No antenatal care. First baby. Fast, hard labour with a partner present for some of the time. They were both visibly upset by the baby's feet and there's a note in the file that the guy was angry and abusive.

'The next morning Wendy discharged herself and the baby against medical advice. There were no grounds to involve the police but staff did notify Social Services. The maternal health nurse has tried to make home visits but each time she's found gates locked and dogs that didn't allow her to go further. There's a phone number but the phone's been slammed down each time she's rung. You might have more luck. You want to try while I check the bridge?'

'What's to check?'

He looked almost dumbfounded, she thought. Man left with abandoned baby. Surgeon way out of his comfort zone.

'I've been listening to the radio and it's still raining up north,' she said evenly. 'There's a vast mass of water coming down. If the water keeps rising it might be a while before you can get her to Social Services.'

'Social Services?'

'Unless we can get her back to her mother—or unless you want her—I assume that's where she'll be placed. Either way, the decision has to be made soon. Those feet need attention now, although I assume you know that.'

'I know it,' he growled, and then he fell silent.

He stared down at the baby in his arms and she thought… there was something there, some link.

Family.

He'd said he didn't have a sister. He'd said he didn't even know her full name.

This was a guy who was an intelligent, skilled surgeon, she thought, a guy who'd know how to keep his emotions under control. But his recent surgery would have weakened him, and a sleepless night would have weakened him still more.

She had a feeling this guy didn't let his defences down often, but they were down now. He was gazing at the child in his arms and his face said he didn't know where to go with this.

Evacuate her? Hand her over to Social Welfare? Keep her until the river went down?

Risk attachment?

She couldn't help him. It was his decision.

'I'll try and phone Wendy,' he said at last, and she nodded and got to her feet and collected her eggs.

'Excellent. I'll leave some of these in your kitchen. Tell me how you go.'

'Maggie?'

She paused. Met his gaze. Saw desperation.

'Stay here while I ring,' he said, and she thought maybe she could at least do that.

But as he handed back the now fed, sleeping Ruby, and she gathered her into her arms and watched Blake head for the phone, she thought…she thought…

She thought this was as far as she should go.

Babies did things to her. Her mother had used that, played on it, trapped her with it. And now…

The sight of Blake was doing things to her as well.

He was all male, one gorgeous hunk of testosterone, but it wasn't that that was messing with her head.

It was the way he'd looked at Ruby—and the way he'd looked at her when he'd asked her to stay.

Under that strength was pure vulnerability.

Maggie had lived most of her life in this valley and she'd heard stories about this family; this man. His mother had been glamorous and aloof and cold, and she'd walked out—justifiably—when Blake had been six. His father had been a womanising brute.

Blake may come from the richest family in the district but the locals had felt sorry for him when he'd been six, and that sympathy hadn't been lessened by anything anyone had heard since.

What sort of man was he now? Like his mother? Like his father?

She couldn't tell. She was seeing him at his most vulnerable. He was wounded, shocked, tired and burdened by a baby he didn't know.

Don't judge now, she told herself. Don't get any more involved than you already are.

Except…she could stay while he rang his sister.

She sank down on the settee and put her feet towards the fire. This was a great room. A family room.

She lived on the other side of the wall. Remember it, she told herself.

Meanwhile, she cuddled one sleeping baby and she listened.

Blake had switched to speakerphone. He wanted to share. She could share, she decided, at least this much.

Blake punched in the numbers Maggie had given him and a woman answered on the second ring. Sounding defensive. Sounding like she'd expected the call.

'Wendy?'

There was a long silence and Maggie wondered if she'd slam down the receiver as she'd slammed it down on the district nurse.

'Blake,' she said at last. She sounded exhausted. Drained. Defeated.

The baby was three weeks old, Maggie thought, and wondered about postnatal depression.

'You know my name,' Blake was saying, tentatively, feeling his way. 'I didn't even know yours.'

'That would be because our father acknowledged you.'

'I'm sorry.'

'Bit late to be sorry now,' she hissed. 'Thirty years.'

'Wendy, what my father did or didn't do to you isn't anything to do with me.'

'You got the farm.'

'We can talk about that,' he said evenly. 'But right now we need to talk about your daughter.'

'She's not my daughter,' she snapped.'I didn't even want her in the first place. Now Sam says he won't even look at her.'

'Too right, I won't,' a man's voice growled, and Maggie realised it wasn't only Blake who was on speakerphone. 'We never wanted kids, neither of us. We're going to Western Australia, but there's no way we're taking a deformed rat with us. By the time Wendy realised she was pregnant it was too late to get rid of it but neither of us want it. We should have left it at the hospital, but all them forms... Anyway, she's getting her tubes tied the minute we get settled, and that's it. If you want the kid adopted, we'll sign the papers, but we don't have time for any of that now. Meanwhile, the kid's yours. Do what you like with it. We're leaving.'

'Let me talk to Wendy,' again, he said. 'Wendy?'

Wendy came on the line again, just as defensive. 'Yeah?'

'Is this really what you want?' he asked urgently. 'This shouldn't be about our past. It's now. It's Ruby. Do you really want to abandon your daughter?'

'Yeah,' Wendy said, and defence gave way to bitterness. 'Yeah, I do, but I'm not abandoning her. I'm giving her to you. My family's done nothing for me, ever, so now it's time. I don't want this kid, so you deal with it, big brother. Your problem.'

And the phone was slammed down with a force that must have just about cracked the receiver at the other end.

Silence.

Deathly silence.

Blake put the phone back in its charger like it might shatter. Like the air around him might shatter.

Maggie looked at his face and looked away.

She looked down at the little girl in her arms.

Deformed rat.

Thank God she was only three weeks old. Thank God she couldn't understand.

Suddenly the way her mother had looked at Maggie's brothers and sisters flooded back to her. Over and over she remembered her mother, exhausted from childbirth, arriving home from hospital, sinking onto her mound of pillows in the bed that was her centre, handing over the newest arrival to her eldest daughter.

'You look after it, Maggie.'

Her mother wasn't close to as bad as this, but there were similarities. Her parents did what they had to do, but no more. Life was fun and frivolous, and responsibility was something to be handed over to whoever was closest.

Her mother liked being pregnant. Her parents liked the weird prestige of having a big family, but they wanted none of the responsibility that went with it.

Deformed rat.

She found herself hugging the little one closer, as if she could protect her from the words. From the label.

Abandoned baby.

Deformed rat.

And then the baby was lifted from her arms. Blake had

her, was cradling her, holding her as a man might hold his own newborn. The way he held her was pure protection. It was anger and frustration and grief. It was an acknowledgement that his world had changed.

'She won't change her mind,' he said grimly, and it was hardly a question.

'I suspect not,' Maggie whispered. 'Not after three weeks. Mothers often reject straight after birth if there's something seriously wrong—or if depression or psychosis kicks in—but she's cared for her—after a fashion—for three weeks now. And the anger… I'm thinking this is a thought-out decision, as much as either of them sound like they can think anything out. After three weeks with this one, there should be an unbreakable bond. If there's not, it won't form now. All we can hope for is to maintain contact.'

'You'd want Ruby to maintain contact with a family who think of her as…?' He broke off, sounding appalled. 'We'll have to organise adoption. Surely there's a family who'll want her.'

'There will be,' Maggie said. 'Of course. But without the papers…she'll need to go into foster-care first.'

'And let me guess, there's no foster-carers over this side of the river.'

'I'm organising evacuation,' she said, and he stared at her. As well he might. This decision had been made a whole two seconds ago.

'Sorry?'

'For both of you,' she said briskly. 'I read up on talipes last night. I haven't seen a baby with it before but I know what needs to be done. She needs careful manipulation and casts, starting now. The Ponseti technique talks about long casts on both legs, changed weekly. I can't do that. Then there's the fact that you had appendicitis with complications a week ago.'

'I didn't have complications.'

'So why didn't you have keyhole surgery?' She fixed him with a look she'd used often on recalcitrant patients. 'Right. Complications. So in summary, I have a man who may end up needing urgent help from previous surgery. I have a baby who needs urgent medical attention. The rain has eased this morning but the forecast is that more storms will hit tonight. I can get you out of here right now. You can have Ruby back in Sydney in the best of medical care, organising foster-care, organising anything you need, by this afternoon. I'll make the call now.'

'You're kicking me out?'

'You have medical training, too,' she said. 'You know it's for the best.'

She was right.

Of course she was right. If she made the call, all problems would be solved. Evacuation was justified. If he didn't accept the offer—the order?—he could well end up stuck here with a baby for a couple of weeks.

He could take Ruby back to Sydney, right now.

He could be home in his own, clean, clinical apartment tonight, with Ruby handed over to carers, and all this behind him.

Maggie was waiting. She stood calmly, her bucket of eggs in her hand, ready to take action.

He thought, stupidly, Who'll eat the eggs if I go?

It was sensible to go.

The phone rang again. He picked it up without thinking. It was still on speakerphone—his father's landline. He half expected it to be Wendy, but it was a child's voice, shrill and urgent.

'Maggie?'

The eggs were back on the floor so fast some must have broken, and Maggie had the phone in an instant.

'Susie, what's wrong?'

'Christopher's bleeding...' On the other end of the line, the child hiccupped on a sob and choked.

'No crying, Susie,' Maggie said, and it was a curt order that had Blake's eyes widen. It sounded like sergeant major stuff. 'You know it doesn't help. What's happened?'

'He slid on the wet roof and he cut himself,' Susie whimpered. 'His blood is oozing out from the top of his leg, and Mum's screaming and Pete said to ring and say come.'

'I'm coming,' Maggie said, still in the sergeant major voice. 'But first you listen, Susie, and listen hard. Get a sheet out of the linen cupboard and roll it up so it's a tight, tight ball. Then you go out to Christopher, you tell Mum to shut up and keep away—can you do that, Susie? Imagine you're me and just do it—and tell Pete to put the ball of sheet on his leg and press as hard as he's ever pressed in his life. Tell him to sit on it if he must. He has to stop the bleeding. Can you do that, love?'

'I... Yes.'

'I'll be there before Mum even stops yelling,' Maggie said. 'You just make Pete keep pressing, and tell everyone I'm on my way.'

CHAPTER FOUR

ONE minute she was readying Blake for medical evacuation. The next she was heading a mile down the road to the ramshackle farmhouse where her parents and four of their nine children lived.

With Blake and baby.

How had it happened?

She hardly had time to wonder. Her entire concentration was on the road—apart from a little bit that was aware of the man beside her.

She'd headed for the door, out to the wagon, but by the time she'd reversed and turned, Blake had been in pants and shirt, standing in front of the car, carrying Ruby.

'If he's bleeding out, you'll need me,' he'd snapped, and she hadn't argued. She'd fastened a seemingly bemused Ruby into the baby carrier she always carried—as district nurse her car was always equipped for carting kids—and now she was heading home and Blake was hauling his shoes on while she drove.

Christopher was twelve years old. He'd had more accidents than she could remember.

'I should never have left them,' she muttered, out loud but addressed to herself.

'You should never have left home?' Blake had tied his shoes and was now buttoning his shirt. He was almost respectable. Behind them, Ruby had settled into the baby carrier, like this was totally satisfactory—baby being taken for an after-breakfast drive by Mum and Dad.

Mum and Dad? Ha!

'My parents aren't responsible people,' Maggie said through gritted teeth. 'They should have been neutered at birth.'

'Um…there's a big statement.' Blake looked thoughtful. 'That'd mean there'd have been no Maggie.'

'And none of the other eight they won't look after,' she snapped. 'But Nickie, Louise, Raymond and Donny are out of the valley now, studying. Susie's ten—she's the youngest. I thought they were getting independent. With me only a mile away I thought they'd be safe.'

'They're as safe as if you were living there and gone to the shops for milk,' Blake said, and she let the thought drift— and the tight knot of fear and guilt unravelled a bit so that only fear remained.

And the fear was less because this man was sitting beside her.

But she still didn't know what she was dealing with. If Chris had cut his femoral artery…

'She said oozing,' Blake said, as if his thoughts were running concurrent with hers. 'If it was the artery she'd have used a more dramatic word.'

The fear backed off a little, too. She allowed a glimmer of hope to enter the equation, but she didn't ease her foot from the accelerator.

'No hairpin bends between here and your place?' Blake asked, seemingly mildly.

'No.'

'Good,' Blake said. 'Excellent. No aspersions on your driving, but Ruby and I are very pleased to hear it.'

* * *

They pulled up outside a place that looked like a cross between a house and a junkyard. The house looked almost derelict, a ramshackle, weatherboard cottage with two or three shonky additions tacked onto the back. The veranda at the front was sagging, kids' toys and bikes were everywhere and Blake could count at least five car bodies—or bits of car bodies. An old white pony was loosely tethered to the veranda, and a skinny, teenage girl came flying down from the veranda to meet them.

'Maggie, round the back, quick…'

Maggie was out of the car almost before it had stopped, and gone.

Blake was left with the girl.

Maggie had left her bag. The girl was about to dart off, too, but Blake grabbed her by the shoulder and held on.

'I'm a friend of Maggie's,' he said curtly. 'I'm a doctor. Will you stay with the baby? Take care of her while I help Maggie?'

The girl stared at him—and then stared into the car at the baby.

'Yes,' she whispered. 'Blood makes me wobble.'

As long as babies didn't, Blake thought, but it was cool and overcast, Ruby was asleep and in no danger of overheating, and Maggie might well need him more.

He thrust the girl into the passenger seat and she sat as if relieved to be there. Then he hauled open Maggie's bag. Maggie was methodical, he thought. Equipment was where he expected it to be. He couldn't handle the whole bag but he grabbed worst-case scenario stuff and headed behind the house at a run.

His stitches pulled, but for the first time since the operation, he hardly noticed.

Behind the house was drama. Maggie was already there, stooped over a prostrate child. Around them was a cluster of kids of assorted ages, and a woman was down on her knees, wailing. 'Maggie, it's making me sick. Maggie...'

The kids were ignoring the woman. They were totally intent on Maggie—who was totally intent on the child she was caring for.

Christopher was a miniature version of Maggie, he thought as he knelt beside her to see what they were dealing with. Same chestnut hair. Same freckles.

No colour at all.

Maggie was making a pad out of a pile of sheets lying beside her. An older boy—Peter?—his face as white as death—was pressing hard on a bloodied pad on his brother's thigh. As Blake knelt beside her, Maggie put her own pad in position.

'Okay, Pete, lift.'

The boy lifted the pad away, and in the moment before Maggie applied her tighter pad, Blake saw a gash, eight to ten inches long. Pumping. Not the major artery—he'd be dead by now if he'd hit that, but bad enough.

Leg higher than heart.

Maggie had replaced the pad and was pressing down again. Blood was oozing out the sides.

Whoever had grabbed the sheets had grabbed what looked like the contents of the linen cupboard. He grabbed the whole pile and wedged them under the boy's thighs, elevating the leg. Maggie moved with him and they moved effortlessly into medical-team mode.

The oozing blood was slowing under her hands, but not enough. Pressure could only do so much.

Maggie was looking desperate. She knew what was happening.

Blake was already checking and rechecking the equipment in his hands. Hoping to hell her sterilisation procedures were thorough. Knowing he had no choice.

He'd wrapped the stuff in a sterile sheet he'd pulled from

plastic. He laid it on the grass, set it out as he'd need it, then hauled on sterile gloves.

'On the count of three, take your hands away,' he said to Maggie, and she glanced up at him, terror everywhere, saw his face, steadied, and somehow moved more solidly into medical mode.

'You're assisting, Nurse,' he said flatly, calmly. 'Don't let me down. Pete, hold your brother's shoulders, tight. Christopher, I'm about to stop the bleeding. It'll hurt but only for a moment. Grit your teeth and bear it.'

He'd swabbed and slid in pain relief while he talked but he didn't have time for it to take effect.

'Ready?' he snapped to his makeshift theatre team.

'R-ready,' Maggie faltered.

'You stay calm on me,' he snapped. 'Pete, have you got those shoulders? Not one movement. Use all your strength to hold your brother still. Chris, are you ready to bite the bullet, like they say in the movies? We need you to be a hero.'

'I... Yes.'

'Good kid,' Blake said. 'You don't need to pretend—you are a hero. I need to hurt you to stop the bleeding but I'll be fast. This is superhero country. Pretend you're armed with kryptonite and hold on.'

Maggie was terrified.

She was a nurse assisting a surgeon in Theatre, and somehow the second took priority over the first. Blake's calm authority, his snapped, incisive instructions, the movements of his fingers...it was all that mattered. It had to be all that mattered.

Instead of being a terrified sister, she was a theatre assistant and only that. She was focussed entirely on anticipating Blake's needs, swabbing away blood so she could see what he was doing, handing him what he needed as he needed it.

A torn artery…

Worse, it had retracted into the wound. She could see the blood seeping from the top of the rip in the skin. This was no exposed artery to be simply tied off.

If there was time for anaesthetic…

There wasn't, and she held her breath as Blake produced a scalpel and fast, neatly, precisely, extended the tear just enough…just enough…

Chris jerked and cried out, but magically Pete held him still.

She swabbed and could see.

He was before her. The scalpel was back in her hand—not dropped when they might need it again—and forceps taken instead. Somehow she'd had them ready.

Blake was working inside the wound, manoeuvring, while she tried desperately to keep the wound clear, let him see what he was dealing with.

'Got it,' he said, amazingly calmly, as if the issue had never been in doubt, and almost as he said it, the bleeding slowed.

He was using the forceps to clamp.

'Suture,' he said.

She prepared sutures faster than she'd thought possible. She watched as his skilled fingers moved in and out, in and out.

She swabbed and cut and cleaned and she thought, Thank you, God.

Thank you, Blake.

He'd done it. The bleeding had slowed to almost nothing. He sat back and felt the same sense of overwhelming dizziness he always felt after such drama.

Cope first, faint second? It was an old edict instilled in him by a long-ago surgery professor when he'd caught his knees buckling.

'There's no shame in a good faint,' the professor had said. 'We all suffer from reaction. Just learn to delay it.'

He'd delayed it—and so had Maggie. In no other circumstances would he have permitted a relative to assist in a procedure on a family member. For her to hold it together...

She'd done more than that. She'd been calm, thorough, brilliant.

They weren't out of the woods yet. What was needed now was replacement volume. He felt Chris's pulse and flinched. With this blood pressure he was at risk of cardiac arrest.

They needed fluids, now.

But Maggie's capacious bag had provided all he needed. Thank God for Maggie's bag. Thank God for district nurses.

While Maggie worked under orders, applying a rough dressing that kept the pressure up—he'd need to remove it later when the pain relief kicked in fully to do a neater job— he lifted the boy's arm, swabbed it fast and slid in the IV. A moment later he taped it safely, grabbed a bag of saline and started it running.

He checked the pulse and checked again that he had adrenalin close.

He checked the pulse again and decided not yet.

'Do we have plasma?' he asked.

'At the clinic,' Maggie said. 'Ten minutes' drive away.'

It wasn't worth risking driving for yet. He'd run the saline and wait.

The lad seemed close to unconscious, dazed, hazy, hardly responding, but as the saline dripped in and the drugs took effect, they saw a tiny amount of colour return.

The pulse under Blake's fingers regained some strength.

Around them the family watched, horrified to stillness, willing a happy ending. As did Blake. As, he thought, did Maggie. Her face was almost as white as the child's.

This child was her brother.

Brothers and sisters.

He thought suddenly of the baby he'd seen thirty years before when he'd been six years old. His sister. He'd never had this connection, he thought, and then he thought of Ruby and wondered if this was a second chance.

It was a crazy time to think of one tiny baby.

Think of Christopher.

The saline dripped in. He kept his fingers on the little boy's pulse, willing the pressure to rise, and finally it did. Christopher seemed to stir from semi-consciousness and he whimpered.

'Christopher, love, keep still,' Maggie said urgently, but he heard the beginnings of relief in her voice. 'It's okay. You've cut your leg badly, so you need to keep it still, but Dr Samford's fixed it. It'll be fine. What a duffer you were to try and climb on the wet roof.'

'You slide faster when it's wet,' he whispered. 'But it hurts. I won't do it again.'

Blake let out his breath. He hadn't actually been aware that he hadn't been breathing but now…

He remembered another rule instilled into him a long time ago by the professor who'd taken him for his paediatric term. 'Rule of thumb for quick triage. If a child is screaming, put it at the end of the queue. If it's quiet but whinging, middle. If it's silent, front, urgent, *now*.'

Christopher had suddenly moved from front of the line to the middle.

He glanced at Maggie and she seemed to sag. There was relief but also weariness. Desperation.

He glanced around and he thought, How many times had this scene played out? Maggie, totally responsible.

The mother—a crazy, hippy-dressed mass of sodden hysteria, was incoherent in the background, slumped on the grass crying, holding onto yet another kid, a little girl who looked about ten. As Blake watched, the little girl tried to pull away to come across to Maggie, but her mother held her harder.

'Hold me, Susie,' she whimpered. 'I'll faint if you don't. Oh, my God, you kids will be the death of me.'

Let her faint, he thought grimly, and glanced again at Maggie and saw a look…

Like a deer trapped in headlights.

How much responsibility did this woman carry for this family?

'Swap places and I'll bind it,' he told her. He needed to take the pressure off Maggie so she could react to the needs of these kids—to Chris but also to brave Pete, who'd held his brother all this time, and to Susie, who'd held her mother. 'Do we have somewhere we can stitch it properly?' He glanced at the house—and Maggie's mother—and thought, I just bet it's not clean inside.

'Maggie's not stitching me,' Christopher whimpered. 'She hurts.'

'You've stitched your brother before?' he demanded, astounded.

Maggie gave a rueful smile. 'Not unless I've have no choice,' she told him. 'But Christopher doesn't give his family many choices.'

'You have a choice now,' he said, still seeing that trapped look. 'I can do this. You said you've set up a clinic. With a surgery?'

'A small one.'

'Excellent.' He smiled down at Christopher. 'If you'll accept me as a substitute for your sister, we'll bind your leg so you don't make a mess of her car, then we'll take you to the clinic she's set up. I'll fix your leg properly where I have equipment and decent light. I need to check for nerve damage.' But already he was checking toes and leg for response, and he was thinking Christopher had been lucky.

'But what about Ruby?' Maggie demanded

And he thought...*Ruby*.

Uh-oh. Ruby.

His baby?

She was not his baby, he told himself harshly. She was merely his responsibility until she could be evacuated or her mother reclaimed her. No more.

'Your sister's caring for her,' he told Maggie. 'In the car,' he added, and hoped she was.

'If she's with Liselle, she'll be fine,' Maggie assured him. 'Liselle loves babies. She makes money babysitting.' But she was frowning, obviously thinking ahead.

'Blake, Chris obviously needs careful stitching.' She glanced at the leg Blake had now bound so tightly the bleeding had completely stopped. 'I think...even if Christopher's okay with it, it might be too big a job to do here. I can cope with simple suturing, but this might need more. On top of that, Ruby's legs need attention. The sooner the pair of them get professional care, the better. Added to that, I don't want the responsibility for your appendix. The sensible plan is to organise evacuation for the three of you. I'll get the chopper in now—they'll fly you all over to the hospital.'

'I don't want to go to hospital,' Christopher whimpered, sounding panicked, and suddenly Blake was right there, concurring.

'I don't either,' he said. 'I can fix this.' He put a hand on Christopher's shoulder, settling him. 'I'm a surgeon and I do a neat job of stitching,' he said. 'No criticism of your sister but she's a girl. What do girls know abut needlework?'

That produced a faint smile on the boy's wan face. 'Yeah, right.'

'So it's okay if I put your leg back together instead of you sister? Without sending you to hospital?'

'Okay,' Christopher whispered, and Maggie hugged him

Blake wondered why Maggie was doing the hugging instead of the wimp of a woman that was their mother.

'I'm going to make myself a nice cup of tea,' the woman was saying, staggering to her feet. 'I'm Barbie, by the way. Barbara, but my friends call me Barbie. Maggie, you might have introduced me.'

Right, Blake thought. Introductions before saving her son's life?

Christopher was slipping towards sleep. The saline was pushing his blood pressure up. The painkillers were taking effect. They had time to think this through but what he was suggesting—staying here—still seemed sensible.

Even to him.

'What about Ruby?' Maggie asked as her mother disappeared, jerking him back to his baby, his responsibility.

But responsibilities weren't only his. His thoughts were flying tangentially, from a wounded child to a baby—and to one lone nurse.

One look at this family and he'd seen what Maggie was facing. The mother was feeble and hysterical, the father was nowhere to be seen, and these kids were too young to be alone. Maggie seemed to be caring for everyone. More than that, she was taking on the medical needs for the entire population of this side of the valley. Until the water receded, she was on her own.

Christopher would live. If Maggie had been on her own, he might well not have. They both knew that. Maggie's white face told him she'd seen it and was still seeing it. But together they'd worked well. They'd worked as a team.

He was on leave. He needed to sort the house. How hard would it be to provide back-up for this woman?

And care for a baby while he did?

She'd help him with Ruby, he thought. Maggie was that sort of woman.

'No,' she said.

'No?'

Her eyes narrowed, and she made her voice resolute. 'I know what you're thinking and no. I'm *not* helping look after your baby and you *are* being evacuated.'

'I wasn't asking you to look after my...my sister's baby,' he said, and thought, Okay, he might have been going to suggest it but he wasn't now. 'And you don't need to look after my appendix. In case you hadn't realised it, most appendectomies result in removal of same, and I've left mine safely in Sydney.' Then, as she opened her mouth to protest some more, he held up his hand to pre-empt her.

'Plus,' he said, 'I was looked after by colleagues, medical mates who know they'll get joshed for ever if I'm hit by complications, so I have enough antibiotics on board to protect a horse. I'm healing nicely. Plus...' she'd opened her mouth again... 'if you send Ruby to hospital the first thing they'll do is to organise an orthopaedic surgeon opinion. I'm suspecting Corella Valley doesn't run to an orthopaedic surgeon. The nearest orthopaedic surgeon would therefore be me, and I'm on this side of the river. Maggie, not only can I assess Ruby, I can manipulate and cast her legs. I can do everything she needs until the water comes down.'

'And look after her?'

'I... Yes,' he said, and he met her gaze full on. 'And Wendy knows where she is right now,' he said. 'She might change her mind. That option's not available if Ruby's sent to the city.'

'I doubt—'

'So do I doubt,' he said softly. 'But Wendy's my sister so maybe I should care for this little one for a week or two and give her that chance.'

'Would you want her to go back to...that?' she demanded, appalled.

'No,' he said truthfully. 'But I do want to talk to Wendy. I do want to figure this mess out. I don't want to walk away...'

'From your family,' she said, her voice softening.

'I've figured it,' he told her, glancing up at the roof. 'Risks are everywhere. If I turn my back, the next thing I know Ruby will be roof-sliding.'

'You'll take responsibility for her?'

'For a week or so,' he said, wondering what on earth he'd let himself in for. But there was something about this moment...something about the way this woman was shouldering so much responsibility—that made him think, One baby for a week. Was that a lot to ask?

Family for a week.

He could do this, he thought, and somehow...maybe it'd be his only chance to make reparation for a sister who'd never had a Maggie.

Why?

Because he'd thought of Wendy. For whatever reason, he'd thought of that baby, glimpsed only that once.

He hadn't had a great childhood, but many had it worse. His mother had had enough strength to walk away from her abusive husband. She hadn't been a particularly affectionate mother but the man she'd married next had been distantly kind. Money had never been an issue. He'd gone to a great school, to an excellent university.

Wendy, though...

He knew enough of his father to know there'd have been no support for an illegitimate child. He didn't know who her mother was, but he remembered hysteria, threats, floods of tears, and he thought... He thought Wendy must have had the worst side of the deal by far.

You've got the farm... She'd thrown that at him as an accusation.

Did he have the right to accept it? For the first time he was questioning it.

Maggie was watching him. Waiting for him to realise what he was letting himself in for. Waiting for him to realise that evacuation was the easiest way to go.

But then he thought back to that moment all those years ago. Seeing a child... Thinking for one amazing moment that he had a little sister.

Family.

He didn't do family. He was a loner. Miriam was all he needed—a woman as caught up in her career as he was in his.

Miriam would think he was nuts.

'Hey, mister, I think your baby's filled her nappy. You want me to change it? I can but I charge babysitting rates.' It was a yell from the far side of the house and it jerked him out of introspection as nothing else could have. It even made him smile.

'He's coming, Liselle,' Maggie said. She was cradling Christopher, hugging him close, surveying Blake like he was an interesting insect species. She was watching to see what he'd do. 'There's no need for him to waste money employing nappy-changers, and there are no nappy-changers available for hire anyway. There are nappies in my bag,' she told him. 'Or there's still the choice of evacuation. What's it to be?'

And he looked down at Christopher—who'd need to be evacuated with him—that wound needed careful stitching and it was too much to expect Maggie to do it. He looked at Maggie, who'd taken on responsibility for the valley.

He thought about Ruby, whose need had just graphically been described.

'I guess I'm staying,' he said, and Maggie smiled up at him. It wasn't a confident smile, though. Maybe she still thought he'd be more trouble than he was worth.

'You're a brave man,' she told him. 'Changing nappies isn't for sissies.'

'Then I guess I can't be a sissy,' he told her, grinning back at her. Thinking this could be a very interesting week. Thinking Here Be Dragons but he could just possibly tackle them and do this woman a favour in the process. 'I can't be a sissy until the floods subside.'

'Or until after you've coped with one nappy,' Maggie said. 'Nappy or floods…take your pick.'

'I have a feeling I'm facing both.'

They tucked Christopher into the back seat of Maggie's wagon. It was a tight fit around the baby seat but they stuffed the leg space with cushions so he could lie down, they wrapped him in blankets and he settled. It wasn't only the drugs that made him relax, Maggie thought. Whenever one of the kids was ill it was 'We want Maggie.' More, it was 'We *need* Maggie.' And they did.

She slid behind the steering-wheel, checked on her now sleeping little brother, an awake but changed and clean Ruby—and one recovering appendectomy patient beside her.

Mother hen with all her chicks.

Blake wasn't quite a chick.

He was staying.

She should be relieved. She was relieved. He'd been brilliant with Christopher. She might have got the bleeding checked in time, but she might not have. The odds said not. She glanced again at Christopher and her heart twisted.

She glanced at Blake—and something inside twisted in a different direction.

Weird?

Yes, it was weird. This guy was a doctor, a surgeon. He was here to help and she should be overjoyed, in a purely professional capacity. But there was a little bit of her that wasn't professional, which was reacting to the sense of this guy sitting beside her, which was saying that Blake deciding to stay might cause problems…

What problems? She was being ridiculous. It was the shock of what had just happened, she told herself firmly. It was the shock of almost losing one of her family.

She loved the lot of them. All eight. They held her heartstrings and she was tied for life.

So put the weird way she was feeling about Blake right away—forget it.

'Why did you decide to leave them?' Blake asked and she concentrated on the road for a while, concentrated on getting her thoughts in order, concentrated on suppressing anger and confusion and whatever else was whirling in her traitorous mind.

'You think I should still be living with them?'

'I don't think,' Blake said mildly. 'But I'm wondering if your father's a bit more capable than your mother.'

'He's not,' she said shortly. 'And he doesn't live there any more.'

'I'm sorry.'

'I'm not,' she said. 'It's one less responsibility.' Then she caught herself. 'Sorry. That sounds like they're all hard work. They're great kids. Nickie, Louise and Raymond have scholarships and are at university. Donny's in his last year as an apprentice motor mechanic. They're all safe.'

'How did you train?' he asked, mildly, thinking if she had been responsible for them all…had she left and come back?

'Luck,' she said briefly. 'Dad was restless and moved us all to Cairns. It was dumb—we knew no one there and ended up reliant on Social Services but it took four years to get enough money together to come back, so I was able to do my basic nursing training while I lived with them. Otherwise I'd be stuck with nothing.'

'Stuck with your family?'

'That's it,' she said quietly. 'And it's a quandary. The kids love me and need me, but they're growing up. Gradually they're making their way into the world, so I need to work out my own independence as well. I know I have eventual escape, but Liselle, Peter, Christopher and Susie are seventeen, fifteen, twelve and ten and too young to be left with the cot case that's my mother. But I didn't have a choice—until your father's farm became available.'

'You're saying you left your family to take care of my father's farm?'

'I left my family for me,' she said grimly, and there was a moment's silence while she obviously decided whether to reveal more of herself. And came down on the yes side.

'My dad left two years ago,' she told him. 'He's as bad as my mum. Totally irresponsible. Six months ago, just as your dad was dying, he turned up with a new young partner in tow. Sashabelle. What sort of name is that? Anyway they giggled and mooned over each other and Sashabelle kept saying how cute Susie was and how she'd love to have a daughter—all in my mother's hearing—and then Dad looked at me and grinned and said to her, "Yeah, sweetheart, you know I love travelling but if you really want a kid…if worst comes to worst we can always bring her home to Maggie."'

'And I thought that's exactly what would happen. Just like Wendy's dumped Ruby on you—only I've already cared for eight and I'm d— I'm darned if I'll look after more. So I told him no more, ever, I was moving out. Then I had to find somewhere where I could reach the kids in a hurry when they need me, but my useless parents know that I've drawn a line and any more kids—no way. Once Susie's left home, I'm out of it. Good ole Maggie… I love my brothers and sisters to bits but the end's in sight.'

'So that's why you won't take on Ruby?'

Her face froze. 'No,' she said through gritted teeth. 'It's not why I won't take on Ruby. I'm not taking on Ruby because she's not my family, and it's totally, crassly, cruelly irresponsible for you to ask it of me. I'm your tenant, Blake, but if babies are involved you won't see me for dust. Put that in your pipe and smoke it—and don't forget it. And here we are.'

They'd pulled into the grounds of the local hall. A dumpy little lady in her forties was tacking a banner to the fence.

'*Medical Clinic, Temporary, Corella Valley East.*'

A sign hung on a nail in front of it.

'*Maggie's Not Here.*'

As Maggie swung into the gate the lady at the fence beamed, waved and swapped the sign over.

'*Maggie's Here.*'

'Very professional,' Blake said dryly, and Maggie cast him a wry look.

'So how would you organise it, city boy?'

'Regular hours?'

'And when another kid falls off a roof I still stay here because I need to be regular? I'll be here when I can.' She climbed out of the car and hugged the lady doing the signs. 'Ronnie, this looks great. Fantastic. And we have our first patient. Christopher.'

Ronnie sighed and tugged away to look into the back seat. 'Oh, Christopher, what have you done now?' And then she paused as Blake emerged from the passenger seat. 'Oh…'

'This is Blake Samford,' Maggie said briefly. 'He's Bob's son—and a doctor. He's offered to help. Blake, this is Veronica Mayes. Ronnie. She's a schoolteacher, but the school's on the other side of the river.'

'You're a doctor.' Ronnie's eyes grew huge. 'A medical doctor—here? On this side. Oh, Maggie, that's wonderful.' She peered again into the back seat. 'But Christopher…?'

'Sliding on roof ended badly,' Maggie said curtly. 'Badly cut thigh. It needs stitching and Blake's offered to help.'

'And…the baby?' She was still staring into the car.

'Ruby,' Maggie said. 'Blake's baby. If he asks nicely, he might be persuade you to take care of her while he stitches.'

'You've brought your family here?' Ronnie demanded of Blake, beaming her excitement.

'Just his baby,' Maggie said. 'I suspect Blake thinks that's enough.'

The wound on Christopher's leg was jagged and bone deep. He was incredibly lucky to have escaped nerve damage, Blake thought as he cleaned, debrided and inserted internal stitches as well as external to hold everything together. They'd sedated the boy heavily, so he wasn't out of it completely but he was wafting in a drug-induced haze. Maggie was doing the reassurance, prattling on about some weird video game Christopher loved, but at the same time she was giving him every inch of assistance he needed.

She was an excellent nurse, Blake thought. The valley was lucky to have her.

As he started the final suturing and dressing, Ronnie poked her head round the door and said apologetically, 'Maggie, love, Joan Kittle's here with Angus with asthma.'

'I can handle Angus's asthma,' Maggie told Blake. 'Mild asthmatic, hysterical mum.'

'There seems to be an abundance of hysterical mothers in this valley,' he noted, keeping on working. 'Christopher, is it okay if your sister goes out to take care of a child with asthma?'

'Yeah,' Christopher said sleepily. 'You'll look after me, and everyone always needs Maggie.'

They did. He had that pretty much figured by now.

He finished stitching and dressing and tucked the little boy under blankets. Ronnie appeared again with a sleepy Ruby in her arms. He asked her to stay with Christopher and went to find out what was happening.

Angus was obviously sorted. Maggie was now examining a toe, attached to a very large, very elderly guy who looked like he'd just come in from the cowshed. He sat slumped in a rather rickety chair in the makeshift waiting room, his boot off and his foot stuck straight out in front of him.

Maggie turned as he entered and he was hit by a smile of sheer, anticipatory gratitude.

'Mr Bowen has a splinter,' she said.

'Went out to chop the wood in me slippers,' the old man said. 'Dumb. Coulda chopped me foot off with an axe. Didn't. Hit the wood with the splitter, though, and a bit of wood went right in. I've been digging round all morning with a needle and can't get it. Maggie says you're a doc.'

He was an orthopaedic surgeon, Blake thought faintly. Was he supposed to go digging for splinters?

But that's what he did. He inserted local anaesthetic. He did a part resection of the nail of the big toe and managed the careful removal of a shattered splinter.

He administered a decent shot of antibiotics—the guy had indeed been digging into the wound and Blake hated to imagine what he'd used to do it. He added a tetanus booster and a dressing and the man was ready to heave himself up and leave—but not before commenting on what had happened and on who Blake was.

'Bob's son, eh?' he said jovially. 'You sure don't take after your old man. I can't see Bob Samford pulling splinters out of anyone's toes—he'd be more likely driving them in. And Ronnie tells me you're here with your daughter. How about that? A whole new generation for Corella Valley Homestead. I'll tell the wife to bake a cake.'

And before Blake had a chance to rebut or even answer,

he was hit by a slap on the back that made him stagger and the guy was gone.

Leaving him...speechless.

Blake Samford returns to the family property with daughter...

Not so much.

Maggie was cleaning up. She had her back to him. She didn't say a word.

He wanted to see her expression. He badly wanted to see her expression.

She'd better not be laughing.

'All finished,' Ronnie asked, opening the door so they could see through to Christopher. 'Chris wants to go home. Is he going back to your mum, Maggie, or will you take him back with you?'

'He'll need to come with me,' Maggie said doubtfully. 'Mum won't keep him quiet.'

'Then you'll need Liselle,' Ronnie decreed. She eyed Blake thoughtfully while she spoke, obviously planning ahead. 'At seventeen Liselle's more than competent to do some babysitting,' she told Blake. 'And she'll love getting away from her mother's weird music so she can do some serious study. Unless *you're* happy to stay home all the time.' She arched her eyebrows at Blake, and grinned.

'That's exactly what Blake should be doing,' Maggie retorted. 'He's recovering from appendicitis.'

'Really?' Ronnie was bug-eyed. 'You've come home to recover? Isn't that nice.'

'I've come home... I've come *back* to put the farm on the market,' he growled, and she grinned.

'That sounds more like your dad. But you're going to be useful while you do it, which isn't like your dad at all. So... Christopher and Liselle...they won't fit in that tiny apartment of yours, Maggie.'

'Christopher can share my bed. You know we do that when any of them are ill. Liselle can sleep on the sofa.'

'I've seen your sofa,' Ronnie said darkly. 'Charity-shop reject if ever I saw one. Poor Liselle.' Then she looked—archly—at Blake. 'Your house, though, has more bedrooms—and more beds—than you can poke a stick at. If you're going to be useful, why not be properly useful? Let Liselle and Christopher stay in your part of the house. Maggie won't even go through your door except to dust, and it's always seemed such a waste.'

'Ronnie,' Maggie snapped. 'You know—'

'I know you've made a huge effort to get away from your family and I know why,' Ronnie said. 'But this wouldn't be you taking them in. It'd be Dr Blake taking them in, in exchange for Liselle occasionally looking after his baby. She can't get to school but she needs to study. I suspect she'll get more study done at your place than at your mother's.' Then, as Maggie looked doubtful, she said, more gently, 'Surely your mum can cope with just Peter and Susie?'

'I guess...' Maggie said slowly. 'I worry about Pete—those mates of his are wild but he has two new computer games he's obsessed with, and he's promised... And Susie'll be fine. She spends her time with the little girl next door. But—'

'Then there you are,' Ronnie said, beaming, refusing to listen to buts. 'Problem solved. Corella Homestead will have two adults and three kids. It's built for more but it's a start.'

'Ronnie, it's Blake's house.'

'But he's helping,' Ronnie said, pseudo innocent. 'It's a flood. Everyone helps in a flood. Isn't that right, Dr Samford?'

Open his house up, Blake thought, floundering. To three kids and one nurse? This hadn't been in the contract when he'd taken Maggie in as a tenant.

The house was built for more.

He thought of the house as he remembered it, exquisitely

furnished by his mother. It still was, even though the furnishings were long faded. She'd set up all the bedrooms for guests who'd never come—one hint of his father's temper had been enough to drive them away.

He had five bedrooms, plus the tiny apartment that was Maggie's.

What harm in letting them be used?

Letting a family into his life…

Don't be dramatic, he told himself harshly, and another voice in his head said it would diffuse the situation. He wouldn't be stuck with one baby. He didn't need to bond. With a house full of people Ruby would be just one more.

'She's starting to fret,' Ronnie told him, and before he could demur she'd handed Ruby over, an armful of needy baby. 'Get out of here. Go home and feed your baby. Maggie, your wagon's full. You want me to go and fetch Liselle and bring the kids' gear over?'

'Blake hasn't even said yes yet,' Maggie said, a trifle desperately, and Ronnie put her hands on her hips and fixed him with a schoolmarm look.

'He hasn't either,' she said. 'So what's it to be, Dr Samford? Do you want me to fetch Liselle, or can you look after your baby all by yourself? She does babysitting for pocket money. She's studying for her university entrance exams. She has Maggie for a sister. She's good.'

'But Maggie herself…' he said, feeling helpless.

'Maggie's busy,' Ronnie snapped, glancing at Maggie. 'It's Liselle or nothing. And you might be generous. You don't have to be like your father, you know.'

'That's blackmail,' Maggie retorted, and Ronnie grinned.

'I know but it's working. Look at his face.'

And of course it was. *You don't have to be like your father…*

It was a powerful statement.

The valley was flooded. These were emergency conditions. A man had to pull his weight.

By letting a family into his life?

He didn't do family.

He was holding family in his arms.

'Fine,' he said, and Ronnie's grin widened.

'That's very gracious. You might say fine and mean it. Liselle's lovely and almost as competent as her sister. Christopher's fun. Maggie's magnificent. You're getting a very good deal, Dr Samford.'

'Fine,' he repeated, but this time he managed a weak smile. 'Let's do it.' He met Maggie's gaze and for the first time he realised she was looking almost as trapped as he was.

She was Maggie the magnificent, he thought—who also didn't do family. Or who didn't want to. She was Maggie who was more trapped than he was.

'Fine,' he said for the third time. 'We can do this, can't we, Maggie? For a week or so… For a week or so we can put up with anything.'

CHAPTER FIVE

BEFORE they left the clinic Blake took basic X-rays of Ruby's legs—enough to confirm what he needed to know. Then they went back to the homestead, with Blake taking what he needed with him.

Ruby's feet needed urgent attention. The X-rays showed there was no underlying complication, but at birth the tissues were soft and pliable and every day that passed meant manipulation would be harder and the treatment longer. By six months she'd be facing surgery, but at three weeks of age there was still time for the feet to be manoeuvred into the right position.

Maggie settled Christopher and Liselle into the bedrooms closest to her part of the house. He listened to their amazement at the opulence of his parents' former life while he did what he'd needed to since last night.

He did a careful, thorough examination of Ruby's feet.

A full CT scan of her feet would be good, but that meant evacuation. He could scarcely justify using emergency services when he felt sure the X-rays had shown enough. But there were other factors at play. If he accepted evacuation with Ruby and he went with her, it seemed a statement that he wasn't ready to make. That she somehow belonged to him. But if he didn't leave with her, if he sent her away on her own, that meant welfare. Foster-parents. Losing control.

No. Not yet. For some strange reason he was starting to feel that, whatever this little girl's future was, he wanted a say in it.

Since last night he'd been holding her, feeding her, cradling her, and somehow she was starting to change him. She was starting to make him feel as he'd never expected to feel.

He and Miriam had never talked about having children. Children weren't on their horizon. Now, though, as he held Ruby, as he felt her tiny head nuzzle into the crook of his neck, searching for the security of his warmth and his strength, he felt his world shift a little.

The thought kept coming back...the memory of the tiny girl he'd seen once when he'd been six years old.

She'd been wailing and he'd wanted to do something. He'd wanted to shout at the adults to stop fighting and make the baby better.

He hadn't realised it had had such an impact, but now, all these years later, this baby was in his hands, and maybe he could help this time.

To make her better?

Maggie had thrust this baby at him. She expected him to help.

She wasn't with him now. She was caught up settling Christopher, but it felt like she was right here, watching.

Judging?

Do no harm. That was the first principle of medicine. He examined the X-rays and was satisfied. He carefully manipulated Ruby's tiny, twisted feet and he grew more and more certain that this was straight congenital talipes equinovarus with no other factors coming into play.

There was no major deformity—it had just been the way she'd lain in utero, her feet twisted and gradually setting in a position that, if left untreated, would cause lifelong problems.

He'd set her on Maggie's cashmere rug in the middle of

his bed. She'd just been fed but she wasn't asleep. It almost seemed like she was enjoying him playing with her feet, gently massaging, gently manipulating.

Her eyes were huge. She was up to focussing, but not smiling. He thought, though, that she was almost there.

He was examining her feet but he was also trying to make her smile.

'Five weeks,' Maggie said from the door, and he started like he'd been caught stealing. Trying to steal a smile?

'What…?'

'Babies are generally five weeks old until you can reliably say the smile's not wind. But not your baby, of course.' She grinned. 'Every parent thinks their baby's far, far smarter and it's not wind at all. So what's the prognosis?'

Every parent…

The words hung. He should refute them. He did, in his head, but he didn't say it out loud.

It was something to do with the way Ruby was looking up at him. The contact was fleetingly—her focus was short lived—but he had established eye contact.

Part of him wanted to say, *I am not this child's parent*, but to do that when he'd been trying to make her smile…

'They twist your heartstrings, don't they?' Maggie said gently. 'Family. I have Christopher next door. He's settling to sleep and my heart's only just beginning to beat again.'

And Christopher was twelve, Blake thought. Twelve years of heartstrings. And for Maggie that was multiplied by eight.

He couldn't begin to comprehend that sort of commitment.

'Will the other two be okay with their mother? Pete and Susie?'

'You mean should I bring them here, too?' she asked wryly. 'Um, no. Mum'd come then, too, and Dad and his girlfriend might well decide why not come as well, and where would you be then?'

He stopped looking at Ruby. He looked...stunned. How many Tildens?

'Don't worry,' she told him, and grinned. 'Your dad did you a favour. The whole district knows the Samfords are mean and grumpy. I doubt Mum'll dare to come close—she doesn't care enough about Christopher to try. But she's not a terrible mother, if that's what you're worrying about. She doesn't drink or belt the kids. She just goes about making dandelion tea or goat's-milk balm or practising her latest yoga moves while the kids do what they like. I think they'll be safe enough—and I'm here as back-up.'

'So I don't get your whole family under my roof?'

'Heaven forbid,' she said, quite lightly but he could hear a whole depth of emotion behind those words. 'So you're tackling Ruby's feet. Do you want help?'

And here she was again, practical Maggie, moving in to do what was necessary—and then moving out again.

He was starting to see, very clearly, exactly how and why those boundaries had been put in place.

'I brought back the things I need,' he told her.

'I saw you collecting them from the clinic. Like what?'

'The makings for casts,' he told her, going back to massaging the little girl's feet. 'I'm sure this is straightforward congenital talipes. See how I can move them? It's not causing her pain when I manipulate—the tissue's still incredibly pliable. The trick is to get the feet into the right position before we lose that pliability. Which is now.

'What we do is manipulate the feet back as far as we can, then apply casts. We leave the casts on for a week, then remove them and do the same thing again. We're inching her feet into correct position. The majority of cases can be corrected in six to eight weeks. Before we apply the last plaster cast we'll probably need to cut the Achilles tendons—an Achilles tenotomy—but that's a small procedure, nothing lik the drama of a torn Achilles tendon in an adult. But that's weeks away.'

'You mean…she'll be cured within a few weeks?'

'They'll be back in position then, but if left they'll revert. She'll need to wear a brace for twenty-three hours a day for three months and then at night-time for three to four years. She may end up with slightly smaller feet than she otherwise would, and her feet might not be exactly the same size, but by the time she goes to school she'll be essentially normal.'

'Wow,' Maggie breathed. 'That's awesome. I learned about talipes in training but I've never seen it. I was imagining disability for life.'

'I imagine that's what Wendy thought, too,' Blake said grimly.

'Are you going to tell her?' She hesitated. 'You know, if Wendy thought she had a normal baby girl she might not have abandoned her.'

'I've thought of that.'

He'd also thought… He could phone her. Come and get your daughter because she's normal.

He raked his hair and thought about it some more. He looked down at his niece and he thought…

Deformed rat. The vindictiveness of what had been said. The bruise on her shoulder. And Wendy hadn't stood up for her.

'Not yet,' he said, and it came out harshly. 'Let's see if she misses her first.'

She'd have to make some effort, he thought. Make some contact. For him to hand this little one back to a pair who'd tossed her aside…

'You're falling in love with her,' Maggie said on a note of discovery and he thought…he thought…

Actually, he thought nothing. The statement left him stunned, like all the air had been sucked from the room.

Love.

What sort of statement was that?

He gazed down at the baby and while he he was looking at her thought he saw a tiny flicker of a smile.

'Wind,' Maggie said.

'It was a smile.'

'See,' Maggie said, and grinned. 'Parents.'

The air disappeared again. Parents. Family.

'So what do we do?' Maggie said, and there was another word.

We.

It made what was happening less terrifying, he thought.

'If you're happy to help…'

'Of course I am.'

'Unless I ask for babysitting.'

'That's not my job and you know it's not—Doctor,' she said primly. 'Let's keep this professional. So what's the plan?

If she was to be professional, so could he. He looked down at those tiny feet and thought of what had to be done.

'The first manipulation aims to raise the first metatarsal, decreasing the cavus,' he told her, thinking it through as he spoke. 'We'll apply long leg casts to hold everything in position after the manipulation. You had everything we needed back in the clinic. Are you treating greenstick fractures yourself?'

'Hopefully not, but if I have to I will. We can't depend on evacuation. That's why the X-ray machine.'

'It's great for us that it's there. It makes me confident of what we're dealing with, and I can feel pretty much what I need to feel now. We'll get the feet into position and in casts. In a week we take them off. The next manipulations involve abduction of the forefoot with counter-pressure on the neck of the talus. Carefully. You don't pronate—and you never put counter-pressure on the calcaneus or the cuboid.'

'I promise I won't,' she said—and she grinned. 'Doctor. Whatever calcaneus or cuboids are. Wow, isn't Ruby lucky to have an orthopod as an uncle?'

'I wouldn't call Ruby lucky,' he said grimly.

'I don't know,' Maggie said, suddenly thoughtful. 'If you'd told me a week ago that being born into the Samford family was lucky I'd have said you had rocks in your head—for all this place is worth a fortune. But now...I'm seeing a seriously different Samford and I'm impressed.'

'Don't be,' he growled. 'I'm out of here in a week.'

'So you're being nice for a week?'

'Until the bridge is safe.'

'Well, then,' Maggie said briskly, 'tell me what you need to do and we'll start doing it. If Ruby and I only have a week of niceness, we'd best make the most of it.'

The procedure to manipulate and cast Ruby's legs was straightforward enough, but it was also enough to show Maggie that in Blake she had a seriously skilled operator.

This was one tiny baby. His fingers were as gentle as a mother's, fingering the tiny toes, carefully, gently massaging, moving, wiggling, taking all the time in the world so Ruby felt no pain. Instead she seemed to be enjoying it, lying back on pillows, wide awake, seemingly savouring the sensation of this big man caressing her twisted legs, playing with her—and smiling at her while he did it.

He'd be a good surgeon, Maggie thought with sudden perception. If she were an old lady with a broken hip, she'd like it to be this man treating her. She thought suddenly, Samford or not, this smile was not just for this baby.

He'd used it on Christopher who, terrifyingly reckless at the best of times, was usually a total wimp when it came to doctors and needles. Christopher was tucked up in bed, happy and safe, because of this man.

Ruby was having her legs encased in casts and she looked not the least bit perturbed. She looked as if she had total trust in Blake as well.

In a Samford.

In a man no one knew anything about.

Maggie reminded herself of that, over and over, as she handed Blake what he needed, as she held the little legs in position as Blake wound the dressings, as she watched as he took the first steps to make this little girl perfect.

And she thought... Uh-oh.

This was one sexy male, and there weren't a lot of sexy males in Maggie's orbit. She needed to keep a clear head and remember—this guy was a Samford. Son of the local squattocracy. She was a Tilden. Daughter of the local welfare bludgers.

As well as that, he was here for a week. She was here for life.

So she'd better stop what she was thinking right now, she told herself. Just because the man had the sexiest, most skilful hands and was smiling at Ruby with a smile to make a girl's toes curl...

Maggie couldn't understand why Ruby wasn't beaming back—but a girl had to keep her feet firmly on the ground and remember relative positions in the world. This guy was her landlord and she needed to stay professional and get back to her side of the wall, *now*.

But Liselle and Christopher were on this side of the wall and Blake would need her advice with Ruby so she'd be on his side of the wall at other times, and boundaries were blurring.

It was up to her to keep them in place—and stop looking at this guy's smile!

By the time they were finished, Ruby was fast asleep. So much for a traumatic medical procedure. She was snuggled on her pillows, dead to the world, sucking her fist and totally, absolutely contented with her lot.

As Maggie cleared the remains of the dressings, Blake looked down at his niece as if he didn't quite know what to do next.

'How about sleep?' Maggie suggested, and he looked at her like he'd forgotten she was there.

'She's already asleep.'

'You,' she said gently. 'Appendicitis. Recovery. I just bet your surgeon said get lots of rest.'

'He might have.' It was a grudging admission.

'Then sleep.'

'I need to move her,' he said, sounding helpless, and she grinned.

Ruby was on the left side of the bed. She took two pillows and tucked them against the edge so even if Ruby managed a roll—pretty much impossible at three weeks—she'd go nowhere.

'That leaves you the whole right-hand side of the bed,' she said. 'She'll sleep better knowing you're close. Babies sense these things.'

'Nonsense.'

It might be nonsense, Maggie thought, but she wasn't telling this guy that. What she was aiming for—what Ruby needed more than anything in the world—was for someone—anyone—to bond with her. To bond so tightly that they'd fight for her for life.

'There's lots of room for both of you,' she said briskly. 'Bed. Now! Would you like me to bring you a cup of tea? Toast?'

'No,' he said, sounding revolted. 'I'm not a patient.'

'But you're not fully healed,' she told him. 'And I'm treating you like the goose that lays the golden eggs. In you I have a qualified surgeon on my side of the river and there's no way

I'm planning on letting you have a relapse. Bed. Now. Egg on toast, coming up.

'Maggie?'

'Yes' she said, and raised an enquiring brow—like an old-fashioned matron faced with an impertinent patient who should know better than to question her medical edicts.

'Never mind,' he said, and she grinned.

'Good boy. You just hop into bed with your baby and let Nurse Maggie judge what's best.'

And how was a man to respond to that?

Everyone seemed headed for a nap. Even Liselle had been shaken enough by the morning's events to want to snooze. She'd brought books to study but she was ensconced in one of Corella View's gorgeous, if faded, guest rooms, she had an entire double bed to herself and she couldn't resist.

'This place is fabulous, Mags,' she whispered as she snuggled into an ancient feather eiderdown and a pile of goosedown pillows. 'I could stay here for ever.'

'Blake's selling the house and he'll be gone in a week,' Maggie said, a bit too waspishly, and Liselle looked up at her in concern.

'Does that upset you?'

'I… No.'

'It means you'll come home to us,' Liselle said sleepily. 'That's good. I like sharing my bedroom with you.'

Maggie smiled at her—but she didn't mean that smile. Going home to her family…

But where else could she live in this valley that wasn't home? Blake had been charging her peppercorn rent in return for caring for the house and dogs. She was a mile away from her family, and that was about the extent of safe range. Today had proved that.

She left her sister to sleep, made herself tea and toast and went out to sit on the veranda.

It was starting to rain again.

She was sick to death of rain.

She was sick to death of this valley.

Actually, it wasn't true. She loved the valley. Her parents' time in the city had been a nightmare and she'd returned home with them feeling nothing but relief.

But she wanted to be free.

What would it be like, she wondered, to spend a couple of weeks lying on a beach somewhere it wasn't raining? Somewhere all by herself?

It couldn't happen. The kids needed all her spare income for their schoolbooks and extra expenses. The welfare payments her mother received could only go so far. They depended on her.

So no holidays for Maggie.

So you might as well quit whinging, she told herself, and glanced back at Blake's bedroom window as though he might have heard the thought.

She hoped he was asleep.

Her cellphone beeped. She checked it and winced. Old Ron Macy from up on the ridge had fallen and his ulcerated leg was bleeding. She needed to go.

But at least she had support. Blake was here, with Liselle as back-up.

She didn't even need to tell him she was leaving, she thought, and she thought back to last night, to Blake calmly handing over the baby to her. *Here you are, your problem.*

She couldn't help grinning. She could go now, and the whole household would be *his* problem.

Blackie was restless. The dogs had learned by now that the phone usually meant she had to go. He was whining and she knew why. She rubbed his ears and then she tiptoed through the house to Blake's bedroom and stealthily unlatched the door to Blake's bedroom. Thunderstorms were due. The forecast was horrendous, and Blackie was probably already hearing thunder in the distance.

If storms hit in earnest Blake would find himself with two dogs on his bed—or under his bed—but it'd be better than them turning themselves inside out with fear.

She was leaving Blake with baby and dogs and her siblings.

He was recovering from an appendectomy.

'He's a big boy,' she said, hardening her heart, but she didn't have to harden it too much. Blake was snuggled in bed while she had to brave the elements.

And then she thought she didn't mind this. A house full of people where she didn't have responsibility.

It was sort of like a holiday, she told herself—only different.

Blake woke up and Ruby was wailing, two dogs had their noses in his face and two wan kids were huddled in the doorway.

And the sky was falling.

Okay, it wasn't quite, but that's what it sounded like. It was either dusk or the storm was so bad the light had disappeared—the natural light, that was, because the lightning was almost one continuous sheet. There was no gap between the lightning and thunder. The rain was pounding so hard on the roof it almost felt as if the house itself was vibrating.

He must have been tired to have slept until now, but suddenly he was wide awake. Wet dog noses would do that to you. Both the dogs were shivering wrecks. The next bout of thunder boomed, and Ruby's cry turned to a yell—and the kids from the door saw he was awake and suddenly they were right in bed with him.

Dogs, too. Why not? This was a huddle of quivering terror and he was in the middle.

'Um…it's just a thunderstorm, guys,' he managed, trying to wake up, and in response they cringed closer. He moved over and lifted Chris nearer so his bandaged leg wasn't squashed. With Ruby on the other side of him he was practically a Blake sandwich. 'You should be in your own beds.'

'We don't like thunderstorms,' Liselle said. 'And Maggie's gone.'

Gone. For one appalling moment he had visions of Maggie doing what Ruby's parents had done—cutting and running. Heading over the threatened bridge, taking off for Queensland, leaving him with Ruby and Christopher and Liselle and Blackie and Tip.

'There….there's a note on the kitchen table,' Liselle quavered. 'Mr Macy on the ridge has fallen over and she had to go up and put a dressing on his leg. She says she'll be back by teatime but if I'm worried about Christopher then talk to you.'

'You shouldn't be worried,' Christopher said, not very stoutly. 'I'm okay.'

Except he was scared and he was hurting, Blake thought wryly. He shouldn't have tried bearing weight on that leg.

'The dogs are scared, too,' Liselle whispered, and the dogs whimpered in response. Blackie edged closer, edging around Christopher, her ancient nose pushing his chest—and suddenly she got what she wanted. The bedclothes were pushed back a bit and she was right down the foot of the bed so she was a mound of dog, like a wombat in a burrow, nestled hard against his feet.

Christopher giggled.

Ruby's wails grew louder.

Way back in Sydney, a really long time ago, Blake had wondered what he should do during his enforced convalescence. He had an excellent apartment with views over the harbour. Miriam was there in the evenings. He had a house-keeper to keep the place in order—everything he wanted. More. There were other medics—colleagues—in his apartment block and he wasn't left alone. His mates dropped in at all hours—*just to keep you company*. The decision to come here had been made partly for practical reasons but also because for some reason he was craving privacy.

Privacy had always been an issue for him. He'd learned early, in his parents' conflicted household, to disappear into his own world, and as an only child, even when his mother had remarried someone more reasonable, he'd known he'd been expected to fade into the background.

Isolation kept him out of emotional drama. It was a defence. Maybe that's why he and Miriam got on so well together—they instinctively respected personal space.

But he'd been at the same hospital for eight years now and lots of his colleagues no longer respected that space. Hence he'd decided that coming here was an option.

'I…I'll make Ruby's bottle, shall I?' Liselle quavered, and he looked at the slight seventeen-year-old who was obviously just as nervous as her brother.

'I'll get it,' he said, and swung back the covers, dislodging Tip in the process, who cast him a look of reproach. Then the next thunderclap boomed and the dog was down under the covers with Blackie.

'Maggie said you had to rest,' Liselle said.

'I'll rest. I'll get the bottle first.'

'And then you'll come back to us?'

To us. To a bed that was big but was now decidedly crowded. Two kids, two dogs, one baby.

'Yes,' he said, goaded.

'Maggie should be here,' Christopher whispered.

'Maggie wouldn't fit,' he retorted. 'You lie still and don't move that leg.' And then he went to fill his niece's very vocally broadcast requirements.

Maggie was heading home, feeling guilty.

So what was new? She'd felt guilty all her life. From the time her mother had made it very clear she needed her, anything Maggie had ever wanted to do for herself had been wasted time.

Now…she'd sort of wanted to stay in the big house and play with one baby and watch one guy bond with that baby, but she'd had no choice but to head up the valley to see Roy Macy. His leg was a mess but there was no way he'd come to her. His neighbour would have driven him but she knew exactly how he'd respond. 'No, don't fuss, leave it be.'

Left alone it'd turn into a septic mess, so good old Maggie had headed out into the storm and fixed it.

And left Blake with her responsibilities.

No. Ruby was his responsibility.

Why did it feel like she was hers?

Because she was used to feeling guilty. She'd sort of wanted to stay—but she'd felt guilty about leaving.

'I should have loaded Christopher into the car with me,' she said out loud. 'Just so I wouldn't feel like this.'

But she still would have. Guilt was unavoidable. Baby Ruby had crept round her heart like a small, needful worm and no matter how much she told herself she was nothing to do with her, she knew it wasn't true.

'It's only until the river level drops,' she told herself, looking bleakly out into the driving rain. 'Then they're out of here. I don't know what he'll do with Ruby, but it's not my problem. Not My Problem. Blake Samford is on his own. Just let the rain stop. Just let the river drop before I fall any deeper for one baby…'

And for the man who went with her?

'I'm not attached to Blake,' she said, astonished at the places her thoughts were taking her. 'As if. Yes, he's gorgeous, but as if I have time...'

Time to notice how gorgeous he was?

She'd noticed.

She did not have time. She did not have the inclination.

Liar. Of course she had the inclination, only what chance was there ever for a love life for her when there were still four kids almost totally dependent on her?

'You'll start singing sad love songs next,' she told herself dryly. 'It's just the way things are. Get over it. And stop thinking of Blake Samford's body. Blake Samford's smile. Blake Samford's hands as he cradles his tiny niece...'

Whoa.

'The sooner the river drops the better for all concerned,' she muttered, and then she paused.

The thunder had been booming almost continuously since she'd left home and it was still booming, but over the noise she could hear...something else.

It was a roar, building from maybe imagined to real, growing more real by the moment.

Instinctively she swung the car away from the river road, up the slope of the valley.

To a place where she could see the massive force of water bursting down the valley as the dam upstream gave way.

To a place where she could see the bridge disappear in a maelstrom of rushing water, and the shallow slopes of the valley disappear within it.

CHAPTER SIX

'The heifers…'

Blake was still in bed. He'd heard the bridge go. One part of him thought he should go and investigate the noise. The other part thought this farm was high and safe, he'd just got Ruby to sleep, the kids were settled, and there wasn't a lot he could do about a collapsing bridge.

Until Maggie burst in.

'The dam's burst upstream,' she said. She sounded exhausted, as though she'd run. She was soaking, her shirt was almost transparent, her curls were dripping round her shoulders, and the drips were making a puddle around her. 'Your heifers are trapped.'

'*My* heifers?' He didn't get it.

'Your calves,' she snapped. 'Your dad's yearlings. The water's come up too fast. I thought the bridge might go but not the dam. They're in the paddock on the far side of the road from the river, but the road's now under water. So's most of their paddock. There's a rise in the middle but it only holds half a dozen and the rest are already being forced to swim. If I can get them away from the rise, I can drive them to higher ground, but all they can see is the stupid island that's only going to let six or so survive. Liselle can't swim. She's scared of deep water and no one else is close enough to help. I know you're recovering but I don't have a choice. We can't let them drown. I need your help and I need it now.'

With Liselle left in charge of Christopher and Ruby—there was no choice but to depend on her—they drove the tractor to the calves' paddock.

Actually, Maggie drove the tractor. Blake stood on the footplate and hung on, feeling like a city kid, totally out of his depth.

He hadn't been on a tractor since he'd been six. He was riding as sidekick to save his cattle. He was Maggie's sidekick. He felt ludicrous.

Then he saw the calves and any temptation he had to laugh died right there.

They were in deathly trouble.

'The water's still rising,' Maggie whispered as she cut the engine. 'Oh, dear God, they'll drown.'

He stared out at the mass of water, at the terrified calves, at the impossibility of what lay before them. The calves could swim—most of them were swimming now—but they were all focussed on one thing and one thing only—the tiny island that was growing smaller while they watched.

'It's too late,' Maggie moaned. 'I thought I might be able to wade out there and drive them off. We could hack a hole in the fence higher up and you could guide them through. Once they see any of their mates on dry land they'll follow. But neither of us can swim out there and herd cows at the same time.'

They couldn't. Even if they were incredible swimmers, to swim and make cows follow directions would be impossible. Blackie was with them but a dog was useless as well.

There was a deathly silence while man, woman and dog watched the heifers struggle.

Then…

'The canoe,' Blake said, almost as an extension of his

thoughts. All his focus was on the heifers. These calves were strong but how long until the first slipped under?

'Canoe?' Maggie's voice was a desolate whisper, but Blake's thoughts were firming.

'There's a two-man canoe under the house, or there was last time I was here. It's ancient. I've done some kayaking. I can handle it. But, Maggie, I can't do this alone. My stitches need protecting, plus I know zip about herding cows. But I don't think I'll pull my stitches paddling. Not if I don't push myself.'

'What are you talking about?'

'I need to get the canoe up on the tractor. That'll require both of us lifting, but Liselle can help. We need to get it here and launched. Then...if we stick Blackie in the front, do you reckon you could persuade him to bark?'

'He'll bark on command.' And Maggie was with him.

'So we could get the canoe amongst them with a barking dog. If you told me what to do herding-wise...'

'Yes!' she said, and the desolation was gone. It was practically a shout. Maggie was suddenly a woman of action—a woman with a plan where there'd been no hope. She was already swinging herself back onto the tractor. 'What are we waiting for?'

It took them ten minutes to get back to the calves. Liselle had come out when they'd yelled and had helped heave the decrepit canoe out from under the house and get it up on top of the tractor in the driving rain. Somehow Maggie managed to drive with Blake holding the canoe steady—or as steady as possible, which wasn't very steady at all.

He had internal stitches, he thought ruefully. If he had been his patient, he'd tell him he was out of his mind.

Eighty drowning calves didn't give him that option.

Maggie was gunning the tractor, not worrying about bumps, cutting corners, just going for it.

'Your other career's as a racing-car driver?' he demanded faintly, and she grinned.

'Eat your heart out. Oh, Blake, they're still there.'

She'd rounded the bend, the road disappeared under water and they could see them again, swimming in panicked circles around that tiny rise, fighting for a foothold.

In seconds the tractor was stopped. They shoved the canoe off—much easier getting it off than getting it on—then pushed it through the submerged road gate and into the water.

Maggie had brought bolt-cutters. As he climbed aboard and organised the paddle, she heaved the bolt-cutters in, lifted Blackie in as well, and slid in herself after that.

'Can you take me round the back?'

To the far side of the paddock? He could see why she needed to go there. The fence there was also under water but beyond the fence the land rose sharply. The dry land beyond was obvious, as it wasn't obvious where they were now. For the last couple of hundred yards they'd driven over a road a foot deep in water.

'I'll cut the fence there,' she said. 'I'll get them out if you and Blackie can scare them into swimming in my direction. They're terrified, but they'll follow a leader and they're not dumb like sheep. If you get the canoe near the island and shoo the calves there into the water they'll look for the next best option. Which will be me and a cut fence and dry land behind me. We can do this. Go.'

He went.

He'd had his appendix out a week ago.

She was under no illusions that this man should not be pushing a canoe through floodwater. He should be lying around in bed, convalescing.

She should never have asked him to help.

But the alternative had been to let eighty calves drown. She hadn't been able to do it, and neither could he.

Like he couldn't send away a baby?

He was soft in the middle, Maggie thought, but outside he looked as tough as the heavy-duty bolt-cutters she was holding.

He was wearing fawn chinos and a soft cotton shirt, with the top buttons undone and the sleeves rolled up to the elbows. He'd kicked off his shoes. The water was plastering his shirt to his body, delineating every muscle. His dark hair was soaked from the rain. Rivulets of water were running down his face but he wasn't brushing them away. He was totally focussed on what he was doing.

He looked like a warrior, she thought, suddenly and inappropriately. He looked lean and hard and dangerous.

She had a sudden flash of what this man would be like as a surgeon. She'd done a theatre stint in training; she'd watched men like this at work. They took lives into their hands…

She'd never been able to figure how they found the courage to take that first cut, but she could see it now. Surroundings were forgotten. Pain was forgotten—and he must be in pain—a week after an appendectomy it'd hurt even to laugh, and here he was, slicing the old-fashioned paddle through the water with total rhythm, total focus—as if he was paddling for the Olympics and not for cows.

'Blake…'

'Yes?' His response was clipped, hard, sharp, a surgeon in Theatre, wanting to know why a nurse was interrupting. He was focussed totally on what he was doing, but not so focussed that he forgot outside complications were possible.

She wanted to help. The stupid canoe only had one paddle. She could only sit like a princess, in the bow of the boat, holding Blackie.

'Steer well around the island,' she managed. 'I don't want them panicked further before I've cut the fence.'

'Fair enough.' The canoe's course altered slightly, and she thought that was no mean feat either. This canoe was ancient and high and wobbly. There were all sorts of obstacles in the water and the water itself was a mass of whirls and eddies. She was sitting as still as she could, as centred as she could, holding Blackie tightly as if by sheer concentration she could help this man.

He must work out. He must…she didn't know…run? He must do something to keep that lean body whip-sharp. His face was a study in concentration as he sliced across the current, and she could only guess how hard it must be.

She glanced across at the calves and saw one slip from the island, then get pushed under by another struggling to find purchase.

She held her breath but it surfaced again.

Eighty young cows, depending on one ailing surgeon.

Maggie, depending on one ailing surgeon.

Finally they reached the far fence. The water here was only eighteen inches deep. As soon as she could grab the fence wires, she was out of the boat, steadying her bolt-cutters.

'Stay,' she snapped at Blackie. 'Sit. Stay.'

He was a great dog. He whined but he stayed in the bow as Blake turned the canoe and headed back out to the middle.

She hacked into the wires with a strength born of desperation then, as the last wire fell away, she headed out of the water, up the rise, so hopefully the calves could see the gap in the fencing, and see her standing on dry land beyond.

'Oi,' she yelled, trying to make the panicked calves look at her. 'Oi, Oi, Oi, Oi, Oi.'

Blake was behind the island now, cutting his way through the calves in the water, heading for the few on dry land.

'Speak,' she yelled to Blackie, and Blackie did just that.

He barked and barked, while Maggie yelled, and Blake manoeuvred his shaky little craft behind the herd, beached himself on the island, stood on the tiny piece of dry land and proceeded to remove the calves' last place of refuge.

He knew nothing about calves. They knew nothing about him, and maybe that was a good thing because they reacted to him and to the barking dog as if they were worse threats than the water.

The calves headed away from him, away from their target island. He was waving his arms like an idiot and Blackie was barking, so they launched themselves in the opposite direction—and suddenly they were swimming towards Maggie.

Maybe they knew her voice, or maybe she'd herded more cows than he had in his lifetime, but the calves seemed to be instinctively turning toward her.

If he was a calf, he'd turn toward Maggie.

There was a stupid thought.

He was hurting. He was standing on the only piece of dry land for fifty yards. He was waving and shouting like a fool—and he still had time to think… Think that Maggie was gorgeous?

She was wearing faded jeans and a shirt that had become almost transparent. She was soaked to the skin. Her chestnut curls were dripping around her shoulders, plastered to her face. Her feet were bare, she was yelling louder than he was… and the calves were heading toward her. And he knew why.

What was beautiful about her?

Bone structure? Facial features? Sense of fashion?

Um…none of those things, though the freckles and the gorgeous curves surely helped.

But it was the sheer courage of her. The way she tackled life head on.

The way she'd refused to care for his baby?

But she would care. He knew instinctively that she would. If he hadn't been here, if she hadn't figured he was more than capable of caring for his niece, then he knew she'd have taken her on, as she'd taken in Christopher last night, and Liselle, and he knew there only had to be a drama and she'd have more people sharing her tiny living space. That he'd offered to share his side of the house had seemed a blessing and a surprise to her. He wondered how many dramas she'd had since she'd moved into his tiny housekeeper's residence—but he knew without being told that without his urging, she'd never have let her life edge through the dividing door into his home.

Only it wasn't his home. It was a mausoleum of a homestead, redecorated in the fashion of the time by his mother and not touched since.

This morning, in bed, it had felt more like a home than it ever had in his childhood.

Because of Maggie?

'Oi!'

Her yelling had grown more insistent, riveting his attention totally on what was happening. The calves were shoving together in the water, seeking safety in numbers, swimming as a herd, but they weren't heading totally in the right direction.

They hadn't seen the gap in the fence.

Okay, boy, he thought grimly. Back in your boat.

'Are you okay?' Maggie called, and he thought all this and she was remembering his stitches.

'Blackie and I are fine,' he called. 'I'm bosun, he's cox. If I can just persuade these calves to join us, we'll be a crew.'

His side was hurting. Badly. What had his surgeon said? No stretching for six weeks. Ha. Block it out, he told himself, and he headed for the calves, paddling hard, cutting through the water, focussing doggedly on what he was doing rather than the pain in his side. He was cutting the calves off from heading back to the island, herding them forward but sideways. He had to turn and turn again as the calves took fright and tried to scatter, but between them, yelling, barking, shoving the canoe at them, he and Blackie made them swerve and kept going.

They were exhausted, he thought, and he was expecting at any minute that one would slip under. They had to see...

The fence was about four feet high, so the gap was obvious. If they could see it they'd be safe.

'Oi,' Maggie yelled again, and Blackie barked, and he veered the canoe behind them—and the calf in the lead lifted its head as if casting round for one last desperate chance...

And saw.

And then the entire herd was surging through the gap. Maggie was stepping aside, the calves were through, rising out of the floodwater, finding their feet, scrambling onto dry land.

The calves bolted upwards as if the water was chasing them. As they realised they were safe they turned into calves again. They looked like kids after a scary adventure, one they could boast about to their mates. A few kicked their heels like this was fun, yay, dry land, safe.

He was still paddling. He reached the gap and Maggie started pulling the canoe out of the water almost before he was out of it.

'I can...' he said, reaching down, but she slapped his hands away.

'You shouldn't.' And he saw she was weeping. 'I should never have let you. You'll have burst all sorts of internal stitches. I didn't realise until I saw you...how hard it was... that paddling was awful... I should never have let you do it and you'll have killed yourself and it's my fault.'

Okay, let's get rid of the drama, he decided. She'd been frightened enough for one day. He'd take himself out of the equation.

'I suspect I've killed my phone,' he admitted, hauling it out of his soaking back pocket and looking at it with apprehension. 'But otherwise I'm alive. And pretty damned pleased with myself.' Then, despite her objections, he helped her haul the canoe to dry land. What harm would another pull be when there'd been so many?

But she still looked terrified. She still looked...like the sky was about to fall.

He tried not to notice. He looked at the calves, turning into kids again. Then, because he couldn't help himself, he looked again at this bedraggled slip of a woman, standing with the rain mingling with her tears, and he felt something change inside him...

Something he'd never felt before.

She was gorgeous, he thought. She was simply, unutterably, indescribably gorgeous.

She'd put everything she knew into saving these calves, and now she was feeling guilty. Guilty for saving calves that weren't even hers. Guilty for risking hurting him. Guilty even for his damaged phone?

She was unbelievable.

And before he knew what he intended, before he even realised what he was doing, he'd tugged her into his arms and held her close.

She'd been terrified, and in truth he'd been the same. Out of his comfort zone. Hurting. Worried the dratted calves would drown.

It wouldn't hurt to hold her, to comfort her—and to take comfort in return.

But...was this about comfort?

He held her close, closer, and he felt the thump of her heartbeat against his, and thought maybe it wasn't.

'Yay for us,' she whispered, and her voice was muffled by his chest. 'You were great. Are you sure you're not hurt?

'I'm not hurt,' he said, and then as her heart kept on thumping, he thought it had been terror for him as well as terror for the calves that was making her heart race.

He cupped her chin with his hand and tilted her face so he could force her to look at him. Her eyes were huge. Her eyes still held remorse and fear.

'I'm fine,' he said. 'I'm great and you're terrific.'

And then, as she kept gazing up at him, he couldn't resist.

He kissed her.

One minute she was feeling like she was losing eighty calves and ripping Blake's stitches to bits and there wasn't a thing she could do about it.

The next she was being kissed so thoroughly, so amazingly that there wasn't a thing she could do about that either.

Not that she wanted to.

If she wished, she could pull away. He wasn't holding her so tightly, so strongly that she couldn't tug back and get him to release her.

But how could she tug back when she was being kissed... like this.

Fire meeting fire.

Fire?

How could she be feeling heat, when she was cold and dripping and shaking from reaction to what had just happened? There was no answer and even as she asked the question, she forgot it.

She forgot everything.

There was only the feel of this man's mouth. The fire, the heat, the strength and warmth and...the maleness of him.

There'd been too few men in Maggie's life. Too little opportunity. Too little time.

This was hardly an opportunity, hardly the time, but there was no way she was pulling back.

Her lips opened, seemingly of their own accord, welcoming him, wanting him.

Wanting him?

Yes. She did want him. Her body seemed to mould itself to him all by itself. Her breasts crushed against him, their wet shirts disappeared almost to nothing, so nothing seemed between them but white-hot want.

His mouth was exploring hers. His hands were in the small of her back, tugging her closer, and hers did the same to him. She was melting into him, dissolving, aching to be closer, closer, closer...

She'd never felt like this. She'd never dreamed she could feel like this. Her entire body was on fire, every sense screaming that here was her man, she was part of him, she belonged.

Maybe it was supposed to be a kiss of relief and of comfort. It was surely a kiss of need—both of them needed the assurance of human contact, that they were safe and life went on and they'd succeeded—but it was more than that.

It was a kiss that changed her. It was a kiss that made her feel as she'd never felt—as if every sense was suddenly alive.

Sleeping Beauty, wakened by a kiss?

Well, that was ridiculous.

There was a tiny part of her mind that was still analysing. It was like she was falling off a cliff and thinking as she fell, How am I feeling right now?

She was feeling pretty good, actually. No matter about the ground rushing up, she was feeling pretty amazing.

Where had this heat come from? What was making her feel like her entire body was sizzling, waking from slumber and turning into something she didn't know it was possible to be?

She was falling and she didn't care.

So far it was so wonderful.

How high was the cliff? How long could she stay in free-fall, savouring this moment, the feel of him, the strength, the way his hands held her, the way she seemed totally enfolded, protected, frail even...

Strong Maggie, melting at a man's touch.

Strong Maggie, melting and loving it.

And then Blackie barked.

He'd done his bit. He was expecting praise. Expecting attention. Or maybe it was that his mistress was being mauled by a strange man and the dog was confused and wondering what he should do about it.

He barked again, and finally, achingly, Maggie tugged away.

Freefall over, she'd reached her destination. She almost expected to feel shattered. That was crazy but she did feel... Bruised? Dazed? Exposed?

Confused was the least of it.

'Well, that was unexpected,' Blake murmured, and something in his deep, growly voice said he was almost as confused as she was. 'Adrenalin, do you think?'

'Either that or it's something in the water,' she managed, and carefully turned away and looked up the hill.

The calves were settling. They were high up on the hill, and as they watched, a couple put their heads down and started to graze.

Back to life as they knew it.

Right, she told herself, trying not to feel breathless. Trying to make this strange, needy...*kissed*?...sensation go away. Trying to go back to life as she knew it. 'That's that fixed. Well done, us. And thanks, Blake, I could never have done it without you.'

'They're my cattle.'

'They haven't been your responsibility for a very long time.'

'Maggie?' He hadn't turned to watch the cows. He'd stayed

watching her the whole time—which wasn't doing anything for the state of her discombobulation.

'Mmm?'

'They're my responsibility, and thank you,' he said. 'And thank you for the kiss. It was…'

'Nice,' she said hurriedly, before he could say anything more. 'It was very nice indeed, but there's no need for you to be worrying that I expect to take it further. We might be staying in the same house but there's a door with a lock between us.'

'And two kids and a baby.'

'That, too.' She hesitated. 'I don't know what came over me.'

'Over *us*.'

'Over us,' she repeated, though she wasn't sure where me and us separated in the kissing stakes. 'But…' She tried hard to get her feet on firm ground—a bit hard when she was standing in six inches of water. 'I…I have work to do. Are you sure you're okay? Can I check your scar?'

'No!'

'I didn't think so,' she said, and she managed a chuckle. 'But you would tell me if there was something wrong, wouldn't you?'

'Probably not.'

'That's reassuring.'

'I hurt,' he told her. 'But there's no piercing pain. I think I've pulled but not torn. Bruised but not broken. Should we take this canoe back over the far side and see if we can get it back up on the car?'

'Let's not,' she said faintly. 'For eighty calves I was prepared to let you risk it. Now I'm thinking of your stitches again. We'll secure it here in case it's needed again but that's it. I'll walk the long way round and bring the tractor home.

You head over the rise and reach the house without getting even more wet.'

'Maggie...'

'Mmm?'

He stared down at her. She was adjusting the canoe, tying the rope to a fencepost.

She was suggesting—no, decreeing—they go their separate ways.

That was surely sensible. That's what this woman was. Sensible.

She was also vulnerable—and beautiful.

She was also saddled with kids and family and responsibility, chained to a life that was alien to everything he knew.

Maggie waded back to the tractor, skirting the worst of the high water.

The road was only a few inches underwater. They could never have headed the calves this way—to push them forward when all they could see was water would have been impossible—but the road was still safe enough to drive on.

She'd still be able to get back and forth to her clinic, she thought, which was just as well.

She'd be needed.

The locals had never thought the dam could burst. She made a fast mental list of the houses close to the river and thought none would be so close to water level that they'd be flooded. The early settlers had been wary of floods and had built accordingly. There'd have been more than just Maggie and Blake desperately trying to move stock in a hurry, though. People would be doing stupid things, putting themselves at risk.

As Blake had put himself at risk.

She should never have asked it of him. The man was a

week out from an appendectomy, and for him to manoeuvre the canoe as he had…

He could sue her, she thought grimly, but then she thought, They were his calves. He could have said let them drown.

He couldn't—as he couldn't evacuate Ruby and hand her over to others.

Her thoughts were running off at crazy tangents. She was thinking of the way he held Ruby—of the way he looked at her. There were things going on in Blake's background she had no idea of. He looked at Ruby and he almost looked… hungry.

She grinned at that, thinking, Nope, big bad wolf wasn't the image she was going for.

So, hungry for what?

What sort of childhood had this man had? His mother had been glamorous and flighty—the local gossip was that she'd married for money. His father had been an oaf. Where had that left him?

And why had he kissed her?

She put her fingers to her lips as she walked, thinking they felt…different.

Why had he kissed her?

'Well, who wants to know?' She said it out loud and kicked a spray of water up in front of her. 'You? You know already. We thought the calves would drown, we got them out, and in moments of triumph, people kiss.'

Only it hadn't been like that. At least, it hadn't been like that for her.

'And that's because you're close to a thirty-year-old spinster without a life of your own,' she snapped, and kicked up more water. 'That's because every minute of every day is taken up with your work or your family, and your hormones are telling you it's not enough.

'So what are you intending to do about it?'

She laughed at that, morosely, because some questions already had answers. Some questions weren't even worth asking.

What was she intending?

One big fat nothing.

She had a job. Almost half her pay went towards helping the kids out with what they needed so they'd get the qualifications she had, tickets out of the valley, escape paths from the cloying demands of her mother. Apart from one tiny, tiny nest egg, the rest of her money went on living. Putting one foot in front of another. Doing her job and keeping the kids safe.

In a couple of weeks the water would be down and Blake would be gone. End of story.

But maybe, while he's here…

'Don't even think about it,' she told the silence, and she kicked so hard the water went up and over her, making her wetter than ever. 'He's my landlord and if he hasn't burst anything today he's a doctor who can help if I need him. Nothing more. Put yourself back in your box, Maggie, and stay there. Now.'

CHAPTER SEVEN

HE got back to the homestead—and there were more kids.

Plus Maggie's mother.

Liselle was on the veranda, clutching a sleeping Ruby, and looking almost as if she was holding her mother at bay.

'Dr Samford,' Liselle breathed when she saw him, and there was real relief in her voice. 'I...I didn't invite her.'

Then Maggie arrived. She pulled in through the gate, climbed from the tractor, squelched across and joined him—and looked at her mother.

'Mum,' she said blankly, and Barbie beamed. She was standing by an ancient family wagon. She hauled up the tail-gate and lifted out a suitcase.

'This is lovely,' she said. 'I was so pleased Dr Samford's decided to share. Did you remember our living-room roof is leaking? I told you last week, Maggie, and you've done nothing about it. And now the dam's burst and the kids are scared.'

She was dressed as a hippy. Fiftyish, long, flowing skirt, beads everywhere, vivid dyed-blonde hair hanging past her shoulders.

Shudder territory.

And obviously Maggie thought so, too.

'You're not staying here,' she said, in a cold, dead voice that had Blake glancing at her sharply. She sounded like she was in pain.

'Well, I'm not staying in that house by myself.' Her mother's voice became shrill and accusing. 'You can't expect me to. I had to sleep in Susie's bed last night because there was a drip right by mine, and both the kids are whining for you.'

Susie verified the statement by sidling across to Maggie and tucking her hand in her big sister's.

Blake saw Maggie's shoulders slump.

She looked like a deer caught in headlights, he thought. She'd escaped her family, but her family had tracked her down.

'Can you carry my suitcase inside, Dr Samford?' Barbie said—and simpered.

It was her right to be looked after.

Blake looked at her and looked at Maggie. Barbie was a world away from the woman who'd been his own mother but there were similarities. He was sure she'd married his father for money and she'd gone on to marry three other men who were expected to look after her every whim. Right now she was in the States with yet another besotted lover.

Maggie's mother had never had the beauty or the style to attract lovers to obey her commands but the way she was looking at Maggie now, he knew the story. Maggie had been the servant. Maggie still was the servant.

No more. A line had to be drawn, and Maggie's face had him drawing it.

'Maggie's brothers and sisters are welcome to stay until the waters recede,' he said. 'But no one else. The evacuation notice says that if anyone's worried, they can camp in the local hall. If the kids want to join you there, that's fine.'

'You're not separating me from my kids!'

'Of course I'm not.' Blake strode up the veranda steps and lifted Ruby from a stunned Liselle's arms. 'I'm not fussed if your kids stay here or not,' he said, in a bored voice that told her to take it or leave it. 'If Maggie wants them to, then that's fine. If you don't permit it, then that's fine, too. All I'm saying is that the invitation is for kids only. Sort it out between you. I need to feed Ruby.'

And he walked in the front door—on his side of the house—and closed the door behind him, leaving all the Tildens on the other side.

Maggie came to find him ten minutes later. He was in his kitchen, fixing formula. He had Ruby nestled in her drawer-cum-bed by the fire stove. He was feeling incredibly domestic.

He was also feeling like he'd been sucked into another world. Babies and kids and dogs and cows and mothers.

And Maggie.

She opened the kitchen door and it was all he could do not to drop the bottle he was holding and take her into his arms. He'd never seen a woman look so…caged.

'I'm so sorry,' she managed. 'But they all want to stay. I can't make them go with her.'

'She's not staying.' He made his voice flat, definite, sure. He spooned formula into the bottles and when he glanced at her again a little of the tension had eased.

'She thinks you mean it. She's not game to call your bluff.'

'It's no bluff. She walks in, I'll pick her up and throw her out.'

'Can…can I ask why?'

'Because she makes you cringe,' he said. 'That's good enough for me. I don't know what's gone on in your past, Maggie, but I know appalling parenting when I see it. I avoided my father and I continue to avoid my mother. You should be allowed to do the same. Has she gone?'

'Yes, but all the kids are here.'

'The whole eight?'

She managed a smile at that. 'No. Just four.'

'Then it's five, counting Ruby. We have ourselves a houseful.'

'Blake, I didn't mean to impose—'

'If you had meant to impose—like your mother certainly meant to impose—I would have sent you packing as well,' he told her, still concentrating on his bottles. Surgical precision was required. Ruby wasn't going to get anything but perfect milk on his watch. 'I extended the invitation, Maggie, not you,' he added. 'I can see the kids are scared and they need you. They're welcome to stay here, but only until the road is open again. This isn't open-ended.'

'You're fantastic.'

'I'm not,' he said shortly.

'Yes, you are,' she said, and her eyes misted. 'Heroic. Like you told Chris he was. But you've done more. You've saved him, you've saved your cows and now…you've taken in my whole family.'

'But you don't want them here.' It was a question, a guess—and it found its mark.

She stilled. She watched him, then watched her feet and took her time answering.

'I have this dumb dream,' she said at last. 'From the time I first remember, it's always been: "Maggie, watch your brother. Take Liselle for a walk. Stay home from school today because your father and I have a gig…" It's just…how it is. Mostly I accept it, only every now and then I dream that I'm backpacking round Europe, sipping kir in a café on the Left Bank in Paris, or watching the sunset over the Nile and having no one talk to me for hours on end.

'It's a dumb dream but it stays. When the kids are older, that's what I decided I'll do. Then recently—when Mum and Dad split—I realised they're getting dependent as well. I'm starting to be scared that after looking after their kids all my life I might end up looking after them.'

'It's not going to happen.'

'No,' she said softly. 'That's why I moved out. Blind terror, if you like. But the kids still need me. I'll probably end up going home.' She took a deep breath. 'But not tonight. Tonight you solved my problem for now. You let me care for the kids and you've forced Mum to be independent—and it didn't even have to be me who was nasty to do it. Plus you saved all those heifers. To watch them drown would have killed me. I should never have asked you but I couldn't bear not to. But now...'

She glanced down at Ruby, who was wide awake but not complaining yet. There was time. 'Now I'm checking your tummy,' she decreed. She motioned to the leather-covered bench at the side of the huge kitchen. 'Sit. Lie. I want to see.'

'There's no need.' To say he was astonished was an understatement. She'd been grateful and emotional, but suddenly she was brisk again, efficient—and bossy. 'I'm fine.'

'For me,' she said, still implacable. 'If you think I can calmly sleep tonight knowing you might have done yourself damage...'

'Maggie...'

'You're a hero,' she said, and she grinned at him. 'Heroes are brave enough to bare a little skin.'

'I'll check myself.'

'Doctor, heal thyself?' she quoted. 'I don't think so. Humour me. Lie down.'

'Maggie...'

'Just do it.'

He gazed down at her and she gazed back—implacable, immoveable, strong as iron. This woman had raised eight children, he thought, and right now he felt like a ninth.

'Now,' she said, and lifted the bottle from his hand and set it on the bench. 'Do it.'

Why not?

Because he felt vaguely foolish? Because he felt exposed; vulnerable? Because he didn't want this woman thinking of him as a patient?

All of which were dumb reasons.

He was sore. He had pulled his stitches.

Sensible was the way to go—surely.

He sighed—and went and lay on the bench and tugged his shirt up and undid his belt.

If this was Miriam he wouldn't mind, he thought. Their relationship could be professional—it usually was. So what was different about Maggie?

He had no answer. He could only lie and wait and submit.

He had hurt himself. She'd seen him wince as he'd climbed from the boat. She'd also seen a tell-tale spattering of blood on his pants and she'd known she'd have to check. He also knew it was sensible, she thought. The guy in him didn't want her near him. The doctor in him said submit.

He submitted. He hauled his shirt up, undid his belt, and she unzipped his pants before he could protest.

His abdomen was rock hard, muscled, ripped. As his shirt fell open she was hit once more with the sight of a male body that was pure muscle. She felt the strength of him as her fingers touched his skin while undoing his zip.

She glanced up at him and saw his face set hard. She wasn't hurting him. She was barely touching him.

This man didn't like being exposed, she thought. This was a guy who walked alone.

But not tonight, she thought ruefully. Five children, two dogs, and her. She was taking over this guy's life.

She wouldn't mind…

Um, no. For the sensation of that kiss had flooded back, and suddenly Maggie Tilden wasn't feeling professional at all. She was bending over a near-naked man—which she'd done before, she was a nurse, for heaven's sake—but she wasn't feeling like a nurse. She wanted...

She could want all she liked. She couldn't have—*and this man was a patient*.

Focus.

She focussed.

He had torn the wound open, just a little, right at the top. The internal stitches must still be holding, she thought, examining the wound with care, as there was no sign of swelling, no sign of internal bleeding. And Blake might look uncomfortable but he wasn't writhing in pain.

There was only an inch or so that had pulled apart a little and bled, and even that wasn't terrible.

'It's okay,' she told him, glancing up at him and seeing him with his hands behind his head, staring straight at the ceiling with a look so grim he might as well be expecting her to attack with a scalpel. 'Hey, I'm not about to dive in and have a fish around,' she joked. 'I thought I might settle for a wash, some disinfectant, some steri-strips and orders for a good sleep.'

His face lost a little of its severity but, she thought, he was forcing himself to relax. He was well out of his comfort zone.

'Want to tell me what's going through that head of yours?' she asked, expecting him not to answer, or to deflect the question, but to her surprise he did answer.

'The last time I lay on this couch, it was because my father hit me,' he said. 'I must have been about five. He spilt my face above the eye. Minor stuff. My mother put a plaster on and screeched at him the whole time. Funny thing, though. No matter how much he hit me—and he did—it took the knowledge that he'd been sleeping around before she took me away.'

'Then I guess you have Ruby—or Ruby's grandmother—to thank that she finally did take you,' she said, forcing her voice to be light. She was carefully cleaning, focussing on the wound, not the man—but part of her was thinking this man had been incredibly isolated. She was so surrounded. Which was worse?

Blake's childhood, she thought. Her parents were dodgy as parents went, but they'd never hit, and the tribe of nine kids had provided their own love and support to each other.

She dared another glance at his grim face and thought, Absolutely, crowds every time.

She'd crammed his house with kids and dogs. She was doing him a favour, she decided—and she grinned.

'What's funny?'

'I'm just thinking of the great protective screen I've erected round you,' she said. 'Five kids and me and the dogs... No one can hit you now, Blake Samford.' She dried his skin with care and thought that no one could hit him anyway. Not with those muscles. But she wasn't telling him that. There was no way she was admitting—even to herself—how awesome she found his body. She started adjusting steri-strips, gently tugging together the slight gaps where the wound had parted. Her concentration was absolute.

He didn't speak, just lay and stared at the ceiling, but the rigidity had gone. She'd defused the moment, she thought. Kids had to be good for something.

'I'll dress it...'

'I don't need a...'

'Remind me to ask next time I need medical advice,' she said severely. 'You'll be dressed whether you want it or not.'

'Very civilised,' he said, and she chuckled, and dressed her carefully applied steri-strips and then went to tug up his zip.

His hand closed over hers.

'I can do that, at least,' he said, and his hand held...for just a moment too long.

He needed to sit up. Instead of tugging her hand away, she gripped his and tugged—and he rose a little too fast.

She was a little too close.

A lot too close.

They'd been here before. She'd kissed this man. This man had kissed her.

He was so close. He was so…so…

Compelling? For he'd placed his fingers under her chin and was tilting…

'No.' Somehow she managed to say it. Somehow she hauled some vestige of common sense from the back of her addled brain and made herself step back.

Her foot hit the bowl of water on the floor, it spilled and she was almost glad.

'Look what you made me do,' she said, a trifle too breathlessly. A lot too breathlessly.

'If you'd let me kiss you, you wouldn't have tripped.'

'You don't want to kiss me.'

'And you know that because…?'

'Because I come with encumbrances.' She stalked over to the pantry—she'd spent six months nursing Blake's father so she knew her way around this place—and grabbed a wad of old dishcloths. She tossed them onto the floor, then went down on her knees and started drying. 'I'm a workhorse,' she said, scrubbing with more ferocity than she needed to. 'Not a show pony. You're only kissing me because I'm the only female available.' She sat back on her haunches and glared. 'But you're wrong. You have Ruby who has need of all the kisses you can give her. Concentrate on what's important, Blake Samford.'

'I'm thinking you're important, Maggie Tilden.'

'Then think again,' she snapped. 'You're trapped, you're wounded, you're exhausted, and I have the right chromosomes. Nothing more. Get a grip.' She pushed herself to her feet, which was hard when she realised he'd stepped toward her to help and she had no intention of letting him help. She gathered the bowl, the dressing wrappers, the dishcloths and turned away.

'This is the main house,' she muttered. 'I live in the servants' quarters. My brothers and sisters might have infiltrated their way over here but me...me, I'm scared stupid. Leave it, Blake. I have a flood, a dependent community and a dependent family, and I need no other complications. None. Your wound is fixed. You need to feed Ruby and put yourself to bed. By yourself,' she added, as she saw what looked suspiciously like laughter in his dark eyes.

'You're overreacting.'

'That's the story of my life,' she muttered, stalking to the door. 'Setting boundaries and hoping people respect them. And being told I'm overreacting when they don't.'

'Maggie...'

'I have to check I'm not needed at the clinic. Liselle will look after my kids.' She glanced down at Ruby. 'You look after yours. Goodnight, Blake.'

And she walked out and closed the door behind her.

What had just happened?

Blake stared at the closed door and thought he'd just been hit over the head with a sledgehammer. That's what it felt like.

He'd really, really wanted to kiss her. The need had felt extraordinary, but it hadn't been a simple sexual urge. It had been all about the smattering of freckles on her nose. The shadows under her eyes. The way she'd stood in the top paddock and yelled, 'Oi, oi, oi.'

It had been about the way her fingers had felt, gently touching his skin. She was a nurse. She'd been doing her job but it hadn't felt like that. It had felt...electric. It was as if everywhere she'd touched there had been this frisson, this connection, two halves desperate to come together.

But it wasn't true. His half was all for it. Her half was backing away like a startled rabbit.

Did she think he was about to seduce her? Local land-owner taking advantage?

His father's reputation had gone before him.

She didn't know him.

And he didn't know her, he told himself. She was like no one he'd ever met. There was no artifice about her—what you saw was what you got. She was taking care of this valley, taking care of her siblings, taking care of…him?

At his feet Ruby finally tired of waiting. She'd been perfectly patient while her uncle had been treated, but enough was enough.

She opened her mouth and she wailed.

Maggie wasn't taking care of Ruby. Fair enough, he thought ruefully. He could hardly expect it of her.

As if in rebuttal, her head appeared around the door.

'You should be in bed,' she said, and she sounded reluctant, like this was her conscience talking. 'If you like, I'll feed her and we'll take care of her on our side for the night. Only for tonight, mind.'

'You're going back to the clinic.'

'There are five of us. One thing the Tilden kids learned early is to take care of each other. For tonight only, we can do it.'

She would, too, he thought. She was looking at him and seeing a guy who was recovering from appendicitis, who'd pushed himself too far.

He did not want to be this woman's patient.

'Ruby and I will be fine,' he said, a bit too shortly.

'You're sure?'

'I'm sure.'

'Knock if you change your mind,' she told him, sounding

relieved. 'And I'll check when I get home. Sleep tight, Blake. Sleep tight, Ruby.'

She closed the door again—and he felt even more...

Like he wanted the door to stay open.

He fed Ruby.

He wandered out to see what the kids were doing.

Ruby had gone to the clinic. The rest of the kids were in his big sitting room.

Liselle was hunched over a side table with a bunch of books in front of her that looked truly impressive.

'Calculus?' he asked, checking over her shoulder.

'Yes,' she said tersely.

'Trouble?'

'This,' she said, and pointed hopelessly. He sat and helped her integrate a complex equation, with techniques he thought he'd long forgotten, and felt absurdly pleased with himself when it worked.

If Maggie was out saving the world, he could at least do maths.

Susie was under the table with her dolls.

Christopher was propped up on cushions, his leg high in front of him. The painkillers would be making him feel sleepy but he'd obviously decided he wanted to be with his siblings. He was watching something violent on television. Was it suitable for a twelve-year-old? But then he thought these kids must be pretty much independent by now.

'It's okay,' Liselle said briefly, seeing him watching the TV and reading his doubt. 'Maggie and Chris go through the guide once a week, Chris reads out the reviews of what he wants to watch and they negotiate.'

Fair enough, he thought, feeling awed.

He looked down at Ruby, who was still in his arms, and wondered who'd negotiate for her.

What was this baby doing to his head? He'd had one image of his baby sister, embedded in his memory thirty years ago. He'd hardly thought of her since, and yet this little one, a baby of that baby, was calling to something he hadn't been aware he had.

A need for family?

He gazed round the living room, at the kids sprawled over the furniture. Sleepy Christopher with his bandaged leg, who'd come so close to death but was recovering fast. Susie, spilling out from under the table with her dolls. Pete with his video games and Liselle keeping vague watch as she studied. Maggie must have lit the fire before she'd left—or maybe Liselle had. They were independent kids, but he just knew...

Threaten one and you threatened them all.

Family.

Ruby was dozing in his arms. He should put her to bed. He should put himself to bed, he thought. He didn't understand the way he was feeling...

It was all about weakness, he decided. It was the aftereffects of appendicitis, the shock of Ruby's arrival, working with Christopher and the physical demands of rescuing the calves.

And the way he was feeling about Maggie?

Um...no. Family. Maggie. That was emotional stuff, feelings he'd long suppressed because they ought to be suppressed. He had a very practical, very satisfactory life and the sooner he could go back to it, the better.

'You look tired,' Liselle said. 'You want me to cuddle Ruby until Maggie comes home?'

So Maggie could come home and see that he hadn't managed one baby?

'Thank you,' he said gravely. 'But I'm fine.'

'Call us if you need us,' Pete said, emerging from his com-outer game for a moment. 'I've buried nappies before,' he offered nobly. 'One spade, one hole and the job's done.'

The kids chuckled and so did he, and then he escaped.

They were great kids, he thought, and then he thought of Maggie.

They weren't great kids because of their parents, he thought. They were great kids because they had a great big sister. An awesome big sister.

A really cute, really sexy, big sister.

That was exactly what he didn't want to think. He needed to think of practicalities. Ruby. Bed.

Not Maggie.

She had two patients to see at the clinic. Both minor complaints. Aida Batton had cricked her neck lifting piglets out of a sty that was becoming waterlogged. Anyone else would have figured that driving the sow out first and leaving the piglets to follow was the best option, but Aida considered herself an earth mother, and thought the sow might slip in the mud and squash one of her babies—and now she was paying the price.

Maggie gave her a gentle massage, sent her home with anti-inflammatories and a heat pack, and was promised a side of bacon in exchange.

Robbie Neal—a mate of Christopher's—had decided to use the run-off from the hill beside his house as a water slide. He'd used a tyre tube, there hadn't been a lot of control from the beginning and he'd hit a tree. He had grazes and bruises everywhere but as far as Maggie could see, the damage was superficial.

No hint of loss of consciousness. No sign of head injury. She cleaned him up and sent him home with his long-suffering parents.

She cleaned the clinic, walked through into the hall where the locals had set up a temporary evacuation centre, noted

that her mother wasn't there—she'd be sponging on any o
half a dozen neighbours, she thought grimly, no commu-
nal evacuation centre for Barbie—and then she thought she
shouldn't care.

How did you turn off caring?

She drove home thinking just that. And also…how did yo
stop yourself starting to care?

For a guy who'd kissed her?

It was nothing, she told herself fiercely, but unbidden he
fingers wandered to her lips as if she could still feel…

'I can feel nothing,' she said harshly into the silence. '
can't afford to feel anything. Honestly, how many complications do you want in your life? A womanising Samford i
exactly what you don't need.'

A womanising Samford…

She was tarring him with the same brush as his father, sh
thought. Was that fair?

Of course it wasn't. Up until now he'd been awesome. He'
helped her care for her little brother. He'd saved his life. He'
saved his cows. He'd dispatched her mother.

He'd kissed her.

'Which has turned you into a simpering schoolgirl,' sh
snapped. 'Grow up, Maggie. It was only a kiss.'

Only it didn't feel like just a kiss. It felt…so much more.

The house was silent. It was eleven o'clock and she was dea
tired.

She checked the fire, checked each of the kids, made sur
Christopher was okay.

Christopher and Liselle both stirred and hugged her a
she leaned over them—something they'd done since they'
been babies.

Part of her loved it.

How could she ever walk away?

She couldn't, she thought, as she tucked them in and kissed them goodnight. When Blake sold the farm she'd move back home. Of course she would. The events of the day had shown her just how dangerous it was to leave the kids with her mother.

Tonight she didn't even have the luxury of her own bed. Susie had demurred at sleeping in a big, strange bedroom by herself. She was very definitely sharing with Maggie.

It's fine, Maggie told herself. You've had six months' luxury of having your own place. That's it.

She was so tired…

But she did need to check on Blake. Just in case, she told herself. He'd pushed himself past the limit this afternoon. If he was bleeding internally, if he was in pain, would he call her?

Maybe he wouldn't and the nurse in her wouldn't let herself go to bed without checking.

She slipped through the darkened house. His bedroom door was open, just a crack.

She had no wish to wake him—or Ruby—if he was asleep. She pushed the door just enough for her to slip inside.

He had the curtains wide open. The clouds had cleared for once, and the almost full moon was lighting the bed, the man sleeping in it, and the baby tucked in her bed beside him.

They were both soundly asleep.

Blake was bare to the waist. He was sleeping right on the edge of the bed, and his arm was trailing down so his fingers were resting beside Ruby's face.

It was as if he'd gone to sleep touching her. Giving her human contact. Letting her know he cared?

Something was twisting…

This man…

Don't, she told herself fiercely. No. Put your hormones right back where they belong.

He stirred and she backed out of there so fast she almost tripped over her feet. He was fine. She didn't need to check again.

She didn't need to go near this man when he was half-dressed, or in his bedroom, or when he was smiling, or when he was feeding Ruby, or when he was doing any of the stupid, dumb things that were mounting up that made her feel...

Like she had no business feeling. When the river went down he'd head back to his city hospital, to his independent life, and she'd just...

Just...

She needed to get a grip. Any minute now she'd be putting something violinish and maudlin on the sound system and start weeping into her beer.

The phone rang and she grabbed it with real relief. Work. That way lay sanity—not looking at half-naked men in the moonlight.

But the phone call wasn't for her.

One problem with sharing Blake's house was that she shared his phone.

Bob Samford's existing line had never been disconnected. An extension of that same line rang in her apartment. She'd been covering the costs since she moved in.

Maggie had a cellphone. The locals knew it, but they disliked using the longer phone number and contacting her cellphone was a more costly call.

When she'd lived with her mother, no matter how much she'd discouraged it, they'd rung her there. As soon as she'd moved, they'd simply phoned here. So when the phone rang as she reached the hall, she answered it fast, to stop it waking the house.

'Maggie Tilden,' she said, polite and professional.

'Who is this?' a female voice demanded.

Uh-oh. She didn't recognise this voice. It was cool, slightly arrogant and startled. Like she was expecting someone else.

She guessed this was Blake's call.

'I'm the district nurse,' she said, a tad too quickly. 'Maggie Tilden.'

'The woman living at the back of Blake's house?'

How could you dislike a woman after two sentences? Not possible. She got a grip and managed a bright smile. Someone had said smile on the phone and the person at the other end could hear it. She tried—hard.

'That's right,' she said, determinedly chirpy. 'Did you wish to speak to Blake?'

'Yes.'

'I'm sorry, but he's asleep.'

'It's only eleven.'

'Yes, but he's had a very big day. He had to save his calves from drowning and Ruby needs feeding in the night.' She paused. 'I'd rather not wake him.'

'He's not answering his cellphone.'

'He dropped it in the water. I don't believe it's working.'

There was a deathly silence. Then, 'He's been in flood-water?'

'I… Yes.'

'To save calves?' It was practically a screech.

'Yes.' She was trying to be polite—but this was hurting her ear.

'You won't look after the baby—*and you expect him to save cows?*'

'They're his cows,' she said mildly. 'And it's his baby.'

'It's not his baby.'

'He's taking responsibility for her.'

'He has no right—'

'It's his sister's baby,' she said gently. 'He has more right than most.'

'You're the midwife. He says you won't—'

'Be professional? I'm being exceedingly professional. I don't take patients home.' She glanced behind her and winced at the mess the kids had made of Blake's fabulous, faded living room—and thought actually she'd brought everything else home.

'Blake needs help,' she snapped. 'He's ill. If you're a nurse, help him.'

'I'm doing what I can.' She'd coped with belligerent patients before—and their relatives. She was deliberately keeping her voice calm, unruffled—but implacable. 'I don't believe there's any need to worry. I'd prefer not to wake him, though. If you give me your name, I'll tell him you called.'

'Miriam Donnington,' she snapped. 'Dr Donnington. Blake's fiancée.'

Why did her stomach lurch? No reason at all.

Or lots of reasons. How stupid did she feel? How had her hormones led her down a path she didn't know she was treading until right now?

Blake belonged in another life. He was a city doctor with a city fiancée. He was trapped here. The kiss they'd shared had been the result of adrenalin, from shared danger and from victory and nothing more. She'd known it. She just… knew it better now.

So why was she standing silent, she demanded of herself, as if she was in shock? Get over it, she told herself harshly—and sensible Maggie emerged, as sensible Maggie always did.

'I didn't know he was engaged,' she managed, and somehow she kept her smile firmly in place. 'Congratulations. I can see why you're concerned. I'll let him know you've called. I suspect his phone might still be out of action even when it's dried, but you can usually raise him on this number. Unless he's asleep. I'm trying my best to keep him in bed.' She listened to how that sounded and decided maybe she'd better lighten it. Make it even more professional. 'He's not a very co-operative patient,' she confessed, nurse to doctor.

'Blake knows what's good for him,' Miriam snapped. 'He doesn't need a nurse telling him what to do. What he needs is peace, not a nurse and a baby complicating his life.'

'Plus my four kids,' she said, letting her temper emerge just a little, deciding why not tell it like it is? Even wind it up a little.

He'd kissed her. He had a fiancée. Toe rag!

'Four kids?'

'Blake doesn't mind,' she said cheerfully. 'All my kids are here. Pete says Blake's even been playing his computer games with him. Now, was there anything else you wanted?'

'I... No.' She sounded stunned.

'Goodnight, then,' Maggie chirped, still managing to smile, and she put the phone down—and turned to find Blake watching.

He was leaning against the wall, arms crossed, bare chested, bare legged, ruffled from sleep—simply watching.

He destroyed her professional detachment, just like that.

Nurse, midwife...woman? With Blake around she was all woman, and her body reacted accordingly.

Fiancée. Fiancée.

Keep your head. Get off that dratted path.

'Miriam?' he asked, and she nodded.

'Your fiancée.'

'That's what she told you?'

'She wanted me to wake you. I refused. I'm sorry. You can ring her back.'

'I will.' His eyes searched her face. 'She gave you a hard time?'

'For not looking after you—which might be justified. If you were being flown out right now with internal bleeding,

I'd be to blame.' She was sounding so calm she was proud of herself.

'As you said,' he said mildly, 'they're my cows. My choice. And, yes, Maggie, Ruby's my niece.'

'Will Miriam help you take care of her?' It was none of her business, she thought. She shouldn't ask, but the question was out there now, like it or not.

'Someone has to,' he said. 'Unless I take Pete's way out and bury the nappies.'

She managed a half-hearted smile back at him. 'Pete'd bury dishes, too, if it was up to him. But good luck. You should ring her back. She sounds genuinely worried.'

'I will. And, Maggie…'

'Mmm?' He was too close, she thought. Too close, too big, too bare.

'I'm sorry she upset you.'

'She didn't.' How was that for a lie? 'I'm accustomed to my patients' worried relatives.'

'I'm not a patient,' he said, so softly that she shivered.

'You ought to be,' she managed. 'It'd be a whole lot easier if you were.'

And before he could retort she'd turned and headed into her own small apartment, closing the door very firmly behind her.

He should ring Miriam right back. Instead, Blake stood and watched the closed door for a very long time.

Maggie was behind that door.

She'd be in bed with her ten-year-old sister. His father's two dogs would be under her bed. She was surrounded.

Miriam would be at her desk in their cool, grey and white apartment with a view of the harbour.

His fiancée?

She wasn't. Why had she said it?

To protect him, maybe? To stop Maggie thinking she could take advantage?

Was she taking advantage?

No. Ruby would be here even if Maggie wasn't—and he'd invited her siblings to stay. As well as that, he'd talked to the doctors who'd cared for his father. Without Maggie the old man would have been hospitalised far earlier. Bob had been no one's idea of an easy man but Maggie had worked to make his last months as good as they could be.

She was not a woman to take advantage...

Fiancée...

He rang and Miriam answered on the first ring. 'Blake... I knew you'd be awake. That woman wouldn't fetch you.'

That woman. It sounded...wrong.

That woman was Maggie.

'She's doing a hell of a job,' he said mildly. 'She's taking care of the whole valley.'

'Not you. Were you really dumb enough to stand in flood-water?'

'If I hadn't, eighty calves would have drowned.'

'For heaven's sake, Blake, what's worth more? All that skill, all that training...'

'Not to mention me,' he said mildly. 'Even without the medical degree I'd still have missed me.'

'For heaven's sake,' she snapped.

And he thought...he thought...

Fiancée?

They'd drifted into this relationship. They'd competed against each other at university, studied together, pushed each other. They were both driven.

He wondered suddenly whether, if he didn't have his medicine, would he have Miriam?

Would she want him?

Would he want her?

It was a crazy thing to think at midnight, when his feet were cold on the floorboards and he could hear Ruby starting to stir in the background, but think it he did.

'When the water comes down,' he said, speaking slowly, thinking it through as he spoke, 'I'd like you to visit here before I come back. I'd like you to get to know Ruby. Help me make a decision about her.'

There was a sharp intake of breath.

'What sort of decision?'

'She's my family, Mim.'

'I'm not Mim.' Suddenly her voice was almost shrill. 'I'm not taking on anyone else's baby. I don't even know if I want one of my own yet.'

'Of our own?' he queried.

'I... Yes.'

'Fiancée?'

There was a moment's pause. It turned out longer. It ended up stretching a very long time indeed.

'I said it for your benefit,' she said at last. 'I thought you might need it. If you're staying in the same house...'

'We have five kids staying here now,' he said gently. 'They're chaperons enough. But...are you thinking I'd need them?'

'I don't care what you do,' she said fretfully.

There was another silence at that. 'Really?' he said at last, and he looked at the closed door and thought of Maggie in bed with Susie and the dogs underneath and he thought... Maggie was a woman who cared.

'Look, this is a dumb conversation,' Miriam snapped at last, regrouping. 'What we have is sensible, Blake. Do you want to mess it up?'

'Would it mess it up if I was unfaithful?'

'If I were to know about it, yes.'

'And if you didn't?'

'Look, I don't care,' she snapped. 'I'm tired and I have a long day tomorrow and if you want to have a torrid little affair with your tenant/nurse—*who has how many children*?—then it's fine by me. But there's no way I'm coming down there.'

'No,' he said bleakly, and he glanced behind him, to his open bedroom door, where he could see Ruby's bedclothes wriggling. Any minute now she'd open her mouth and yell.

And then, suddenly, he was thinking of Maggie again, and Christopher, and his television rules. Boundaries. And he thought…if ever he had an affair with Maggie she'd give him boundaries—and they wouldn't be do what you like but don't tell me about it.

'I'll be moving apartments when I get back to Sydney,' he said, and he heard Miriam's breath draw in with shock and with anger.

'So it's true. Your stupid little nurse…'

'It has nothing to do with Maggie,' he told her, though maybe it did, and it was simply too soon to acknowledge it. 'But it has to do with family. You and me, Mim…we're friends. Colleagues. But we've never been family and it's too late to start now. Our relationship needs to stop. It's going nowhere and it's time we acknowledged it. I'm sorry, Mim… Miriam, but it's over.'

'So you're starting…what, a family? Down there?' The viciousness in her voice was appalling.

'I have no idea where or what I'm starting,' he told her. 'All I know is that we're wrong. Thank you for trying to protect me, Miriam, but I don't need a fiancée. I'm not sure what I need. Oh, actually, yes, I am. I need to make one bottle for one baby and then go back to bed. Right now, I'm not capable of thinking further.'

CHAPTER EIGHT

THE river stayed impassable. The rain was interminable. There was nothing for it but for the valley to hunker down and wait.

If anyone had told Blake he could spend a week trapped in a farmhouse with five children and be…almost content, he'd have labelled them crazy, but that's exactly what he did.

Maggie was frantically busy. That rush of water through the valley had caught everyone unprepared. There'd been stock loss—nothing dire, but farmers had been caught by surprise and there were sprains and bruises from rushing to save stock, grazes that had turned septic from floodwater, leg abscesses that had got wet and stayed wet too long, back problems as people heaved belongings higher than the water.

Blake helped when he could, relishing the times he could go out with her to the outlying farms, helping to debride ulcers, double-checking her diagnoses, or just plain giving reassurance that Maggie was right, they didn't need evacuation to the hospital over the river.

To his surprise, he was enjoying it. He'd never thought of country medicine, but its variation was almost…fun.

But frustrating for Maggie.

'What is it about having doctor in front of your name?' she demanded. She'd spent an hour telling Maisie Goodall her leg was starting to heal and the antibiotics were taking effect, but Maisie was still frightened. Blake had walked in, examined the ulcerated leg for a whole two minutes and smiled his reassurance.

'This is healing beautifully, Miss Goodall. See the faint film over the edges? That's slowly working its way in to form a seal. Try and keep it elevated and dry, watch lots of telly, cuddle your cats—' the woman was surrounded by them '—and I reckon by the time the water's down you'll be good as new.'

Maisie almost purred as loudly as her cats, and Maggie climbed back into her car beside Blake and glowered.

'I can speak until I'm blue in the face,' she muttered. 'But you walk in with your doctor-ish bedside manner and you don't do a single thing and suddenly Maisie doesn't want a helicopter, she just wants another visit from you tomorrow.'

'Basic Bedside Manner,' Blake said smugly. 'Taught in med school. Kept secret from nurses for generations.'

'You mean you're good looking, you're male and you smile at her,' she snapped.

'There is that.' He looked smug and she had to chuckle.

'Okay, it's useful,' she conceded. 'If I could just bottle you and keep you in my medical kit…'

'I won't be put.'

'No.' She sighed. 'You shouldn't even be out here.' She'd brought him out of desperation because Maisie had been so scared, but she kept reminding herself that he, too, was a patient. But he was recovering. He was moving with ease, the stiffness and the grimacing had gone and he was well on the way to recovery.

They had Ruby in the baby seat. Bringing her with them for the minor stuff meant Liselle could keep studying and, besides, patients liked it. Maggie had no doubt there'd be a pair of bootees from Maisie's knitting needles by the end of the week. That was okay as well because it meant Maisie would sit with her leg up while she knitted. That'd help her healing—but healing was what Maggie should be organising for Blake, rather than letting him accompany her on her rounds.

But he seemed to enjoy it, she conceded, and he was very skilled, very efficient, very friendly—and very useful. Also accepted. Because of his links to the valley the locals treated him as one of them. Local boy made good.

Also local boy made interesting—and there was the complication. Interest meant speculation. The locals looked at Blake, they looked at Maggie, they looked at Ruby—and Maggie could see exactly what the valley was thinking. That made her think…and thinking was exactly what she was trying not to do. It was bad enough having Blake sitting beside her, but a girl didn't need to think about it.

She glowered at the steering-wheel—and the ignition light lit up.

Excellent—a diversion.

Or maybe not excellent. Ignition light…trouble?

She should be driving a Health Services car on her rounds. Normally she would, but the bridge closure had happened earlier than expected, catching them all by surprise. Her dependable hospital car was on the other side of the river and she was left with her own.

Which wasn't so dependable. She used it in emergencies, but patients had been known to groan when she pulled up in her battered wagon.

Ignition light…

'What's wrong?' Blake asked as she pulled over to the verge.

'Sister, farmer, nurse, mechanic,' she said. 'You've met three. Welcome to the fourth.'

She climbed out and hauled up the bonnet, and he climbed out after her.

Cars weren't his thing. Yeah, he could drive them, but his

garage was right by the hospital and apart from the odd tyre change he'd never concerned himself with them.

Underneath the bonnet looked as decrepit as the outside of the car, and a lot more mysterious, but Maggie was sighing and heading for the rear.

'Panty hose,' she said.

'Panty hose?'

'A girl's best friend. Never go anywhere without them.' She hauled out a pair of black tights that looked like they'd seen better days. 'Can you find some scissors in my bag and chop the legs off?' she asked. He did, while Maggie did… other stuff.

'Fanbelt?' he guessed, thinking he ought to try and sound intelligent. They were in the middle of nowhere. Where was the nearest tow truck?

But Maggie wasn't thinking about tow trucks. 'You've got it.' She was head down in the engine, tossing out a very decrepit belt. 'I did a course a while back to learn what to do. The fanbelt transmits drive from the engine to the alternator and water pump. Without it, the battery doesn't charge and the engine overheats. It's okay. I have a spare at home and the panty hose will get us there. I just need to make a smooth knot so it'll spin. I'll loosen the alternator mounting bolts and push the alternator towards the other pulleys. Then I'll slip on my pantyhose, lever the alternator until the loop's tight and do up the bolts. I'll only use the crank and pump pulleys. It's hard to make the panty hose tight when it's fitted over more.'

'Right,' he said faintly, and she glanced back up at him and grinned.

'So mechanic doesn't fit in your job description.'

'No.'

'Lucky you.' She straightened and took the chopped pantyhose leg from him. She had a smudge of grease on her nose. He thought she looked…she looked…

'Hop back in the car,' she said gently. 'I can cope on my own. Miriam would have my hide if she could see me dragging you with me on my medical rounds—and I don't need you to hold my spanner.'

'Miriam's not my fiancée,' he said, and she paused and stared at him—and then bit her lip and dived under the bonnet again.

'Not?'

'She's a colleague.'

'She said—'

'She's been my partner. Sort of. We studied together at university. When we got jobs at the same hospital, we figured we could afford an amazing apartment if we got it together.' He hesitated. 'That doesn't totally sum up our relationship,' he said honestly. It's drifted past friendship but the other night… I realised it needs to stop drifting.'

'Because I was sharing a house with you?' she said, not looking at him, concentrating fiercely on whatever it was she was concentrating on. 'Because you kissed me? If you think I'm taking responsibility for breaking up your relationship…'

'I didn't say that.'

'You want me to phone her and tell her there's an oak door and five kids between us?'

'I already have.'

'Then it's ridiculous.'

'Is it?'

'Of course it's ridiculous.' She thumped something with a spanner. 'You've lost a potential fiancée. Why aren't you sounding heartbroken?'

'Because I'm not in love with Miriam. Neither of us has ever pretended to be in love with the other. Because, even though I've known you for less than two weeks, even though it makes no sense at all, the kiss we shared was electric and

I've never felt that with Miriam. Ever. So moving on from Miriam...it had to be done. It's not fair on anyone to continue.'

There was a moment's silence. Deathly silence. Actually, it was more than a moment. It lasted for a very long time.

Then the spanner thumped again. She went back to work. He waited—and he thought...

Why had he said that? Confessed all?

Because her backside under the bonnet was really, really sexy? Because the smudge of grease on her nose made him want to wipe it away for her and then kiss it? Because the whole package of Maggie, woman, sister, farmer, nurse, mechanic was doing something to him he couldn't understand and he couldn't fight?

She was the most desirable woman he'd ever met.

He'd suggested what they had together was unique. One kiss?

He'd done this all wrong. He'd confessed he'd been blown away by a kiss, while the woman in question was covered in grease and doing something a guy would traditionally do but which he had no hope of doing.

Had he scared her?

He *had* scared her. He saw it in her body language. He saw it in the way she concentrated fiercely on doing what she had to do.

He'd been really, really stupid.

Why?

He thought up a barrage of excuses. Appendix. Floods. Baby. Maggie herself.

The kiss.

Together they were a package designed to knock any man off kilter, he decided—and maybe Maggie realised it. When she finally hauled herself back from under the bonnet she had her face under control.

She dropped the bonnet into position with a bang, wiped

her hands on the remains of the panty hose, slid into the driver's seat and waited until Blake had climbed back into the car beside her.

She started the car, watched the ignition go out with satisfaction, pulled back onto the road and finally, eventually she spoke.

'I hope what you said back there was an aberration,' she said.

'It was…a fairly awesome kiss,' he said, thinking caution was the way to go here.

'Fairly?'

'Okay, very,' he conceded. 'And just now… There was grease on your nose. You looked sexy as hell. I love a girl with a spanner.'

She managed a smile at that, but it was a wobbly smile.

'Just as well I've put my spanner away, then,' she said. 'Blake…' Her voice turned serious. 'Don't read anything into what happened between us, and for heaven's sake don't call things off with Miriam because of me. I come with a lot more encumbrances than a spanner, and I'm not in the market for a relationship. One kiss does not a relationship make.'

Where could he fit caution into this reply? He tried, but failed. When in doubt, opt for honesty. 'One kiss makes me feel like I've never felt before,' he said, and it felt okay. It felt right.

'It was a good kiss,' she conceded. 'But don't even think of taking it further. I'm heading for Africa.'

'Africa?' he said, startled.

'And possibly Siberia. Not to mention Sardinia, Istanbul and Paris. All by myself. I have a bank account…' She took a deep breath, glanced at him—quickly—and obviously decided to go on. 'When I was a kid I used to collect drink cans,' she told him. 'Outside footy matches, from the richer kids at school, wherever I could find them. I squashed them and sold them by weight. They made me a pittance but it was *my* pittance. When things got bad at home I used to escape and search for cans. Even today I think of escape in the form of drink cans.'

She hesitated then, and he wondered why she was telling him this—why she was turning what must surely be a joking conversation—a mistake?—into a conversation about saving. But something in her expression told him this was important. And maybe it was something she'd told no one else.

'Mum and Dad were always broke,' she told him. 'Desperately broke. If they'd known I had even a tiny fund they'd have used it in an instant and it'd be gone, so I kept hiding it and they never knew. All my life I hid it. As a teenager I babysat, like Liselle does. Some of the money I earned went into my secret fund. When I started nursing I kept doing it, squirrelling away my pittances. Ninety-nine per cent of all I've ever earned has gone to keeping me or helping the kids, but one per cent is mine. My tiny fund is almost enough to get me to Africa—but not back.'

'But you will come back?' he asked, startled, and she shrugged and grinned.

'Of course I will. I suspect the family will always need me—Good Old Maggie. But I will go.' It was a declaration, almost a vow. 'The moment Susie leaves home, I'm off.'

'Susie's ten,' he said faintly. 'That's seven years.'

'I'll have the return fare by then,' she said resolutely. 'More. The less they need me the more I'll be able to save. I'm aiming to travel for at least six months. All by myself... Remember that backpacking dream I told you about? Sitting on the Left Bank in Paris drinking kir, with not one single person to answer to. Lying in the sun on a Greek island. Seeing a rhinoceros in the wild. I really do hope to turn that into a reality one of these days.' She glanced across at him and bit her lip and turned her attention deliberately to the road again. 'So don't you—and Ruby—dare mess with my dream!'

'I wouldn't dare.'

'Good,' she said. 'Just so we understand each other.'

They drove on and he kept right on kicking himself. Of all the morons… Why had he frightened her? Why had he made a big deal out of one kiss? Why had he forced her to tell him her life dreams?

He'd known this woman for little more than a week. He'd kissed her once. To suggest it could be the foundation of a relationship…to tell her it was the reason he'd broken up with Miriam…

The whole thing was dumb.

He was a city surgeon, ambitious, career focussed, totally centred on getting as good at his job as it was possible to get. Maggie lived in Hicksville, surrounded by kids and cows and not even the scent of decent coffee.

And never the twain should meet.

It was cabin fever, he told himself. He'd been trapped with Maggie for a week now. Any more time in this place and anyone with an X chromosome would start looking good. Even a woman with grease spots on her nose.

Only it was more than that, he conceded as they drove on. Maybe Maggie represented something he'd never thought about—or maybe something he'd repressed. A need for home?

He'd lived in this place until the age of six. After that, his mother had moved from place to place, from man to man. This valley must have some sort of long-term emotional hold over him.

And then there was Ruby. He glanced behind at his tiny niece, sleeping deeply in her baby cocoon.

What to do with Ruby?

She needed family, and right now she had it. She had him,

and Maggie as back-up, and she had four siblings, Liselle, Pete, Chris and Susie, who all regarded her as their personal plaything.

She was starting to smile and everyone in the house was working for those smiles.

'Hey, I got one. I'm in front by two.' That had been Chris that morning, crowing with delight, and the memory made him smile.

The way Maggie handled Ruby made him smile, too. While he was unwieldy when Ruby was distressed, Maggie stepped in, calm and sure, and made things right.

But even put together, those things weren't enough to define as love. To start thinking long-term relationship...

Nostalgia. Need. Isolation.

A girl with a grease spot on her nose.

Weakness and need was all it was, he told himself harshly, but now he had Maggie looking at him like he had a kangaroo loose in the top paddock. She'd even felt the need to explain her long-term life plans, spelling out that they didn't include him.

Which was all fine—only why was he sitting here thinking he'd made a huge mistake? It was because something within him was telling him Maggie was important for far more than practical or nostalgic reasons. Maggie was someone the likes of whom he'd never met before and might never meet again.

Maggie. Grease spots. Maggie. Love and laughter.

Yes, she came with terrifying baggage—but to have the right to hold her...

He'd known her a little more than a week and he'd scared her.

'Cabin fever must be getting to me,' he said into the loaded silence, and she cast him a glance that contained...gratitude? He was letting her off the hook. Setting things back to normal?

'It must be,' she said, sounding relieved. 'You should ring Miriam and tell her isolation's playing with your head.'

'Can isolation happen in a house with five kids, two dogs and how many cows?'

'It comes in all forms,' she said, and her voice changed a little, and suddenly he heard a note of desolation. 'I've been surrounded all my life and I've longed for isolation, yet in a sense I already have it. Define isolation?' She took a deep breath. 'Sorry. It's getting to me, too. You're right, cabin fever. We need to avoid kissing—we're likely to jump each other through sheer frustration. But the authorities are saying the water level's starting to drop, and the forecast is for the weather to finally clear. Within a week they'll set up a barge. The kids can go back to school. You can go back to Sydney. Life can get back to normal.'

'Is that what you want?'

'Of course it is,' she said tightly. 'I have a seven-year plan, remember? I've been working on it since I was ten years old and I have no intention of deviating from it now.'

But she was deviating.

Only in her mind, she thought savagely. Only when she let herself turn from practical Maggie into someone who let her mind wander all along sorts of crazy, impractical paths.

Paths that ended with Blake.

She should avoid him. She couldn't.

They went home and it was time to redo Ruby's legs. She'd been wearing casts for a week now. They needed to be removed, the tiny feet manipulated some more, inched closer to normal, and new casts applied.

So Maggie watched and helped as Blake tended his tiny niece with all the care in the world.

At least she could focus on Ruby rather than her uncle.

Left unattended, these feet would cripple this little girl—

they'd make her life a torturous nightmare, with a wheelchair a real, long-term option.

But once the casts came off she could see improvement. The feet had been twisted far back at birth. They were still twisted, and left now they'd revert, but at rest, the little feet lay at an angle that was slightly closer to normal.

'Can you run her a bath?' Blake asked, as he started playing with the tiny feet, and she did. Well, okay, not a baby bath—this place didn't run to it—but the kitchen sink was big, porcelain, perfect. She did a quick scrub, filled it with warm water and lined it with towels so Ruby wouldn't be lowered against the hard surface.

She half expected Blake to hand Ruby to her, but it was he who lowered her into the water. It was Blake who looked down as Ruby's eyes widened with surprise at this strange, new sensation.

They'd bathed her the night she'd come, before the first cast had gone on, but she'd been a very different baby then—malnourished, abandoned, unloved.

This was a Ruby who'd had a full week of regular feeds, regular cuddles—a regular family?

It wasn't exactly regular, Maggie thought, thinking of her weird assortment of brothers and sisters handing her around—but now Ruby had the thing she most needed in the world. A constant.

Blake.

He was holding her as if she was the most precious thing in the world. She hardly needed to have put the towels down—his hands held her with warmth, security and love.

Love?

She looked into his face and saw emotions she didn't understand.

This man was falling for this baby, she thought, and he was falling hard.

Blake Samford was a city doctor, aloof, a stranger. He was nothing to do with this valley or her. He'd sell this farm and be gone from her life.

But today he'd said…

Forget what he'd said. Concentrate on Ruby, not Blake.

But some things were just plain impossible. The way he was looking at this baby was twisting her heartstrings. This was no doctor looking at a patient. Neither was it a man who planned on handing Ruby to foster-parents as soon as he could.

He was an enigma, and even though she'd sworn to stay distant, she couldn't help herself. She wanted to know more.

'Tell me about your sister,' she said, as Ruby discovered she could wiggle her arms and her cast-free feet and feel even more amazing sensations in the warm water. 'About Wendy.'

'I never knew her.'

'I think you must have,' she said gently. 'The way you're looking at Ruby.'

And then, amazingly, he told her. He cradled Ruby and played with her while he talked of a baby he'd seen only once—a baby who'd destroyed his parents' marriage.

He told of being six years old and crouching by the baby while everyone around them yelled. He told her of placing his hand in the baby's carrycot and feeling her finger tightening around his. He told of being six years old and terrified and thinking this baby was his little sister and she must be terrified, too.

And then he talked of the strange woman taking her away, of his parents never speaking of her again, and of his family no longer existing.

'A psychologist would have a field day,' he said, half-mocking.

And she looked up at him and thought…and thought…if he hadn't been holding his baby she'd touch him. She'd run her fingers down that strong cheekbone and caress the lines of pain and self-mockery.

The image of tall, dark, dangerous was receding.

There were worse things than being one of nine neglected kids, she decided. This man had been alone all his life.

But now he'd found Ruby.

Focus back on Ruby, she thought desperately. That was the plan. She had to have a plan around this man because she did not want to feel like she was feeling. It seemed like a vortex, a whirlpool, dark, sweet, infinitely enticing, but who knew what lay inside?

'Don't you need to manipulate?' she managed, and he glanced at her and caught himself and she saw him swap—with difficulty—back to professional as well.

'Of course I do,' he said. 'And it might be easier if we do the first part while she's happy in the water.'

So he handed her over, and as their hands touched as they inevitably had to during handover, and she held his baby while his big, skilled hands manipulated those tiny legs with all the tenderness in the world, as she stood close to him and watched his face and watched his hands, she realised she was in so much trouble.

He'd broken off a relationship with Miriam because of one kiss. That was crazy.

But maybe the condition was catching.

Warm, dry, fed—and confined in her new cast—Ruby was fretful. She'd had a lovely time when her whole body had been free to move, and now she was back to being constricted. It'd be a long haul, Blake thought. Six weeks of casts, an operation to cut the Achilles tendon to let it heal in the new correct position, months of twenty-three hours a day in a brace, then more in a brace at night.

'It's the price you'll pay for being able to dance at your

wedding,' he told her, but she wasn't taking any comfort from that.

She was tired after her bath, and so was he. His mate back in Sydney had been right—the operation had knocked the stuffing out of him. Maggie didn't need him right now. He could settle on his bed with Ruby beside him, and try and settle her.

Tell her stories of what their life would be like together?

For he was keeping her—as simple as that. Some time during the last week she'd twisted her way around his heart and she was staying.

He'd be joining the ranks of single dads.

How did they cope?

How would he cope?

How would he cope without Maggie?

'Is that what the conversation in the car was all about?' he demanded of Ruby. 'Or is it my subconscious knowing it'd be easy if she fell for me—if she took you on as well as her brood. After all, she's stuck here for the next seven years anyway.'

There's a romantic way of looking at a relationship, he thought wryly. Red roses didn't even begin to cut it in comparison.

But it had to be more than that. The way he was feeling…

'How can I know what I'm feeling' he asked Ruby, and watched her eyelids grow heavier and heavier until she drifted off to sleep. 'Yeah, I'm smitten with you, and that's cracking open places I don't want to go. I want my independence.'

How could he be independent and keep Ruby?

Make Maggie fall in love with him? Work out how to bend his career so he could fit in family? Live happily ever after.

Was that independence? There was a part of him that was saying it was a solution to all their problems—but another

part of him was telling him he'd be giving up way too much.
Even if Maggie agreed.

But Ruby was so needy, and that kiss… The possibilities
were there. As he watched his tiny niece sleep and thought of
Maggie next door, with the weight of the world on her shoulders, he decided a man had to try.

The forecast was saying it would be another week before
the river would be safe to cross. He wasn't due back at work
for another two weeks.

Anything was possible in two weeks, he thought.

Including making a family?

He'd never thought about a family. Why was he thinking
about one now?

She had enough of a family without including him. She told
herself that over and over during the next few days, and she
meant it.

As much as possible Maggie kept her brood on her side of
the oak door. They had to use Blake's large sitting room—
there wasn't enough room for them anywhere else—but the
kids were under threat of death not to disturb him. She cooked
for her siblings and fed them in her own small kitchen. The
kids thought they should invite Blake, too, but it seemed…
dangerous? Inviting him into her tiny kitchen or letting her
brood loose in his seemed equally fraught.

She needed to stay apart. That kiss…telling her he'd split
with Miriam… It was a sweet seduction, she told herself
fiercely. He'd get her over to his side of the house, she'd fall
for Ruby and she'd be trapped again. Man gets landed with
abandoned baby, man makes moves on motherly nurse…
Coincidence? Ha.

So she needed to be firm. Doing his own cooking was
part of caring for Ruby, living with her, making a life for her.
It was part of Blake's bonding process that was proceeding

beautifully. She wanted no part in it, and she wasn't interfering with it for the world.

Occasionally she needed him medically. Occasionally he needed her for advice on Ruby. That's all the contact they needed, she told herself, and anything else was scary.

But the kids kept on telling her she was nuts. Even cruel.

'When you're not here he comes in and plays computer games with us, and helps me with maths, and he even helped Susie tie hair ribbons on her doll,' Liselle told her. 'We love playing with Ruby. Only when you come in and he's here, you back out again so he doesn't come in when you're home. That seems mean.'

It did, Maggie conceded. But it also seemed safe. She was being defensive, and somehow she had need of all the defences she could muster.

'And he makes life less boring,' Pete muttered from the couch. 'I'm so-o-o bored. The guys are making mud slides on the far side of the valley. Tom's taking them over in his dad's car. If Tom's dad says it's okay, why won't you?'

Because Tom's father was a moron and Tom behind the wheel was a danger to everyone, Maggie thought, but she didn't say so.

'You know Mum's forbidden it,' she said, more mildly, because she'd worked on this one. Barbie didn't particularly care what her kids did, but Maggie had learned that if she put her under enough pressure—like threatening to withdraw financial help—Barbie could be persuaded to utter edicts. '*You won't drive with Tom.*'

Pete couldn't tell his mates Maggie said no. 'Mum says no' hurt his pride less.

'Mum doesn't care,' Pete said sullenly. 'Tom says she's staying at Archie Harm's place. She hasn't even phoned to find out how Chris is.'

'She does care,' Maggie said, without conviction. 'And you're not to go with Tom.'

'Then let me ask Blake to play this video game with me. It's too hard for Chris, and Liselle won't.'

'Don't disturb Blake.'

'Why not?'

'Because he's not part of our family,' Maggie snapped. 'He's our landlord. Nothing else.'

The week dragged.

The longer the river remained impassable the busier Maggie became. Medical niggles became major. The authorities organised helicopter drops of essentials and evacuation of a few people who'd just got sick of staying.

Maggie's mother was one of them.

'Archie and I are fed up,' she told Maggie on her first phone contact since Chris had hurt his leg. 'You have the kids. Why should I stay? We're visiting Archie's daughter in Sydney.'

'Can you take Pete?' Maggie asked, knowing already what the answer would be but she had to try. 'He's so bored I'm scared he'll do something dumb.'

'You think Archie's daughter wants kids?' Barbie asked incredulously. 'Of course she doesn't. Pete's a good boy. You worry too much, Maggie.'

And she was gone.

Maggie had been using the phone in the hall. She turned and found Blake watching.

Sharing the phone had to stop, she thought. Why wouldn't her mother use the cellphone? Why was Blake watching? And why was her mother's voice so shrill that she knew Blake must have heard?

'Archie?' he asked.

'He's a no-good dropkick from the other side of the valley,' she told him, trying to keep her tone unemotional. 'His wife keeps leaving and then he hangs round Mum. It doesn't last. They'll have a fight, his wife'll take him back and things will get back to normal. As normal as they ever do in our family.'

'So you're totally trapped.'

'The river's trapping me.'

'Even if it goes down...'

'I'm fine,' she said. 'I just need to stay close.'

'When I sell this house, where will you go?'

He saw the colour fade from her face. How many places were available for cheap rent in the farming district close enough to be on call for her siblings? None.

She'd go back home.

'Maggie...'

'It's my business,' she said. 'You have enough on your plate worrying about Ruby.'

'Maybe we could—'

'Maybe we couldn't,' she snapped. 'Maybe there's no we.'

She walked back into side of the house and carefully closed the door behind her. That was rude, she thought. Uncivil. She didn't even know what he'd been about to say.

But there was something about the way he'd looked at her. There's no *we*.

It was true, she thought. No matter how he looked at her, it was simply another tug at her heartstrings. She had too many already. A guy with his needy baby...

A guy as drop-dead gorgeous as Blake?

A guy who'd hand her yet another responsibility?

'Maggie...' It was Chris, yelling from the other side of the door, Blake's side. 'Pete's got the remote and won't give it to me. Tell him he has to.'

'Pete,' Blake's voice boomed. 'Give your brother the remote or I'll switch the channel to the National Bowling Championships and burn the remote. I mean it.'

There was a loaded silence and then a chuckle and then silence reigned from the living room.

She smiled.

She told herself not to smile.

Because that smile was all about thinking *we*.

There was only manipulation and responsibility and she'd had enough of that to last a lifetime.

CHAPTER NINE

THE household grew more and more tense. Maggie was doing her best to keep the kids happy and not bother Blake, but the valley needed her. She was out a lot.

The weather stayed appalling. Half the problems she was called out for were as the result of people having too much time on their hands—and too much imagination.

'Maggie, I've found a lump on my back. I think it's cancer.'

'Maggie, I've got this funny rash on my neck and I've been reading on the internet about Scabies...'

'Maggie, you know that scary cow disease? Jacob something? My mum used to make me eat brains when I was a kid, and how do I know I don't have it?'

If the river's staying up, the valley should be cut off from the internet, she thought bitterly. The internet was the greatest hypochondria feeder of all time, and she was stuck with it.

Luckily she had Blake. He was great at hosing down panic. By the end of the second week they'd worked out a system. She'd take the initial call. If it was minor and practical she'd go. If it was hysterical and sounding like it could be solved by talking, Blake would go—usually with Ruby, as Ruby herself distracted and defused fear.

If it was major they'd both go, but so far there'd been only a couple of real dramas. A local farmer had rolled his tractor onto his leg. Blake had been calm, steady and impressive, and she'd been truly grateful for his presence. Amy Southwell had had a major heart attack. There had been nothing either of them could do there, but Maggie had watched Blake comfort Amy's husband of sixty years, grip his shoulders, simply hold him.

She'd thought again—quite desperately—there was no *we*. How could it ever work? A city surgeon with baby and a country nurse with eight siblings.

So stay separate, she told herself, and she did, mostly, until Pete got too bored to continue to obey, climbed into a car with a kid who shouldn't have a licence—and nearly got himself killed.

Maggie was dressing an ulcer on Rose Chibnell's leg when her phone went. It was Tom's mother. Cindy Blayne was a fluffy piece of silliness, and she and her husband let their son do exactly what he wanted. Tom was eighteen going on twelve, and Maggie hated Pete being friends with him.

'Maggie?'

Cindy's first word had Maggie's catching her breath. She could hear terror.

'What's wrong?' She stepped back into Rose's hall, knowing whatever was coming was bad.

'Maggie, Tom's rolled the car.'

A car accident. It was the worst of nightmares in such an isolated place. Her mind was switching straight into triage. She'd need Blake, she thought, and then she remembered he wasn't home. He'd headed over the ridge to see the Misses Ford, who'd decided they both had jaundice, going on for liver cancer. Thanks to the internet.

His cellphone was still out of action.

She'd ring the Ford house. She had to find him.

'Where's the crash?' she asked. 'Where's Tom?'

'Maggie, it's not Tom who's hurt.' Cindy sounded like a trembling mess.

'What do you mean, it's not Tom?' But her heart did this strange, cold clench. Already she sensed what was coming.

'He picked up Pete from your house,' Cindy quavered. 'I know your mum said no, but she's been away and Tom and Pete thought… Anyway, they were in the car together and Tom's okay but Pete was thrown out and he's down the river bank and Tom can't reach him.'

'Dr Blake?'

Miss Harriet Ford answered the phone and handed it to Blake with all the solemnity of a well-paid secretary. Blake took it and another elderly lady was on the other end.

'Dr Blake, this is Rose Chibnell,' the lady said, primly but urgently. 'Maggie's asked me to try and contact you. There's been a motorcar accident at the junction where the river turns north and the road twists away from it. It's Tom Blayne's car.'

He already knew who Tom Blayne was. It was amazing how many of the valley people he was getting to know.

'Is he hurt?'

'That's why Maggie needs you,' Rose said. 'She doesn't know. At least, she knows Tom's okay, but it seems her brother, Pete, was in the car with him. He was thrown out and Tom can't reach him. Tom thought he heard him groaning but he's too far down the river bank for him to see. Do you want me to call the medivac helicopter? I can ask for it to be put on standby.'

'Yes,' he snapped. 'Please. Now.'

And then he turned and looked at two astonished spinsters who didn't have jaundice, much less liver cancer.

'How are you at babysitting?' he demanded, and handed over Ruby before they could reply. 'Thank you,' he said, and went.

Tom was slumped on the roadside, by the steepest incline down to the river in the valley, and Maggie could see at a glance what had happened.

The edge of the road was sodden. Tom had come round the bend too fast and hit the verge. The verge had started to crumble, he'd swerved, overcorrected, hit the bank with the far side of the car, flipped it and rolled.

He was very lucky the car hadn't gone right over.

Maggie wasn't thinking luck, though. She was thinking... Pete.

She was out of the car, bending over Tom, shaking his shoulder. His eyes looked glazed. Shocked. He wasn't a bad kid. Just stupid.

He was bleeding from a cut above his eye but it was shallow, bleeding sluggishly. It was enough to look dramatic but not enough to distract her from her urgent questioning.

'Tom, are you hurt? Apart from your eye?'

'N-no.' He was staring downwards with horror. She glanced down and her heart lurched.

This was no small landslip. The road had given a little, but a little had become a lot as it had slipped downwards. She saw a swathe of fresh, tumbled mud.

'Pete...'

'There's no seat belt on the passenger side,' he muttered. 'It broke last month. Dad was s'posed to fix it. Pete fell out.'

'Pete's down there?' She'd forgotten to breathe. She'd forgotten everything.

'I can't get down. I tried and the mud moves. I heard him groan at the start but not any more. I can't... You reckon he's dead?'

Dear God.

She stared again at the mud. She cupped her hands and yelled, louder than she'd ever yelled before.

'Pete!'

No answer—but the river was roaring beneath them.

Oh, God, how far had he slipped? How much mud was there? Where…?

Tom was weeping, wringing his hands. She grabbed his shoulders and forced him to look at her.

'I need your help,' she said. 'You know the local numbers. Ring Mrs Mayes, or if you can't get her ring Ted Barnes or Fred Halliday. Tell them I want the emergency chopper with paramedics, and I want tractors and I want as many men as you can get, as fast as they can possibly get them here. And I want them to find Dr Samford. Do you have that, Tom?'

'I… Yes.'

'Ring, fast. Ring everybody. I'm going down.'

'You can't.'

'I'll go down at the edge of the slide,' she snapped. 'I don't have a choice. Phone, now.'

Clambering down a sodden cliff face beside a mass of tumbled mud and debris was easier said than done. It was appallingly difficult.

She had no choice.

She called as she climbed but she felt…hopeless.

There was too much mud. If Pete had been thrown as the mud had slid he could be buried. He could have been pushed into the river.

She was weeping and climbing and yelling—and the bank was too steep. The rocks were giving under her feet.

Slow down, she told herself. You're no use to anyone if you kill yourself—but her feet wouldn't obey.

Dear God, where was he?

The cliff was getting steeper. She pushed herself harder, clambering, clinging, calling.

She paused on a tiny ledge, forcing herself to take a second to work out the best way to proceed, to look down, search…

And she saw him—well, his blue hoodie… He was a kid, sprawled among the rocks and mud by the river bank.

Not buried.

'Pete,' she screamed, and he raised his arm in a feeble wave.

Not dead. Not dead.

She choked back a sob and stepped off her ledge, heading straight for him.

The ground gave way under her.

She lurched and flailed for something to hold onto.

Everything was moving. She was sliding…the whole world was sliding.

'Pete,' she yelled again, uselessly, and then even more uselessly, 'Blake…'

And then a rock rose up to meet her and there was nothing.

Blake hadn't known he could drive so fast. He hadn't known he could be so afraid.

He hauled his car to a halt beside Maggie's, beside Tom's upturned wreck, and he was beside the shaking Tom almost before the car stopped.

'Maggie?'

'Pete's down there somewhere,' Tom said, pointing uselessly downward. Sobbing. 'An' Maggie went after him. Only then the rocks fell and I heard Maggie scream and there's been nothing since.'

CHAPTER TEN

MAGGIE woke up to whiteness—and to the worst headache she'd ever known.

It was blowing her head away. It was making her feel…

A bowl was right where she needed it, strong hands were holding her steady, and there was a voice…

'It's okay, love. It'll pass soon. We've got you safe. We're getting you stronger pain relief.'

Blake.

She was too weak to ask questions. She was too busy concentrating on the dictates of her stomach, but between spasms…

Blake?

White. Blake. Alive.

The spasms eased. The bowl was removed and Blake's hands, strong and gentle at the same time, guided her back to the pillows. Someone in green…someone at the periphery of her vision…was giving her an injection.

She got that. One arm was having an injection. Blake had the other. It was Blake's hand.

What…? What…?

'Pete…' Somehow she managed to whisper it, but inside the word was a scream.

'Pete's copped a broken leg and a dislocated shoulder,'

Blake told her. 'He's had surgery and he's in the next ward. He's fine.'

In the next ward. It was so hard thinking through the fuzz. Ward. Hospital.

Blake.

Kids.

Panic.

'I have to go home.'

'You don't have to go anywhere,' he said gently. 'Ronnie's at home with the kids. They're ringing in every hour to see how you are. They all send their love. They're fine, my love. Close your eyes until the pain eases.'

It was good advice, she decided. It was advice she needed to take. The pain in her head...

She lay back and let the pain take her. She gave in to it, rode it, figured she could live with it if only she stayed absolutely still and didn't let the light in.

'Her pulse is settling,' someone said from a long way away. 'Are you sure about transfer?'

'We can do without it.' That was Blake again. 'Ross concurs. The pressure's not building and she's conscious. She'll want to stay home.'

Home.

Blake.

Kids.

He'd answered all her questions.

His hand was still holding hers and she wasn't letting go. It was helping her ride the pain. She held onto his hand, and it helped.

The waves were receding a bit. A lot? A fog was taking its place—infinitely preferable. She drifted into it, but she still didn't let go of that hand.

'Let yourself sleep,' Blake said, and his voice was right

by her ear. She could feel him breathing. She could feel the
faint rasp of stubble of his face against hers.

Blake. Here. Good.

Why?

'What…?'

'You hit your head,' he told her. 'Hard. We had to drill a
wee hole to ease the pressure.'

'Dr Samford did,' another voice said. A woman. She dared
a glimpse and saw the green again as the voice went on. 'He
operated on you, down in all that mud and slush. Relieved
the pressure before it killed you. How he ever managed it…
It doesn't bear thinking about. Everyone's talking about it.
Maggie, you're so lucky.'

It was Mary, Maggie thought. With the pain receding it
was easier—but not as easy as all that—to think. To figure
things out. To realise she knew this voice in green. It was
Mary Walford, Theatre Nurse at Corella Base Hospital

Falling. Pete.

Drill a wee hole…

Pressure.

'A…a cranial burr-hole?' Her voice was hardly a whisper

'A beautiful, successful drill. Ross Myers helped clean i
up when we got you here,' Mary said. 'But Blake did the ur
gent stuff. He's quite some hero. Now sleep, Maggie, love.'

'Blake…'

'I'm going nowhere,' Blake said, in a voice that was so un
steady she hardly recognised it. His hold on her hand didn'
ease one bit. 'Sleep as long as you like. I'll be here when yo
wake up.'

She slept and woke and slept and woke and every time she
woke he was with her. He seemed to be drifting in and ou
of her fog. Holding her. Telling things were okay. His hand

was her link to reality. Otherwise she'd float, she thought. Disappear.

Every now and then the pain would rise and she'd need that hand even more. Then there'd be a growl from Blake and movement and people and the fog would descend again.

And his hand kept right on holding her. Stopping her disappearing into the whiteness.

He was her one reality, she thought with the only vestige of reality she had left to her. Blake.

'Sleep,' he kept saying whenever she stirred, whenever things started crowding in. 'There's nothing to worry about. There's nothing to do, my Maggie, except sleep.'

And finally, finally, the fog receded and she woke up. She could hardly explain it. One minute the fog was all-enveloping; the next she was opening her eyes and the fog was gone. The sun was shining on the white coverlet.

Blake was asleep in the chair beside her.

He looked appalling. He looked battle worn, unshaved, gaunt, exhausted. He looked like he should be in this bed instead of her.

His hand still held hers.

She looked down at it, at the lean, long fingers, at the strength, at the link.

She glanced out the window and saw sunshine. Water glistening—the river beyond. No rain.

She turned again to look at that hand, and Blake was wide awake and watching her.

'Good morning, sleepyhead,' he said, and smiled, but his smile was different from any smile she'd ever seen. A warrior after battle. A warrior who'd been too close...

'Sleepyhead yourself,' she whispered. 'You're the one who was sleeping.' She glanced out the window again. 'It's morning.'

'It is.'

'I've been in here all night?'

'You've been in here for two days and three nights,' he said, and waited for that to sink in.

There was a bandage on her head. She put a hand up and touched it. Felt the lack of hair.

'We had to cut it,' he said ruefully. 'I was in a bit of a hurry and I'm not much at hairdressing. When the bandages come off we'll find you a stylist.'

'I'll be punk for a while?'

'Maybe you will,' he agreed. 'Lopsided mohawk. It had to be done. You gave yourself one hell of a bang.'

She lay back on the pillows and thought about it. Blake let her hand go, poured two glasses of water, handed one to her—watched to make sure her shaking hand wasn't about to drop it—and then drank himself. He looked like a man who needed it.

Cranial burr-hole. The words came floating out of the fog. Pressure.

'You operated.'

'I was...lucky,' he said. 'You had a massive haematoma and I could see you slipping, but Tom was driving his dad' farm ute. It had a toolbox in the back containing a drill, plus a set of lovely, new, clean drill bits. All sizes. Tom had his phone. I rang a neurologist mate in Melbourne. Tom held the phone while I drilled. Thankfully it took the pressure off instantly. Exciting, huh?'

And she heard his voice shake. She heard the lingering terror in it.

She'd seen burr-holes drilled with patients in nice, clean theatre settings, and they were so often too late.

Pressure from bleeding on the brain...

She touched the bandage again and she knew how lucky she'd been.

'Thank you,' she said simply, and he sat again and took er hand and held.

'I never knew how much I needed you,' he said simply. Until I thought I was losing you. I've known you for two veeks. I can't possibly need you that much but I do.'

'Blake...' He'd taken her breath away. She lay on the pil->ws and watched his face, and saw raw, naked need. Pain.

'Blake,' she said again, and reached out, and he moved, athering her into his arms, gently, tenderly, holding her as he needed to be held. His heart against hers. Washing away he last of the fog. Just holding.

'I need you to marry me, Maggie,' he whispered, and her vorld stilled.

Marry...

He pulled away at that, and saw her face, and he laughed, raw, jagged laugh that contained pain as well as humour.

'Um...let's recall that,' he said, and she saw he was striv-ng for normality, for a place that didn't encompass the fear e'd faced. 'It's way too soon.'

'I...I can't...' The fog was wisping in again. All she wanted > do was say yes, sink into this man's arms and never let go, ut some vestige of the old Maggie was resurfacing, ringing varning bells, stopping her from take this amazing, irrevers->le leap. 'Blake, I can't...think.'

'No,' he said, and he smiled and then he tugged her back > him and he kissed her, a whisper kiss, light, loving on er lips. And then he propelled her back on the pillows. 'Of ourse you can't. And I can't either, my love. I've hardly slept. ou're full of analgesics. We need to sort ourselves out and nd some sort of normality and go from there.'

He smiled at her then, and it was a smile that made her eart turn over. It was a smile that had her forgetting that her ead was starting to pound again. It was a smile that made er world shift.

'I'll ring for some more pain relief for you,' he said. 'And then I'll go and wash and sleep. But then I'll come back. But I'll keep coming back, my Maggie. For now and for always, and that's a promise.'

He left. She slept and when she woke up he wasn't there. Mar was, fussing in the background, adjusting drips.

'Hi,' she said, and grinned. 'Welcome back to the rea world.'

'Blake?' She couldn't help himself.

'Sent home with a flea in his ear,' she said. 'Ross told hin unless he got out of here he'd get Security to eject him. H didn't want two patients and the man's exhausted. He hardl left you for three days.'

'Three days…'

'Oh, he's gorgeous,' Ronnie said happily. 'And his littl girl… We brought her in here, you know, while you were s sick, because Ronnie knew he was torn. Ross decided anothe helicopter trip was worth it to collect her. She's a darling. Ha the hospital's in love with her. But, oh, Maggie, Blake's won derful. What a wonderful solution. You should see him wit Pete. Pete's been beside himself, so scared for you, and ever time you were deeply asleep Blake'd go to him. We'll whee him in to see you later, but Blake's reassured him completel

'Oh, he's lovely… He can be big brother to your tribe— dad almost—and you can be mum for Ruby. Ross is alread talking to him about part-time work here. Apparently he coul work here two days, and Sydney three days. It's a happy ev after. The whole valley's happy for you, Maggie. It's a happ ever after for everyone.'

It took her a few more days before she felt anywhere ap proaching normal. She had more grazes and scrapes than sl wanted to think about. She had broken ribs. She was bei loaded with antibiotics and care and demands for rest, and she was being told over and over that she was the luckiest woman in the world.

She was.

She lay back on her hospital pillows, she watched the sunbeams on the coverlet, she watched the faces of her scared siblings when they visited—apparently they'd finally managed to set up a barge for river crossings. She listened to Pete's stammering apology, she hugged him, she smiled at Blake, and she watched with love as he played with Ruby on her coverlet.

Then, on the day she was due to leave hospital, she told him she wasn't going to marry him.

He'd come in by himself. The kids had pleaded to be allowed to help bring her home but that'd mean four kids and a baby. Pete's leg was in a cast so he'd need the entire back seat. It was all or none so he decreed none.

He drove to the hospital using the freshly organised barge, set in place until the bridge could be rebuilt. The worst of the bad weather was gone. The river level was dropping every day, only the mass of debris on the banks showing the maelstrom it had been.

Blake wasn't looking at scenery, however. He knew this would be decision day, and he walked into Maggie's room and he knew the moment he saw her face what her answer would be.

'Too soon?' he asked, trying to keep the tone light. Trying to ignore the lurch in the pit of his gut.

She was dressed, ready to leave with him. She was wearing her faded jeans and a loose, oversized windcheater that was easy to take on and off over her bandaged head.

She was still heavily bandaged. The Corella Valley hairdresser had come in and clipped her lovely curls on the un-damaged parts of her scalp back to a boyish, elfin crop.

She looked absurdly young, absurdly vulnerable—and absurdly beautiful. All he wanted to do was gather her into his arms, yet her expression said don't.

'I can't,' she said, and her words were anguished.

'No,' he said. He crossed to the bed where she was sitting and because he couldn't help himself he tilted her chin with his fingers and brushed her lips with his. He wanted—more than anything he'd ever wanted in his life—to gather her into his arms and kiss her as he needed to kiss her, but somehow he held back. Somehow he held to the last vestiges of his self-control.

'I can't marry you,' she whispered.

'That's what I thought you meant.'

'Blake, I'm sorry.'

'Don't be,' he said, still striving for lightness. 'It's your life, Maggie.'

'But it's not my life,' she said, and suddenly she wasn't whispering any more.

He stilled. 'Is that why?' he said slowly. 'Because you're encumbered with the kids, with responsibilities? You know I how much I want to share those.'

'That's just it,' she said bitterly. 'Of course you do.'

She turned and looked out the window. The river was flowing peacefully in the distance. From here they could see the far side of the valley. They could almost see the homestead, filled with kids and dogs and…family.

'It's my dream,' she said.

'Your drink-can dream?'

'Don't laugh.'

'I'm not laughing. I would never laugh at you.'

She turned then and met his gaze straight on. She gazed at him and he didn't falter. He looked back at her, calm and

sure, and he tried to put every ounce of love he felt for this
woman into that gaze.

'I know you wouldn't,' she said at last. 'I know. But it still
is a dream, and if I married you...' She hesitated, touched
the bandages on her head as if they hurt—but maybe it was
something else that was hurting.

'Blake, these last weeks have been...stunning. For both of
us. You've taken responsibility for your sister's baby. You've
been immersed in my family up to your ears. You've been
hauled out of your life as an independent city surgeon, engaged—all right,' she added hastily as she saw his face—
'partnered by a colleague you've been with for years. You've
come back to a place that's filled with emotion for you and
I've thrown more at you. You've saved my brother's life and
you've saved mine.

'That's an awesome amount of emotion to jam into three
weeks. Do you think I should ask you to commit for the rest
of your life on the strength of it? It's been a crazy, roller-
coaster ride, Blake. Now you need to get off the roller-coaster,
settle, figure where you want to take things with Ruby and
go from there.'

'I need you, Maggie,' he said, surely and steadily. 'Yes,
it's only three weeks but when I thought I could lose you...'
He broke off and he knew she could hear the power of what
he'd gone through.

At the base of a cliff. Watching the swelling...

It still made him feel ill, but it wasn't helping his cause.

'I never knew what love was,' he said simply. 'Until I
thought I'd lost you. If love is needing, like needing a part
of me...'

'But I'm not needful, Blake,' she said, calmly and steadily.
'I'm grateful—you can't imagine how grateful I am, but I
won't marry you because I need you. Even if...even if your
need is love. I've fallen for you, hard, but I'm seeing you as

a guy who's taken on his baby niece, who helped me save Christopher and Pete, who saved me. And, yes, who needs me. But that's not a basis for a marriage.'

'No, but love is. Surely the two combine. Maggie, I've thought it out. We could organise things... I could work a couple of days in Sydney a week and spend the rest of the time here. We could fill the house with kids. They could come and go as they pleased, back and forth to your mother, back and forth to us. You'd be there whenever they need you. Ruby would have a mother...'

It was the wrong thing to say. He knew it as he saw her expression change. He had this all wrong.

This was not a sure and loving Maggie. This was still a trapped Maggie.

'I would be,' she whispered. 'Ruby's twisting herself around my heart already. But it's not fair.'

'Fair?'

'My heart's already so twisted,' she said. 'From the time I can first remember. "Maggie, push your brother's pram, he's crying. Maggie, your little sister's wet. Maggie, sleep with Liselle, she's having nightmares. Maggie, you need to stay home from school this week, Donny's got measles." And I did it. Every single time, I did it—how could I not? Because I loved them. I love them. And here you are, asking me to love...more.'

'You don't want...'

'Of course I want,' she said, and she tilted her chin and looked at him—really looked at him. 'I'm falling so hard. If you took me into your arms right now...' But she put up her hands as if to ward him off. 'But I don't want you to.

'Really?

'I don't know,' she said, and she didn't sound sure any more. She sounded...scared. Desolate. 'Blake, I don't know. All I do know is that I'm not game to try. I'd marry you and it'd be gorgeous and the whole valley would be happy for me. The kids would be beside themselves and it'd solve all your problems and I'd end up loving Ruby to bits... And one day I might wake up and think, What did I collect all those tin cans for?'

'We could travel,' he said, slowly, trying to sound confident. Trying to sound like he thought her qualms were minor. 'Together.'

'But I've had...*together*,' she said, and she flinched as she said it. 'I know. That sounds appalling when I say I'm falling in love with you in the same breath, but I've never had anything but together. You've come here for three weeks, you've walked straight into my together and you think it's magic. But you've had, what, thirty-six years of You. I've never had Me and I want it. I want to learn Me.'

She shook her head then, falling silent. He watched her, quiet and still, knowing the time for argument was not now. Knowing that pushing her now would do his cause no good—would even do harm. Knowing he had to let her be.

'Blake, I'm scared,' she whispered. 'I'm terrified I'll wake up in ten years surrounded by more kids and more dogs and more drama, and I'll resent it all and become a bitter old lady who snaps at kids and locks herself in the bathroom and sulks...'

'The bathroom?' he said faintly.

'It's the only place I can ever get away,' she said. 'And even then they bang on the door. "Maggie, hurry up, I need a note for school. Maggie, I need to tell you about my boyfriend. Maggie, if this pimple doesn't go down I'll die." And don't you dare laugh, Blake Samford.'

'I won't laugh. I've told you before, I'd never laugh at you, Maggie.'

'And don't be gorgeous either,' she managed, trying to glare, only her eyes were filling. She swiped away tears with anger and the desire to gather her in his arms was overwhelming. He didn't. He was proud of himself that he didn't, but it nearly killed him.

'So, what,' he said at last. 'Back to the seven-year plan, huh?'

'I... Yes,' she said. 'It's better than nothing.'

'I'm better than nothing.'

'Yes, you are,' she said, controlling herself again. Taking a deep breath and moving on. 'But you deserve something more than a woman who's scared that marriage might seem a trap.'

'I'd never marry you if you felt like that.'

'Well, then,' she said, and rose and looked down at her packed duffel bag. At her hospital room crowded with flowers from almost everyone in the valley. At him.

'Well, then,' she said again. 'It's time to go home. Time for you to go back to Sydney. Time for me to find another place to live.'

'I'm not selling the farm, Maggie.'

'You're not?'

'There's not a thing you can do about that,' he told her. 'I've fallen for the farm as well.'

'You're not...going to live there?'

'No,' he said. 'I wouldn't do that to myself. To live next door to you...'

'You'll take Ruby back to Sydney?'

'Yes.'

'Will you cope?'

'I believe I can,' he said, and managed a grin. 'Without calling on Maggie. But, Maggie...'

'Yes?'

'I'm not moving out of your life. Not entirely. I'm your landlord and I'll need to check the farm out from time to time. As well as that, the kids have done some heart twisting as well. I've promised Pete I'll take him to Sydney and get him some driving lessons as soon as he turns sixteen. I'd like to organise an online tutor for Liselle and her calculus.'

'There's no need—'

'There is a need,' he said softly. 'Just because you can't marry me it doesn't mean I can stop caring.'

'You...understand.'

'Yes, I do,' he said with a heavy heart, and he did. 'I wish I didn't, but I do. I wish... I wish...' He hesitated and then he shrugged. 'I'm not sure what I wish,' he told her, and he lifted her duffel with one hand and took her hand in the other. 'But let's take you home, and let's get on with our lives while I figure it out.'

CHAPTER ELEVEN

CHRISTMAS at the Tildens' was always crazy. Everyone was home, and the tiny house was bursting at the seams.

'Let's have Christmas at Blake's,' Liselle had pleaded. 'It's huge and Blake won't mind.'

He wouldn't mind, Maggie thought. He'd been a constant presence in the kids' lives for six months now and they regarded him more as a benevolent uncle than as Maggie's landlord.

He'd only visited twice, flying visits to install a new farm manager—Harold was too old and Blake didn't want Maggie responsible for his cattle—and to check for himself that Pete's leg was healing as he thought it should.

They'd been fast trips and he hadn't brought Ruby. 'I have a fabulous housekeeper-nanny,' he told Maggie. 'And I've given up the job as Head of Orthopaedics. I'm an Indian rather than a chief now, but it means I spend more time with my little girl.'

He'd brought photographs and he showed them to her with pride, but he made no mention of marriage, no mention that he wasn't coping without her, no mention that she'd made the wrong decision.

She hadn't, she told herself over and over, but the kids had his number on speed dial, she heard them chatting to him about trivial stuff, and she felt...jealous?

Ridiculous.

But he was a friend. The boys took their troubles to Blake now, and for that she was grateful.

Liselle got first-class honours in her calculus. 'Blake thinks I can be a doctor,' she'd told Maggie, almost bursting with pride. 'He's going to help me.'

Somehow he'd inveigled himself into their lives and she loved him for it.

But not enough?

Not enough to want Christmas at his house. Not enough to think she'd made a mistake.

Now she woke up on Christmas morning and for about the thousandth time since he'd left she thought of him straight away.

She was back at her mother's house. She was sharing a bed with Susie. Liselle was in the bed beside them. Blackie and Tip were under the bed. All her brothers and sisters were home.

She was surrounded, just like always. Any minute now she'd get up and stuff the turkey. Her mother would waft out for present giving and set up candles on the table or make a new cocktail. Her father might drop in later with the pregnant Sashabelle. Expecting gifts. Not giving any.

But things were easing. Donny had finished his apprenticeship and Nickie had graduated and was choosing between three excellent job offers. Two down, six to go.

Six years left?

To what? Kir on the Left Bank of Paris.

It was losing its gloss.

I'm turning sour already, she thought, and decided, Turkey. She tossed back the covers—and paused.

She'd heard a truck approaching—or trucks? They stopped, just outside the house.

As her feet touched the bare wooden floor there was an enormous whine, like the tray on a truck heaving upwards…

And then a crash that had her jumping out of her skin. That had Liselle and Susie sitting bolt upright in bed and the dogs going out of their minds.

Another crash, bigger than the first.

Amazingly Susie was giggling, whooping, heading for the door. And then she looked back as if she'd forgotten something important. She grabbed an envelope from under the pillow.

'Blake said to give you this,' she said importantly. 'But I have to get mine to put on top.' She dived under the bed and hauled out a huge plastic bag filled with…cans. Empty drink cans.

'And me,' Liselle said sleepily. 'Mine are in the wardrobe. Open it, Susie, love.'

Susie obligingly opened the wardrobe—and let loose a cascade of cans.

'They're from the whole of Corella Valley High,' Louise said proudly. 'Six months' collecting.'

The door opened. The rest of her family was crowding in the doorway.

'Here's ours,' they told her, and they were practically buried in cans.

'What…? What…?'

'I've got some, too.' It was her mother, holding two small bags of cans like they were diamonds. 'I had to change drinking bottled tonic to canned tonic, just for you, love. But it was worth it. You're a good girl, Maggie.'

'But it's mostly from Blake. It's Blake's present.' Christopher was practically bouncing with excitement. 'Come and see, come and see, come and see.'

So she went, pushing through a sea of cans, still clutching her unopened envelope.

Peter had the front door wide, and his beam was almost wider. 'How cool is this?' he demanded. 'Blake says these are from the whole of Sydney Central Hospital for six months. And it's every single person in the valley. And Donny's garage and our school and university, and Blake says we have enough for at least six months...'

'Shush,' Susie said, bossy and exasperated. 'She hasn't read the letter.'

She wasn't looking at the letter. She was looking at a mountain. Cans, cans and more cans. The entire yard was buried under drink cans.

'Two shipping containers,' Pete said, awed. 'Two full shipping containers, plus what we've got. You have no idea, Maggie...'

'Blake...' she breathed.

'Read the letter,' Susie demanded, and finally the little girl lost patience with her big sister, ripped it open, stood in front of her and read out loud.

'"Darling Maggie...". Oooer, darling...'

'Cut it out,' Louise snapped. 'Read it like it is.'

Susie glowered and then grinned and read.

'"Darling Maggie. Seven years is too long. Anything could happen in seven years. They could stop serving kir on the Left Bank. The pyramids might erode. I could wear out waiting. So here's an alternative. We've weighed our cans and we figure they're good for six months' travel. On your own. With what you already have, plus the extras the kids have found since we weighed them, we reckon you can go and see whatever you want in the world. But before you start objecting, you need to listen to the rest of the plan..."'

'I don't need to read this,' Susie said. 'I know.'

'Blake's taking six months' leave,' Liselle said. 'It's paternity leave 'cos he's formally adopting Ruby.'

'And he's staying at Corella View,' Pete said. 'And he's going to teach me cool driving stuff.'

'And we can stay here with Mum or we can stay with him if Mum gets sick of us,' Chris added, with a sideways glance at his mother.

'And Ronnie's promised to look after Ruby if Blake starts feeling…house…house…'

'Housebound,' Louise finished for her. 'But us older ones are planning on coming home often as well. You've done so much for us, Maggie.'

'And Blake and Ronnie have organised you time off work,' Pete added.

'And Blake says he can get you a passport really fast. He says you should go to Africa first 'cos it'll be cold in Europe in winter. But he says it's up to you.'

'Blake…' she managed again.

'A million cans,' her mother said. 'All over my front lawn. I'll give him such a talking to when I see him next.'

'Which would be now,' a low voice said, and she whirled and it was Blake. He was standing on the veranda. Watching. Listening.

He was dressed even more casually than the day she'd first seen him. Faded jeans. A checked, open-necked shirt. Boots. He looked like a farmer rather than a city surgeon.

He was holding Ruby.

Cattleman with baby?

He looked so sexy he made her toes curl.

'You're free,' he said, softly, firmly, lovingly. 'Maggie Tilden, your seven-year plan just turned into now. We've all done it. We love you, Maggie, and we're sending you away.'

'But you'll come back?' Susie asked, suddenly anxious. 'Maggie, you won't forget us? You'll come home?'

Blake was smiling at her. Smiling and smiling. Her heart

was turning somersaults, backward flips, any gymnastic manoeuvre it could think of. All at once.

She wished she wasn't wearing pyjamas. She wished she wasn't surrounded by family. She wished she wasn't surrounded by thousands of tin cans.

No, she didn't. She wished for none of those things because for now, for this moment, there was only this man, only this moment, this smile.

Blake.

'You did all this,' she managed.

'Six months' scrounging,' he said, and chuckled. 'I owe favours to every janitor in Sydney.'

'The kids...'

'Scrounged like champions. See, we all want to get rid of you. Mostly because we figure...if we set you free, you'll fly home.'

'Like a pigeon.'

'I prefer dove,' he said comfortably. 'A lovely, loving white dove. Liselle, do you think you might take Ruby for a moment? I can't see any mistletoe but I'm sure there's some around here somewhere. I need to kiss your sister goodbye.'

'Goodbye...'

'With no promises,' he said, as he headed along the veranda to where she was standing, barefooted in her pyjamas, tousled with sleep. As he gathered her into his arms and held her. Just held her. Asking for no promises. Placing no expectations on her.

'We're giving you yourself back, Maggie, love,' he told her. 'We're giving you the world in the shape of a mountain of tin cans. And if you can see your way to steering this way at the end of your adventures...'

'Kiss her now,' Donny yelled. 'Go on, mate, get it over with.'

'No pressure,' Blake said, and his dark eyes gleamed down

into hers. 'No pressure, Maggie, love, but if you could possibly tilt your chin…'

She did. How could a girl not?

How could a woman not kiss a man who was giving her the world?

Who wasn't asking her to marry him.

Who was setting her free.

She watched giraffes sway majestically across the African savannah. She woke under canvas and in the dawn she heard lions roaring. She had to shoo monkeys from her breakfast. She wrote to Blake about it.

He sent photos back of Ruby and told her how his work was going and talked to her about a new breed of cattle he thought he might introduce to the farm.

She took camel rides around the pyramids. A kid photographed her for money and she emailed the snap home.

Blake sent a snap of himself riding a horse he'd bought. It seemed Liselle was teaching him how to ride.

She watched funeral pyres beside the Ganges and wondered how she could describe the smell, the sights to Blake. She wandered from street stall to street stall and she didn't get sick once. Blake sounded almost irritated. 'Everyone gets sick—what's your stomach made of?'

He sent advice on hygiene and links to sites on intestinal worms. She laughed but he also sent a picture of him at a staff dinner at Corella Hospital and she looked at Mary standing beside him and she thought…she thought…

No. She wouldn't think. She was free.

She walked the Great Wall in China—okay, not all of it but enough to get sore feet—and she gazed at the hidden warriors with awe and gratitude that she could be in this place at this time.

Blake had seen them, too. She wished…

No, she couldn't wish, for who could wish for more than she'd dreamed of?

She drank Guinness in fabulous Irish pubs. She checked out some ancestors and decided she liked being a little bit Irish.

Blake told her about how Mary had been to Ireland last year and researched all her Irish ancestors.

She was interested—sort of. She liked Mary. Mary was a friend.

Why the niggle?

She dived from a caique into the turquoise waters off a Greek isle. She got sunburned, but she didn't tell Blake because he'd lecture her and she liked being free to get sunburned or not. Didn't she?

She wandered the bazaars in Istanbul, Cairo, Morocco. She looked, she tasted, she smelled and she listened. She drank kir on the Left Bank in Paris. She looked and looked and looked and she felt and felt and felt.

And she tried not to wish for more.

Every night she went back to her hotel room or her tent or yurt, or whatever weird and wonderful place she was staying in and she used the fantastic satellite internet Blake had organised for her and she contacted home.

She told the kids what she'd done that day. Sometimes they were interested. Mostly they were more interested in telling her the things that were happening to them.

And almost every night she talked to Blake, who was interested in her. Who asked the right questions. Who got it that she'd been disappointed in kir. Who grinned when she said the Eiffel tower was just too high and she'd taken the lift. Who agreed that seal colonies stank.

Who showed her pictures of a happy, bouncing, healing Ruby with pride, who explained that her legs were almost in line now, and she was sitting up, and teething. Who talked about the valley with love and with pride. Who spoke of the people he was meeting, of Ronnie, who was awesome at helping, and Mary, who was such a friend…

He smiled at her and said goodnight—even when it was morning his time—and he sent her to sleep happy. Or happyish. For the longer she was away, the more she thought. She was living a dream but what if, in following her dream, she was letting another go?

What if she'd made a mistake?

She hadn't. She knew she'd made the right decision. She loved what she was doing and she embraced it with all her heart, but the heart swelled to fit all comers and there was a corner…a Blake corner…

Please, her heart whispered. Please…

And six months later she walked through the customs gates at Sydney airport, feeling jet-lagged, feeling weird, feeling hopeful but almost afraid to hope…

Blake was there.

All by himself.

No kids. No Ruby.

No Mary.

Just Blake.

'My love,' he said as she reached him, and he held out his arms.

She walked right into them. He folded her against his heart, and she stayed there for a very long time.

He'd organised things so Ronnie was with Ruby, so they had the night in Sydney to themselves.

He took her back to his new little bachelor-nursery pad near the hospital and he made her dinner while she spent half an hour under streaming-hot water and washed every part of her. She dressed in jogging pants and a windcheater because she had nothing else clean. Most of her luggage was still in the back of Blake's car, ready to be taken to Corella Valley the next day. She'd kept only her overnight bag. She should have kept something special aside, she thought ruefully. A little black dress?

A sexy negligee?

But she walked out of the bathroom and Blake was stirring something at the stove. He was wearing jeans and an apron. He turned and smiled at her and his smile said it didn't matter one whit what she was wearing. She could be wearing nothing.

She loved this man with all her heart. She'd loved this man around the world and back again—and she'd come home.

'Will you marry me now?' he asked, and her world stood still.

'I think I might just have stuffed that,' he said ruefully as the silence stretched on. 'Patience is not my strong suit. I thought…dinner. Champagne. Something romantic playing in the background. It's just… I look at you and I can't…'

He stopped. He took off his apron. He took the eight steps that separated them and took her hands in his.

'I got it wrong,' he told her. 'I've had months to think about it, almost a year, and I know exactly how I got it wrong. I told you I needed you. Maybe I do; maybe that's part of the equation, but it's not the main thing here. The main thing, the huge, overriding elephant in the room, or more than elephant if I can think of anything bigger, is that I love you, Maggie Tilden. I've loved you since the first moment I saw you. So…can you cope without the violins and roses? Can we look past the need? Can you forget that I ever needed you and can you just love me?'

And how was a woman to answer that?

With an open heart.

'I…I always have,' she whispered. And then, more firmly, because the joy in her heart was settling, fitting into all the edges with a sweetness that made the path ahead seem sure and true and right, 'My love, I always will.'

And they looked at each other, just looked, and something passed between them, so sweet, so strong that Maggie knew a bond was forged right then that would last for ever.

'I'm not asking you to be mother to Ruby,' he said. 'I've organised—'

'Hush,' she told him, and she placed her finger on his lips. 'I'm not asking you to be a brother to my siblings either, but I have a feeling you already are. And Ruby's as much mine as yours. If you're willing to share.'

'Maggie, to ask you to take us on…'

'I don't think it's taking on,' she managed. 'It's loving. It's different.'

'Six months ago…'

'I wasn't where I am now,' she said, steadily, lovingly, because she'd had six months to think this through and every night as she'd talked to Blake she'd become more and more sure of where her heart lay.

'I've been surrounded by love since I was born. Trapped by it, in a sense. What you've done for me, Blake…you've set me free so I can choose love. I've had six wonderful months of being by myself, but I wasn't by myself. I had the kids in the background. I had Ruby. I had Corella Valley. They were my rock, my base, my knowledge that of all the places in the world, there was a place for me. But most of all there was you. My one true thing. My love.'

'Maggie…' He held her, tenderly though, as if she was fragile. As if she might evaporate. As if she might still gather her things and head out that door, back to the world. 'Maggie, are you sure?'

'I've never been more sure,' she whispered.

'I've organised it. I've cut back, hard. I'm a part-time doc tor until Ruby reaches school age. She's my responsibility, Maggie, not yours.'

'I'll be a part-time nurse, too,' she said comfortably. 'If you don't mind sharing.'

'Maggie…'

She pulled back and looked at him—really looked at him. Needing him to see the whole package. 'I still need to stay in Corella Valley,' she said.

'Of course you do,' he said. 'Just lucky there's a fabulous homestead and enough work for both of us. I'm getting on brilliantly with the hospital staff—they've called on me already, and you should see the new bridge!'

'You'd stay there?'

'The Valley needs an orthopaedic surgeon. It also needs a fabulous district nurse-cum-midwife. How lucky's that?'

'Lucky?' she whispered. 'Or meant?'

'I guess meant,' he said as he tilted her chin and gazed into her eyes. 'Maggie, I've loved you to the ends of the earth and back and I always will, but now will you come home with me?'

'I… Something's burning on the stove.' How had she noticed that when all she could feel was him?

'Maggie…'

'Yes, I will,' she said, positively, absolutely, and she wrapped her arms around this man she loved with all her heart. Who cared if the apartment burned—this was more important. 'I may travel again but it'll take ages to collect enough cans. Double this time because wherever I go, you go. Plus Ruby. Plus whoever else needs us.'

'That's a lot of can collecting,' he said unsteadily. 'I wonder if champagne bottles count.'

'I'm sure they do.' The smell was getting stronger. Maybe she could be practical Maggie for a moment. 'Blake, the dinner…'

'I s'pose,' he said, and sighed dramatically and swept her up into his arms and held her close. Two strides took him to the cooker and the gas was turned off.

'Disaster averted,' he told her. 'But I'm not thinking dinner right now.' He was carrying her towards the bedroom, laughing down at her, loving her with his eyes. 'So, Maggie Tilden, love of my life, woman of my dreams, will you marry me? Will you take me on as well as all the other wonderful loves you hold in your heart?'

'You're the biggest,' she said, and she smiled back at him. She smiled and smiled, at this lovely, sexy, toe-curlingly gorgeous man who promised to be a part of her life for ever. 'You're the biggest and the best, and you're my for-ever love. Of course I'll marry you.'

And then they reached the bedroom and there was nothing else to say.

Two people were one.

They were Maggie and Blake, and they were starting their whole life together.

And in Corella Valley...

'I've got two hundred and three,' Susie announced, looking at her pile of cans with satisfaction.

'I'm up to four hundred and sixty,' Chris crowed. 'And Liselle says her dorm's up to a thousand. How many do you reckon before we can all go?'

'I'm guessing trillions but we can do it. Maggie'll be so happy.'

'Maggie *and* Blake,' Chris corrected her. 'But you're right. Gee, it's going to take a lot of cans for all of us.'

'We've got time,' Susie said in satisfaction. 'If we just keep collecting and collecting we'll be able to do anything we want. Do you reckon they'll mind that we've filled Maggie's bedroom with cans as a homecoming present?'

'Nah,' Chris said. 'They've got loads of bedrooms. I reckon they'll only want one from now on.'

'Really?'

'Yeah,' Chris said with thirteen-year-old wisdom. 'I think Maggie's given up being alone.'

* * * * *

UNLOCKING HER
SURGEON'S HEART

FIONA LOWE

To my fellow Mills & Boon Medical authors.
You're all amazing and talented women.
Thank you for the support, the laughs and the
fun times when we were lucky enough to
meet in person.

CHAPTER ONE

'WANT TO CLOSE?'

Noah Jackson, senior surgical registrar at the Melbourne Victoria Hospital, smiled behind his mask as he watched the answer to his question glow in the eyes of his surgical intern.

'Do I support The Westies?' Rick Stewart quipped, his eyes alight with enthusiasm. His loyalty to the struggling Australian Rules football team was legendary amongst the staff, who teased him mercilessly.

'For Mrs Levatti's sake, you need to close better than your team plays,' Noah said, knowing full well Rick was more than capable.

There'd be no way he'd allow him to stitch up his patient unless he was three levels above competent. The guy reminded him of himself back in the day when he'd been an intern—keen, driven and determined to succeed.

'Thanks, team.' Noah stepped back from the operating table and stripped off his gloves, his mind already a long way from work. 'It's been a huge week and I've got the weekend off.'

'Lucky bastard,' muttered Ed Yang, the anaesthetist. 'I'm on call for the entire weekend.'

Noah had little sympathy. 'It's my first weekend off in over a month and I'm starting it at the Rooftop with one of their boutique beers.'

'I might see you there later,' Lizzy said casually.

The scout nurse's come-hither green eyes sparkled at him, reminding him of a previous good time together. 'Everyone's welcome,' he added, not wanting to tie himself down to anyone or anything. 'I'll be there until late.'

He strode out and headed purposefully towards the change rooms, savouring freedom. Anticipation bubbled in him as he thought about his hard-earned weekend of sleeping in, cycling along the Yarra, catching a game at the MCG, eating at his favourite café, and finally seeing the French film everyone was talking about. God, he loved Melbourne in the spring and everything that it offered.

'Noah.'

The familiar deep voice behind him made him reluctantly slow and he turned to face the distinguished man the nursing staff called the silver fox.

'You got a minute?' Daniel Serpell asked.

No. But that wasn't a word an intern or registrar ever said to the chief of surgery. 'Sure.'

The older man nodded slowly. 'Great job on that lacerated liver on Tuesday. Impressive.'

The unexpected praise from the hard taskmaster made Noah want to punch the air. 'Thanks. It was touch and go for a bit and we almost put the blood bank into deficit but we won.'

'No one in this hospital has any doubt about your surgical abilities, Noah.'

Something about the way his boss hit the word *sur-gical* made Noah uneasy. 'That's a good thing, right?'

'There are nine areas of competency to satisfy the Royal Australasian College of Surgeons.'

Noah was familiar with every single one of them now that his final surgical exams were only a few months away. 'Got them all covered, Prof.'

'You might think that, Noah, but others don't agree.' He reached inside his jacket and produced a white en-velope with Noah's name printed on it.

'What's this?'

'Your solution to competency number two.'

'I don't follow.'

The prof sighed. 'Noah, I can't fault you on techni-cal skills and I'd trust you to operate on me, my wife and my family. You're talented with your patients when they're asleep but we've had complaints from your dealings with them when they're awake.' He cleared his throat. 'We've also had complaints from staff.'

Noah's gut clenched so tight it burned and the enve-lope in his hand suddenly developed a crushing weight. 'Is this an official warning?'

'No, not at all,' the prof said genially. 'I'm on your side and this is the solution to your problem.'

'I didn't know I had a problem,' he said, not able to hide his defensiveness.

The professor raised a brow. 'And after this, I hope you won't have one either.'

'You're sending me on a communications course?' The idea of sitting around in a circle with a group of strangers and talking about feelings appalled him.

'Everything you need to know is in the envelope. Just make sure you're ready to start at eight o'clock on

Monday morning.' He clapped a hand on Noah's shoulder. 'Enjoy your weekend off.'

As his boss walked away, Noah's anxiety ramped up ten notches and the pristine, white envelope now ticked like an unexploded bomb. Not wanting to read it in public, he walked quickly to the doctors' lounge, thankfully finding it empty. He ripped open the envelope and scanned the brief letter.

Dear Dr Jackson
Your four-week rotation at the Turraburra Medical Clinic commences on Monday, August 17th at eight a.m. Accommodation, if required, is provided at the doctor's flat located on Nautalis Parade. Collect the key from the real estate agent in Williams Street before noon, Saturday. See the enclosed map and tourist information, which we hope will be of assistance to you.

Enjoy your rotation in Turraburra—the sapphire of South Gippsland.
Nancy Beveridge
Surgical Trainee Placement Officer.

No. No way. Noah's intake of breath was so sharp it made him cough. This could *not* be happening. They couldn't do this to him. Not now. Suddenly, the idea of a communications course seemed positively fun.

Relax. You must have read it wrong. Fighting the red heat of rage that was frantically duelling with disbelief, he slowly reread the letter, desperately hoping he'd misunderstood its message. As his eyes scrolled left to right and he slowed his mind down to read each and every word, it made no difference. The grim message the black and white letters told didn't change.

He was being exiled—sent rural—and the timing couldn't be worse. In fact, it totally sucked. Big time. He had less than six months before he sat his final surgical examinations and now more than ever his place was at the Victoria. He should be here, doing cutting-edge surgery, observing the latest technology, attending tutorials and studying. Always studying. He should *not* be stuck in a country clinic day in, day out, listening to the ramblings of patients with chronic health issues that surgery couldn't solve.

General practice. A shudder ran through him at the thought. There was a reason he'd aimed high and fought for his hard-earned place in the surgical programme, and a large part of it was to avoid the mundane routine of being a GP. He had no desire at all to have a long and ongoing connection with patients or get to know their families or be introduced to their dogs. This was blatantly unfair. Why the hell had he been singled out? Damn it, none of the other surgical registrars had been asked to do this.

A vague memory of Oliver Evans bawling him out months ago flickered across his mind but surely that had nothing to do with this. Consultants yelled at registrars from time to time—usually during moments of high stress when the odds were stacked against them and everyone was battling to save a patient's life. Heated words were exchanged, a lot of swearing went down but at the end of the day it was forgotten and all was forgiven. It was all part of the cut and thrust of hospital life.

Logic immediately penetrated his incredulity. The

prof had asked him to teach a workshop to the new interns in less than two weeks so this Turraburra couldn't be too far away from downtown Melbourne. Maybe he was just being sent to the growth corridor—the far-flung edges of the ever-growing city, the outer, outer 'burbs. That wouldn't be too bad. A bit of commuting wouldn't kill him and he could listen to his training podcasts on the drive there and back each day.

Feeling more positive, he squinted at the dot on the map.

His expletive rent the air, staining it blue. He'd been banished to the back of beyond.

Lilia Cartwright, never Lil and always Lily to her friends, stood on a whitewashed dock in the ever-brightening, early morning light. She stared out towards the horizon, welcoming the sting of salt against her cheeks, the wind in her hair, and she smiled. 'New day, Chippy,' she said to her tan and white greyhound who stared up at her with enormous, brown, soulful eyes. 'Come on, mate, look a bit more excited. After this walk, you'll have another day ahead of you of lazing about and being cuddled.'

Chippy tugged on his leash as he did every morning when they stood on the dock, always anxious to get back indoors. Back to safety.

Lily loved the outdoors but she understood only too well Chippy's need for safe places. Given his experiences during the first two years of his life, she didn't begrudge him one little bit, but she was starting to think she might need a second dog to go running with to keep fit. Walking with Chippy hardly constituted exercise because she never broke a sweat.

Turning away from the aquamarine sea, she walked towards the Turraburra Medical Centre. In the grounds of the small bush nursing hospital and nursing home, the glorious bluestone building had started life a hundred and thirty years ago as the original doctor's house. Now, fully restored, it was a modern clinic. She particularly loved her annexe—the midwifery clinic and birth centre. Although it was part of the medical centre, it had a separate entrance so her healthy, pregnant clients didn't have to sit in a waiting room full of coughing and hacking sick people. It had been one of the best days of her career when the Melbourne Midwifery Clinic had responded to her grant application and incorporated Turraburra into their outreach programme for rural and isolated women.

The clinic was her baby and she'd taken a lot of time and effort in choosing the soothing, pastel paint and the welcoming décor. She wanted it to feel less like a sterile clinic and far more like visiting someone's home. In a way, given that she'd put so much of herself into the project, the pregnant women and their families were visiting her home.

At first glance, the birthing suite looked like a room in a four-star hotel complete with a queen-sized bed, side tables, lounge chairs, television, bar fridge and a roomy bathroom. On closer inspection, though, it had all the important features found in any hospital room. Oxygen, suction and nitrous oxide outlets were discreetly incorporated in the wall whilst other medical equipment was stored in a cupboard that looked like a wardrobe and it was only brought out when required.

The birth centre didn't cater for high-risk pregnancies—those women were referred to Melbourne, where they could receive the high-tech level of care required for a safe, happy and healthy outcome for mother and baby. The Turraburra women who were deemed to be at a low risk of pregnancy and childbirth complications gave birth here, close to their homes and families. For Lily it was an honour to be part of the birth and to bring a new life into the world.

As Turraburra was a small town, it didn't stop there either. In the three years since she'd returned home and taken on the position of the town's midwife, she'd not only delivered a lot of babies, she'd also attended a lot of children's birthday parties. She loved watching the babies grow up and she could hardly believe that those first babies she'd delivered were now close to starting three-year-old kinder. As her involvement with the babies and children was as close as she was ever likely to get to having a family of her own, she treasured it even more.

Lily stepped into the main part of the clinic and automatically said, 'Morning, Karen,' before she realised the receptionist wasn't behind her desk. Karen's absence reminded her that a new doctor was starting today. Sadly, since the retirement of their beloved Dr Jameson two years ago, this wasn't an uncommon occurrence. She remembered the fuss they'd all made of the first new doctor to arrive in town—ever hopeful he'd be staying for years to come—but he'd left after three months. Seven other doctors had followed in a two-year period and all of the staff, including herself, had become a bit blasé about new arrivals. The gloss had long faded from their hope that *this one* might actually stay for the long term and grand welcoming gestures had fallen by the wayside.

Turraburra, like so many rural towns in Australia, lacked a permanent doctor. It did, however, have more than its fair share of overseas and Australian general practitioner trainees as well as numerous medical students. All of them passed through the clinic and hospital on short stays so they could tick their obligatory rural rotation off their list before hot-footing it back to Melbourne or Sydney or any other major capital city.

The cultural identity that to be Australian was to be at one with the bush was a myth. Australia was the most urbanised country in the world and most people wanted to be a stone's throw from a big city and all the conveniences that offered. Lily didn't agree. She loved Turraburra and it would take a major catastrophe for her to ever live in Melbourne again. She still bore the scars from her last attempt.

Some of the doctors who came to Turraburra were brilliant and the town begged them to stay longer, while others were happily farewelled with a collective sigh of relief and a long slug of fortifying beer or wine at the end of their rotation. Lily had been so busy over the weekend, delivering two babies, that she hadn't had time to open the email she'd received late on Friday with the information about 'doctor number nine'. She wondered if nine was going to be Turraburra's lucky number.

Chippy frantically tugged at his leash again. 'Yes, I know, we're here. Hang on a second.' She bent down and slid her hand under his wide silver and indigo decorative collar that one of the patients had made for him. It was elegant and had an air of Russian royalty about it, showing off his long and graceful neck. She released the clip from the leash and with far more enthusiasm than he ever showed on a walk, Chippy raced to his large, padded basket in the waiting room and curled up with a contented sigh.

He was the clinic's companion dog and all the patients from the tiny tots to the ninety-year-olds loved and adored him. He basked in the daily stroking and cuddles and Lily hoped his hours of being cosseted went some way towards healing the pain of his early life at the hands of a disreputable greyhound racer. She stroked his long nose. 'You have fun today and I'll see you tonight.'

Chippy smiled in the way only greyhounds can.

She crossed the waiting room and was collecting her mail from her pigeonhole when she heard, 'What the hell is that thing doing in here?'

She flinched at the raised, curt male voice and knew that Chippy would be shivering in his basket. Clutching her folders to her chest like a shield, she marched back into the waiting room. A tall guy with indecently glossy brown hair stood in the middle of the waiting room.

Two things instantly told her he was from out of town. Number one: she'd never met him. Number two: he was wearing a crisp white shirt with a tie that looked to be silk. It sat at his taut, freshly shaven throat in a wide Windsor knot that fitted perfectly against the collar with no hint of a gap or a glimpse of a top button. The tie was red and it contrasted dramatically with the dark grey pinstriped suit.

No one in Turraburra ever wore a suit unless they were attending a funeral, and even then no man in the district ever looked this neat, tailored, or gorgeous in a suit.

Gorgeous or not, his loud and curt voice had Chippy shrinking into his basket with fear. Her spine stiffened. Working hard at keeping calm and showing no fear, she said quietly, 'I could ask you the same question.'

His chestnut-brown brows arrowed down fast into a dark V, forming a deep crease above the bridge of his nose. He looked taken aback. 'I'm *supposed* to be here.'

She thought she heard him mutter, 'Worse luck,' as he quickly shoved a large hand with neatly trimmed nails out towards her. The abrupt action had every part of her urging her to step back for safety. *Stop it. It's okay.* With great effort she glued her feet to the floor and stayed put but she didn't take her gaze off his wide hand.

'Noah Jackson,' he said briskly. 'Senior surgical registrar at Melbourne Victoria Hospital.'

She instantly recognised his name. She'd rung her friend Ally about him when she'd first heard he was meant to be coming but Ally had felt that there was no way he'd ever come to work at Turraburra. At the time it had made total sense because no surgery was done here anymore, and she'd thought there had just been a mistake. So why was he standing in the clinic waiting room, filling it with his impressive height and breadth?

She realised he was giving her an odd look and his hand was now hovering between them. Slowly, she let her right hand fall from across her chest. 'Lilia Cartwright. Midwife.'

His palm slid against hers—warm and smooth— and then his long, strong fingers gripped the back of her hand. It was a firm, fast, no-nonsense handshake and it was over quickly, but the memory of the pressure lingered on her skin. She didn't want to think about it. Not that it was awful, it was far from that, but the firm pressure of hands on her skin wasn't something she dwelled on. Ever.

She pulled her hand back across her chest and concentrated on why Noah Jackson was there. 'Has the Turraburra hospital board come into some money? Are they reopening the operating theatre?'

His full lips flattened into a grim line. 'I'm not that lucky.'

'Excuse me?'

'I haven't come here as a surgeon.'

His words punched the air with the pop and fizz of barely restrained politeness, which matched his tight expression. Was he upset? Perhaps he'd come to Turraburra for a funeral after all. Her eyes flicked over his suit and, despite not wanting to, she noticed how well it fitted his body. How his trousers highlighted his narrow hips and sat flat against his abdomen. How the tailored jacket emphasised his broad shoulders.

Not safe, Lily. She swallowed and found her voice. 'What have you come as, then?'

He threw out his left arm, gesticulating towards the door. 'I'm this poor excuse of a town's doctor for the next month.'

'No.' The word shot out automatically—deep and disbelieving—driven from her mouth in defence of her beloved town. In defence of the patients.

Turraburra needed a general practitioner, not a surgeon. The character traits required to become a surgeon—a driven personality, arrogance and high self-belief, along with viewing every patient in terms of 'cutting out the problem'—were so far removed from a perfect match for Turraburra that it was laughable. What on earth was going on at the Melbourne Victoria that made them send a surgical registrar to be a locum GP? Heaven help them all.

His shoulders, already square, vibrated with tension and his brown eyes flashed with flecks of gold. 'Believe me, Ms Cartwright,' he said coldly, 'if I had things my way, I wouldn't be seen dead working here, but the powers that be have other plans. Neither of us has a choice.'

His antagonism slammed into her like storm waves pounding against the pier. She acknowledged that she deserved some of his hostility because her heartfelt, shock-driven 'No' had been impolite and unwelcoming. It had unwittingly put in her a position she avoided— that of making men angry. When it came to men in general she worked hard at going through life very much under their radar. The less she was noticed the better, and she certainly didn't actively set out to make them angry.

She sucked in a breath. 'I'm just surprised the Melbourne Victoria's sent a surgeon to us, but, as you so succinctly pointed out, neither of us has a choice.' She forced herself to smile, but it felt tight around the edges. 'Welcome to Turraburra, Dr Jackson.'

He gave a half grunting, half huffing sound and swung his critical gaze back to Chippy. 'Get the dog out of here. It doesn't belong in a medical clinic.'

All her guilt about her own rudeness vanished and along with it her usual protective guard. 'Chippy is the clinic's therapy dog. He stays.'

Noah stared at the tall, willowy woman in front of him whose fingers had a death grip on a set of bright pink folders. Her pale cheeks had two bright spots of colour on them that matched her files and her sky-blue eyes sparked with the silver flash of a fencing foil. He was still smarting from her definite and decisive 'No'. He might not want to work in this godforsaken place but who was she to judge him before he'd even started? 'What the hell is a therapy dog?'

'He provides some normalcy in the clinic,' she said, her tone clipped.

'Normalcy?' He gave a harsh laugh, remembering his mother's struggle to maintain any semblance of a normal life after her diagnosis. Remembering all the hours they'd spent in numerous medical practices' waiting rooms, not dissimilar to this one, seeking a cure that had never come. 'This is a medical clinic. It exists for sick people so there's nothing normal about it. And talking about normal, that dog looks far from it.'

She pursed her lips and he noticed how they peaked in a very kissable bow before flushing a deep and enticing red. Usually, seeing something sexy like that on a woman was enough for him to turn on the charm but no way in hell was he was doing that with this prickly woman with the fault-finding gaze.

'Chippy's a greyhound,' she snapped. 'They're supposed to be svelte animals.'

'Is that what you call it?' His laugh came out in a snort. 'It looks anorexic to me and what's with the collar? Is he descended from the tsars?'

He knew he was being obnoxious but there was something about Lilia Cartwright and her holier-than-thou tone that brought out the worst in him. Or was it the fact he'd spent the night sleeping on the world's most uncomfortable bed and when he'd finally fallen asleep the harsh and incessant screeching of sulphur-crested cockatoos at dawn had woken him. God, he hated the country.

'Have you quite finished?' she said, her voice so cool he expected icicles to form on her ash-blonde hair. 'Chippy calms agitated patients and the elderly at the nursing home adore him. Some of them don't have anyone in their lives they can lavish affection on and Chippy is more than happy to be the recipient of that love. Medical studies have shown that a companion pet lowers blood pressure and eases emotional distress. Like I said, he absolutely stays.'

An irrational urge filled him to kick something and to kick it hard. He had the craziest feeling he was back in kindergarten and being timed out on the mat for bad behaviour. 'If there's even one complaint or one flea bite, the mutt goes.'

Her brows rose in a perfect arc of condescension. 'In relative terms, Dr Jackson, you're here for a blink of an eye. Chippy will far outstay you.'

The blink of an eye? Who was she kidding? 'I'm here for seven hundred and twenty *very* long hours.'

Her blue eyes rounded. 'You actually counted them?'

He shrugged. 'It seemed appropriate at three a.m. when the hiss of fighting possums wearing bovver boots on my roof kept me awake.'

She laughed and unexpected dimples appeared in her cheeks. For a brief moment he glimpsed what she might look like if she ever relaxed. It tempted him to join her in laughter but then her tension-filled aura slammed back in place, shutting out any attempts at a connection.

He crossed his arms. 'It wasn't funny.'

'I happen to know you could just have easily been kept awake by fighting possums in the leafy suburbs of Melbourne.'

Were they comrades-in-arms? Both victims of the vagaries of the Melbourne Victoria Hospital that had insisted on sending them to the back of beyond? A bubble of conciliation rose to the top of his dislike for her. 'So you've been forced down here too?'

She shook her head so quickly that her thick and tight French braid swung across her shoulder. 'Turraburra is my home. Melbourne was just a grimy pitstop I was forced to endure when I studied midwifery.'

He thought about his sun-filled apartment in leafy Kew, overlooking Yarra Bend Park. 'My Melbourne's not grimy.'

Again, one brow quirked up in disapproval. 'My Turraburra's not a poor excuse for a town.'

'Well, at least we agree on our disagreement.'

'Do you plan to be grumpy for the entire time you're here?'

Her directness both annoyed and amused him. 'Pretty much.'

One corner of her mouth twitched. 'I guess forewarned is forearmed.' She turned to go and then spun back. 'Oh, and a word to the wise, that is, of course, if you're capable of taking advice on board. I suggest you do things Karen's way. She's run this clinic for fifteen years and outstayed a myriad of medical staff.'

He bit off an acidic retort. He hadn't even met a

patient yet but if this last fifteen minutes with Ms Lilia Cartwright, Midwife, was anything to go by, it was going to be a hellishly long and difficult seven hundred and nineteen hours and forty-five minutes in Turraburra.

CHAPTER TWO

'I'M HOME!' LILY CALLED loudly over the blare of the TV so her grandfather had a chance of hearing her.

A thin arm shot up above the top of the couch and waved at her. 'Marshmallow and I are watching re-runs of the doctor. Makes me realise you don't see many phone boxes around any more, do you?'

Lily kissed him affectionately on the top of his head and stroked the sleeping cat as Chippy settled across her grandfather's feet. 'Until the mobile phone reception improves, I think Turraburra's phone box is safe.'

'I just hope I'm still alive by the time the national broadband scheme's rolled out. The internet was so dodgy today it took me three goes before I could check my footy tipping site.'

'A definite tragedy,' she said wryly. Her grandfather loved all sports but at this time of year, with only a few games before the Australian Rules football finals started, he took it all very seriously. 'Did you get down to the community centre today?'

He grunted.

'Gramps?' A ripple of anxiety wove through her that he might have driven to the centre.

Just recently, due to some episodes of numbness

in his feet, she'd reluctantly told him it wasn't safe for him to drive. Given how independent he was, he'd been seriously unhappy with that proclamation. It had taken quite some time to convince him but he'd finally seemed to come round and together they'd chosen a mobility scooter. Even at eighty-five, he'd insisted on getting a red one because everyone knew red went faster.

It was perfect for getting around Turraburra and, as she'd pointed out to him, he didn't drive out of town much anyway. But despite all the logic behind the decision, the 'gopher', as he called it, had stayed in the garage. Lily was waiting for him to get sick of walking everywhere and start using it.

'I took the gopher,' he said grumpily. 'Happy?'

'I'm happy you went to your class at the centre.'

'Well, I couldn't let Muriel loose on the computer. She'd muck up all the settings and, besides, it was my day to teach the oldies how to edit photos.'

She pressed her lips together so she didn't laugh, knowing from experience it didn't go down well. He might be in his eighties but his mind was as sharp as a tack and he was young at heart, even if his body was starting to fail him. She ached when she thought of how much he hated that. Losing the car had been a bitter blow.

The 'oldies' he referred to were a group of frail elderly folk from the retirement home. Many were younger than him and made him look positively spry. He was interested in anything and everything and involved in the life of the town. He loved keeping abreast of all the latest technology, loved his top-of-the-range digital camera and he kept busy every day. His passion and enthusiasm for life often made her feel that hers was pale and listless in comparison.

He was her family and she loved him dearly. She owed him more than she could ever repay.

'Muriel sent over a casserole for dinner,' he said, rising to his feet.

'That was kind of her.' Muriel and Gramps had a very close friendship and got along very well as long as she didn't touch his computer and he didn't try to organise her pantry into some semblance of order.

He walked towards the kitchen. 'She heard about the Hawker and De'Bortolli babies and knew you'd be tired. No new arrivals today?'

Lily thought about the tall, dark, ill-tempered surgical registrar who'd strode into her work world earlier in the day.

You forgot good looking.

No. Handsome belongs to someone who smiles.

Really? Trent smiled a lot and look how well that turned out.

She pulled her mind back fast from that thought because the key to her mental health was to never think about Trent. Ever. 'A new doctor's arrived in town.'

His rheumy, pale blue eyes lit up. 'Male or female?'

'Sorry, Gramps. I know how you like to flirt with the female doctors but this one's a difficult bloke.' She couldn't stop the sigh that followed.

His face pulled down in a worried frown. 'Has he done something?'

Since the nightmare of her relationship with Trent, Gramps had been overprotective of her, and she moved to reassure him. 'No, nothing like that and I'm stronger now. I don't take any crap from anyone any more. I just know he's not a natural fit for Turraburra.'

'We're all entitled to one bad day—give the poor guy a minute to settle in. You and Karen will have him trained up in the Turraburra ways in no time flat.'

I wish. 'I'm not so sure about that, Gramps. In fact, the only thing I have any confidence about at all is that it's going to be a seriously long month.'

Noah stood on the town beach, gulping in great lungfuls of salt air like it was the last drop of oxygen on the planet. Not that he believed in any of that positive-ions nonsense but he was desperate to banish the scent of air freshener with a urine chaser from his nostrils. From his clothes. From his skin.

His heart rate thundered hard and fast like it did after a long run, only this time its pounding had nothing to do with exercise and everything to do with anxiety. Slowing his breathing, he pulled in some long, controlled deep breaths and shucked off the cloak of claustrophobia that had come out of nowhere, engulfing him ten minutes earlier. It had been years since something like that had happened and as a result he'd thought he'd conquered it, but all it had taken was two hours at the Turraburra nursing home. God, he hated this town.

He'd arrived at the clinic at eight to be told by the efficient Karen that Tuesday mornings meant rounds at the nursing home. He'd crossed the grounds of the hospital where the bright spring daffodils had mocked him with their cheery and optimistic colour. He hadn't felt the slightest bit cheery. The nurse in charge of the nursing home had given him a bundle of patient histories and a stack of drug sheets, which had immediately put paid to his plan of dashing in and dashing out.

Apparently, it had been three weeks since there'd been a doctor in Turraburra and his morning was consumed by that added complication. The first hour had passed relatively quickly by reviewing patient histories. After that, things had gone downhill fast as he'd examined each elderly patient. Men who'd once stood tall and strong now lay hunched, droop-faced and dribbling, rendered rigid by post-stroke muscle contractions. Women had stared at him with blank eyes—eyes that had reminded him of his mother's. Eyes that had told him they knew he could do nothing for them.

God, he hated that most. It was the reason he'd pursued surgery—at least when he operated on someone, he usually made a difference. He had the capacity to heal, to change lives, but today, in the nursing home, he hadn't been able to do any of that. All he'd been able to do had been to write prescriptions, suggest physiotherapy and recommend protein shakes. The memories of his mother's long and traumatic suffering had jeered at the idea that any of it added to their quality of life.

He'd just finished examining the last patient when the aroma of cabbage and beef, the scent of pure soap and lavender water and the pervading and cloying smell of liberally used air freshener had closed in on him. He'd suddenly found it very hard to breathe. He'd fled fast—desperate for fresh air—and in the process he'd rudely rejected the offer of tea and biscuits from the nurses.

He knew that wouldn't grant him any favours with the staff but he didn't care. In six hundred and ninety-six hours he'd be back in Melbourne. Pulling out his smartphone, he set up a countdown and called it T-zero. Now, whenever the town got to him, he didn't have to do the mental arithmetic, he could just open the app and easily see how many hours until he could walk away from Turraburra without a backward glance.

The fresh, salty air and the long, deep breaths had done the trick and, feeling back in control, he jogged up the beach steps. Sitting on the sea wall, he took off his shoes to empty them of sand.

'Yoo-hoo, Dr Jackson.'

He glanced up to see a line of cycling, fluoro-clad women—all who looked to be in their sixties—bearing down on him fast. The woman in front was waving enthusiastically but with a bicycle helmet on her head and sunglasses on her face he didn't recognise her.

He gave a quick nod of acknowledgment.

She must have realised he had no clue who she was because when she stopped the bike in front of him, she said, 'Linda Sampson, Doctor. We met yesterday morning at the corner store. I gave you directions to the clinic and sold you a coffee.'

Weak as water and undrinkable coffee. 'Right, yes.'

'It's good to see you're settling in. Turraburra has the prettiest beach this side of Wilson's Promontory, don't you think?'

He opened his mouth to say he didn't really have a lot of experience with beaches but she kept right on talking. 'The town's got a lot to offer, especially to families. Are you married, Dr Jackson?'

'No.' He banged his sandy shoe against the sea wall harder than necessary, pining for the anonymity of a big city where no one would think to stop and talk to him if he was sitting on the sea wall at the Middle Park beach.

His life had been put on hold once already and he had no intention of tying himself down to another human being, animal or fish. 'I'm happily single.' If he'd hoped that by telling her that it would get the woman to back off, he was mistaken.

'There's a fine line between happily single and happily coupled up,' Linda said with the enthusiastic smile of a matchmaker. 'And you're in luck. There are some lovely young women in town. The radiographer, Heather Barton, is single.'

One of the other women called out, 'Actually, she's dating Emma Trewella now.'

'Is she? Well, that explains a lot,' Linda said with a laugh. 'Still, that leaves the physiotherapist. She's a gorgeous girl and very into her triathlons. Do you like sports, Doctor?'

He stared at her slack-jawed. Had he been catapulted backwards in time to 1950? He couldn't believe this woman was trying to set him up with someone.

'Or perhaps you'd have more in common with the nurses?' Linda continued. 'I'm sure three of them aren't dating anyone at the moment…'

The memory of ringless white hands gripping pink folders and sky-blue eyes sparking silver arcs shot unbidden into his mind.

'Lucy, Penny and…' Linda paused, turning towards her group. 'What's the name of the pretty nurse with the blonde hair?'

Lilia. He tied his shoe laces with a jerk and reminded himself that he wasn't looking to date anyone and even if he had been, he most certainly wasn't going to date her. Despite her angelic good looks, her personality was at the opposite end of the spectrum. He wouldn't be surprised if she had horns and carried a pitchfork.

'Grace,' someone said. 'Although is she truly blonde?'

Noah stood up quickly, dusting his black pants free of sand. 'That's quite an extensive list, Linda, but I think you've forgotten someone.'

She shook her head, the magpie deterrent cable ties on her helmet swinging wildly. 'I don't think I have.'

'What about the midwife?'

He thought he heard a collective intake of breath from the other women and Linda's smile faltered. 'Lily's married to her job, Doctor. You're much better off dating one of the others.'

The words came with an undercurrent of a warning not to go there. Before he could ask her why, there was a flurry of ringing bike bells, called farewells and the group took off along the path—a bright slash of iridescent yellow wobbling and weaving towards the noon sun.

Lily stared at the appointment sheet and groaned. How could she have forgotten the date? It was the midwifery centre's bi-monthly doctor clinic. Why had the planets aligned to make it this month? Why not next month when Noah Jackson would be long gone and far, far away? The luck of the Irish or any other nationality was clearly not running her way today. She was going to have to work in close proximity with him all afternoon. Just fantastic…not!

As the town's midwife, Lily operated independently under the auspices of the Melbourne Midwifery Unit.

When a newly pregnant woman made contact with her, she conducted a preliminary interview and examination. Some women, due to pre-existing medical conditions such as diabetes or a multiple pregnancy, she immediately referred to the obstetricians at the Victoria or to the Dandenong District Hospital but most women fitted the criteria to be under her care.

However, it wasn't her decision alone. Like the other independent midwife-run birth units it was modelled on, all pregnant Turraburra clients had to be examined by a doctor once in early pregnancy. Lily scheduled these appointments to take place with the GP on one afternoon every two months. Today was the day.

Her computer beeped with an instant message from Karen.

Grumpy guts is on his way. Good luck! I've put Tim Tams in the kitchen. You'll need three after working with him all afternoon.

Karen had been having a whinge in the tearoom earlier in the day about Dr Jackson. She'd called him cold, curt and a control freak. Lily was used to Karen getting defensive with new staff members who questioned her but she couldn't believe Noah Jackson could be quite as bad as Karen made out. She'd offered Karen chocolate and wisely kept her own counsel.

'You ready?'

The gruff tone had her swinging around on her office chair. Noah stood in the doorway with his sleeves rolled up to his elbows and one hand pressed up against the doorjamb—muscles bunched and veins bulging. A flicker of something momentarily stirred low in her belly—something she hadn't experienced in a very long time. Fear immediately clenched her muscles against it, trying to force it away. For her own safety she'd locked down her sexual response three years ago and it had to stay that way.

Unlike yesterday, when Noah had looked like the quintessential urban professional, today he was rumpled. His thick hair was wildly wind-ruffled, his tie was stuffed in between the third and fourth buttons of his business shirt and his black trousers bore traces of sand. Had he spent his lunch break at the beach? She loved the calming effects of the ocean and often took ten minutes to regroup between clinic sessions. Perhaps he wasn't as stuck up as she'd first thought. 'Been enjoying the beach?'

Shadows crossed his rich chocolate eyes. 'I wouldn't go so far as to say that.'

She tried hard not to roll her eyes. Perish the thought he might actually find something positive about Turraburra. *Stick to talking about work.* 'Today's clinic is all about—'

'Pregnant women. Yeah, I get it. You do the obs, test their urine and weigh them and leave the rest to me.'

I don't think so. She stood up because sitting with him staring down at her from those arcane eyes she felt way too vulnerable. Three years ago she'd made a commitment to herself that she was never again going to leave herself open to be placed in a powerless position with another human being. Even in low heels she was closer to his height.

'These women are my patients and this is a rubber-stamping exercise so they can be part of the midwifery programme.'

His nostrils flared. 'As the *doctor*, isn't it my decision?'

Spare me from non-team-players. 'I'm sorry, I thought you were a surgical registrar but suddenly you're moonlighting as an obstetrician?'

His cheekbones sharpened as he sucked in a breath through his teeth and she reeled in her fraying temper. What was it about this man that made her break her own rules of never reacting? Of never provoking a man to anger? Of never putting herself at risk? She also didn't want to give Noah Jackson any excuse to dismiss her as *that crazy midwife* and interfere with her programme.

'I take that back. As Turraburra's midwife, with five years' experience, anyone I feel doesn't qualify for the programme has already been referred on.'

His gaze hooked hers, brimming with discontent. 'So, in essence, this clinic is a waste of my time?'

'It's protocol.'

'Fine.' He spun on his heel, crossed the hall and disappeared into the examination room.

She sighed and hurried in after him.

'Bec,' she said to the pregnant woman who was sitting, waiting, 'this is Dr Jackson, our current locum GP. As I explained, he'll be examining you today.'

Bec Sinclair, a happy-go-lucky woman, gave an expansive smile. 'No worries. Good to meet you, Doc.'

Noah sat down behind the desk and gave her a brisk nod before turning his attention to the computer screen and reading her medical history. He frowned. 'You had a baby eight months ago and you're pregnant again?'

Bec laughed at his blatant disapproval. 'It was a bit of a surprise, that's for sure.'

'I gather you weren't organised enough to use contraception.'

Lily's jaw dropped open. She couldn't believe he'd just said that.

Bec, to her credit, didn't seem at all fazed by his rudeness. 'It was a dodgy condom but no harm done. We wanted another baby so the fact it's coming a year earlier than planned is no biggie.' She leaned towards the desk, showing Noah a photo of her little boy on her phone. 'Lily delivered Harley, and Jase and I really want her to deliver this next one too.'

'It will be my pleasure. Harley's really cute, isn't he, Noah?' Lily said, giving him an opening for some chitchat and hoping he'd respond.

Noah ignored her and the proffered photo. Instead, he pushed back from the desk, stood and pulled the curtain around the examination table. Patting it with his hand, he said, 'Up you get.'

Bec exchanged a look with Lily that said *Is this guy for real?* before rising and climbing up the three small steps.

Lily made her comfortable and positioned the modesty sheet before returning to stand by Bec's head. Noah silently listened to her heart, examined her breasts and then her abdomen. Lily kept up a patter, explaining to Bec everything that Noah was doing because, apparently, he'd turned mute.

When the examination was over and Bec was back in the chair, Noah said, 'Everything seems fine, except that you're fat.'

Bec paled.

'What Dr Jackson means,' Lily said hurriedly, as she threw at him what she hoped was a venomous look, 'is that you're still carrying some weight from your last pregnancy.'

'That's not what I meant at all.' Noah pulled up a BMI chart, spun the computer screen towards Bec and pointed to the yellow overweight zone where it met the red obese one. 'Right now, you're just below the border of obese. If you're not careful during this pregnancy, you'll tip into the red zone. That will put you at risk of complications such as gestational diabetes, pre-eclampsia and thrombosis. There's also an increased risk that the baby may end up being in a difficult position such as breech. All of those things would make you ineligible to be delivered by Lilia at the birth centre.'

'I want to have my baby here,' Bec said, her voice suddenly wobbly.

'Then make sure you exercise and eat healthy foods. It's that simple.' Noah turned to Lily. 'I assume you have information for your patients about that sort of thing.'

'I do,' she managed to grind out between clenched teeth. 'If you come with me, Bec, I'll give the pamphlets to you now as well as the water aerobics timetable. It's a fun way to exercise and there's a crèche at the pool.'

She escorted Bec from the room and gave her all the information, along with small packet of tissues. 'Come and see me tomorrow and we'll talk about it all then in greater detail. Okay?'

Bec nodded and sniffed. 'I kinda knew I'd got big but it was hard hearing it.'

Lily could have killed Noah. 'I'm so sorry.'

'Don't be. It's not your fault.' Bec gave a long sigh. 'I guess I needed to hear it.'

She gave Bec's shoulder a squeeze. 'Only in a kinder way.'

'Yeah.' Bec took in a deep breath. 'I didn't know being heavy could make things dangerous for me and the baby, and I guess it's good that he told me because I don't want to have to go to Melbourne. I know Mandy Carmichael's preggers again and she's pretty big. Maybe we can help each other, you know?'

Lily smiled encouragingly. 'That sounds like a great plan.'

As Bec left, Karen buzzed her. 'Kat Nguyen's rescheduled for later today so you've got a gap.'

As Lily hung up the phone she knew exactly what she was going to do with her free half-hour, whether she wanted to take that risk or not.

Noah glanced up as Lily walked back into the office alone. Her face was tight with tension and disapproving lines bracketed her mouth, pulling it down at the edges. An irrational desire to see her smile tugged at him and that on its own annoyed him. So what if a smile made her eyes crinkle at the edges with laughter lines and caused dimples to score her cheeks? So what if a smile made her light up, look happy and full of life and chased away her usual closed-off sangfroid? Made her look pretty?

He tried to shake off the feeling. It was nothing to him whether she was happy or not. Whether she was a workaholic or not, like the ladies at the beach had told him. Whether she was anything other than the pain in the rear that she'd already proved to be. He didn't have time in his life for a woman who was fun, let alone one with dragon tendencies. 'Where's the next patient?'

She crossed her arms. 'She's running late.'

He'd already pegged her as a person who liked things to go her own way and a late patient would throw out her schedule. 'So that's why you're looking like you've just sucked on a lemon. Surely you know nothing in the medical profession ever runs on time.'

Her eyes rounded and widened so far he could have tumbled into their pale, azure depths. 'Are you stressed or ill?'

'No,' he said, seriously puzzled. 'Why would you say that?'

She walked closer to the desk. 'So you're just naturally rude.'

Baffled by her accusations, he held onto his temper by the barest of margins. That surprised him. Usually he'd have roared like a lion if a nurse or anyone more junior to him had dared to speak to him like this. 'Where's all this antagonism coming from? Did something happen to upset you while you were out of the room?'

'Where's all this coming from?' Incredulity pushed her voice up from its usual throaty depths. 'You just told Bec Sinclair she's fat.'

He didn't get why she was all het up. 'So? I said that because she is.'

She pressed her palms down on the desk and as she leaned in he caught the light scent of spring flowers and something else he couldn't name. 'Yes, but you didn't have to tell her quite so baldly. Do you ever think before you speak?'

Her accusation had him shooting to his feet to rectify the power balance. 'Of course I do. She needed to know the risks that her weight adds to her pregnancy. I told her the truth.'

Her light brown brows hit her hairline. 'You're brutally blunt.'

'No. I'm honest with them.'

She shook her head back and forth so fast he thought she'd give herself whiplash. 'Oh, no, you're not getting away with that. There are ways of telling someone the truth and you're using it as an excuse to be thoughtless and rude.'

She'd just crossed the line in the sand he'd already moved for her. 'Look, Miss Manners,' he said tersely. 'You don't have the right to storm in here and accuse me of being rude.'

Her shoulders rolled back like an Amazon woman preparing for battle. 'I do when it affects *my* patients. You just reduced the most laid-back, easygoing woman I know to tears.'

A pang of conscience jabbed him. Had he really done that? 'She was upset?'

She threw her hands up. 'You think? Yes, of course she was upset.'

He rubbed his hand over the back of his neck as he absorbed that bit of information. 'I didn't realise I'd upset her.'

Lily dropped into the chair, her expression stunned. 'You're kidding me, right?'

No. Man, he hated general practice with its touchy-feely stuff and rules that he hadn't known existed. He was a surgeon and a damn good one. He diagnosed problems and then he cut them out. As a result, he gave people a better quality of life. It was a far easier way of dealing with problems than the muddy waters of internal medicine where nothing was cut and dried and everything was hazy with irrational hope.

He and his mother had learned that the hard way and after that life-changing experience he'd vowed he would always give his patients the truth. Black was black and white was white. People needed information so they could make a choice.

The prof's voice came out of nowhere, echoing loudly in his head. *We've had complaints from your dealings with patients when they're awake.*

His legs trembled and he sat down hard, nausea churning his gut. Was this the sort of thing the prof had been referring to? Propping his elbows on the desk, he ran his hands through his hair and tried to marshal his thoughts. Did Lilia actually have a point? Was his interpretation of the facts blunt and thoughtless?

He instantly railed against the idea, refusing to believe it for a moment. *We've had complaints.* The prof's words were irrefutable. As much as he didn't want to acknowledge it, *this* was the reason he'd been sent down here to Turraburra. It seemed he really did have a problem communicating with patients. A problem he hadn't been fully aware of until this moment. A problem that was going to stop him from qualifying as a surgeon if he didn't do something about it.

'Noah?'

There was no trace of the previous anger in her voice and none of the sarcasm. All he could hear was concern. He raised his eyes to hers, his gaze stalling on the lushness of her lips. Pink and moist, they were slightly parted. Kissable. Oh, so very kissable. What they would taste like? Icy cool, like her usual demeanour, or sizzling hot, like she'd been a moment ago when she'd taken him to task? Or sweet and decadently rich? Perhaps sharply tart with a kick of fire?

The tip of her tongue suddenly darted out, flicking the peak of her top lip before falling back. Heat slammed into him, rushing lust through him and down into every cell as if he were an inexperienced teen. Hell, he had more control than this. He sucked in a breath and gave thanks he was sitting down behind a desk, his lap hidden from view.

He shifted his gaze to the safety of her nose, which, although it suited her face, wasn't cute or sexy. This brought his traitorous body back under control. He didn't want to be attracted to Lilia Cartwright in any shape or form. He just wanted to get this time in Turraburra over and done with and get the hell out of town. Get back to the security of the Melbourne Victoria and to the job he loved above all else.

Her previously flinty gaze was now soft and caring. 'Noah, is everything okay?'

Everything's so far from okay it's not funny. Could he tell her the real reason the Victoria had sent a surgeon to Turraburra? Tell her that if he didn't conquer this communication problem he wouldn't qualify? That ten years of hard work had failed to give him what he so badly wanted?

For the first time since he'd met her he saw genuine interest and empathy in her face and a part of him desperately wanted to reach out and confide in her. God knew, if he'd unwittingly upset a patient and been clueless about the impact of his words, he surely needed help.

She'll understand.

You don't know that. She could just as easily use it against me.

He'd fought long and hard to get this far in the competitive field of surgery without depending on anyone and he didn't intend to start now. That said, he'd noticed how relaxed she was with her patients compared to how he always felt with them. With Bec Sinclair, she'd explained everything he'd been doing, chatting easily to her. She connected with people in a way he'd never been able to—in a way he needed to learn.

He had no intention of asking her for help or exposing any weakness, but that didn't mean he couldn't observe and learn from her. *Don't give anything away.* Leaning back, he casually laced his fingers behind his head. 'Do you have any other fat pregnant women coming in today?'

Wariness crawled across her high cheekbones. 'There is one more.'

'Do you concede that her weight is a risk to her pregnancy?'

'Yes, but—'

'Good.' He sat forward fast, the chair clunking loudly. 'This time you run the consultation, which means you're the one who has to tell her that her weight is a problem.'

She blinked at him in surprise and then her intelligent eyes narrowed, scanning his face like an explosives expert looking for undetonated bombs. 'And?'

'And then I'll critique your performance like you just critiqued mine. After all, the Victoria's a teaching hospital so it seems only fair.'

He couldn't help but grin at her stunned expression.

CHAPTER THREE

L<small>ILY TURNED THE</small> music up and sang loudly as she drove through the rolling hills and back towards the coast and Turraburra. As well as singing, she concentrated on the view. Anything to try and still her mind and stop it from darting to places she didn't want it to go.

She savoured the vista of black and white cows dotted against the emerald-green paddocks—the vibrant colour courtesy of spring rains. Come January, the grass would be scorched brown and the only green would be the feathery tops of the beautiful white-barked gumtrees.

She'd been out at the Hawkers' dairy farm, doing a follow-up postnatal visit. Jess and the baby were both doing well and Richard had baked scones, insisting she stay for morning tea. She'd found it hard to believe that the burly farmer was capable of knocking out a batch of scones, because the few men who'd passed through her life hadn't been cooks. When she'd confessed her surprise to Richard, he'd just laughed and said, 'If I depended on Jess to cook, we'd both have starved years ago.'

'I have other talents,' Jess, the town's lawyer, said without rancour.

'That you do,' Richard had replied with such a look of love and devotion in his eyes that it had made Lily's throat tighten.

She'd grown up hearing the stories from her grandfather of her parents' love for each other but she had no memory of it. Somehow it had always seemed like a story just out of reach—like a fairy-tale and not at all real. Sure, she had their wedding photo framed on her dresser but plenty of people got married and it ended in recriminations and pain. She was no stranger to that scenario and she often wondered if her parents had lived longer lives, they would still be together.

Although her grandfather loved her dearly, she'd never known the sort of love that Jess and Richard shared. She'd hoped for it when she'd met Trent and had allowed herself to be seduced by the idea of it. She'd learned that when a fairy-tale met reality, the fallout was bitter and life-changing. As a result, and for her own protection, and in a way for the protection of her mythical child, she wasn't prepared to risk another relationship. The only times she questioned her decision was when she saw true love in action, like today.

Her loud, off-key singing wasn't banishing her unsettling thoughts like it usually did. Ever since Noah Jackson had burst into Turraburra—all stormy-eyed and difficult—troubling thoughts had become part of her again. She couldn't work him out. She wanted to say he was rude, arrogant, self-righteous and exasperating, and dismiss him out of her head. He was definitely all of those things but then there were moments when he looked so adrift—like yesterday when he'd appeared genuinely stunned and upset that his words had distressed Bec Sinclair. She couldn't work him out.

You don't have to work him out. You don't have to work any man out. Remember, it's safer not to even try.

Except that momentary look of bewilderment on his face had broken through his *I'm a surgeon, bow down before me* facade, and it had got to her. It had humanised him and she wished it hadn't. Arrogant Noah was far more easily dismissed as a temporary thorn in her side than thoughtful Noah. The Noah who'd sat back and listened intently and watched without a hint of disparagement as she'd talked with Mandy Carmichael about her weight was an intriguing conundrum.

She braked at the four-way intersection and proceeded to turn right, passing the *Welcome to Turraburra* sign. She smiled at the '+1' someone had painted next to the population figure. Given the number of pregnant women in town at the moment, she expected to see a lot more graffiti over the coming months. Checking the clock on the dash, she decided that she had just enough time to check in on her grandfather before starting afternoon clinic.

Her phone beeped as it always did when she drove back into town after being in a mobile phone reception dead zone. This time, instead of one or two messages, it vibrated wildly as six messages came in one after another. She immediately pulled over.

11:00 Unknown patient in labour. Go to hospital. Karen.

11:15 Visitor to town in established labour in Emergency. Your assistance appreciated. N. Jackson.

'What have you done with the Noah Jackson I know and despair of?' she said out loud. The formal style of Noah's text was unexpected and it made Karen's seem almost brusque in comparison. The juxtaposition made her smile.

11:50 Contractions now two minutes apart. Last baby I delivered was six years ago. Request immediate assistance.
NJ.

12:10 Where the bloody hell are you?!
N.

'And he's back.' Although, to give Noah his due, she'd be totally stressed out if she was being asked to do something she hadn't done in a very long time. She threw the car into gear, checked over her shoulder and pulled off the gravel. Three minutes later she was running into Emergency to the familiar groans of a woman in transition.

For the first time since arriving in Turraburra, Noah was genuinely happy to see starchy and standoffish Lilia Cartwright, Midwife. 'You don't text, you don't call,' he tried to joke against a taut throat. Trying to stop himself from yelling, *I'm freaking out here and where the hell have you been?*

'Sorry,' she said breezily. 'I was out of range.'

'Seriously?' Her statement stunned him. 'You don't have mobile reception when you leave town? That's not safe for your patients. What if a woman delivers when you're not here?'

'Welcome to the country, Noah. We'd love to have the communications coverage that you get in the city but the infrastructure isn't here.'

'How can people live like this?' he muttered, adding yet another reason to his long list of why country life sucked.

'I always let Karen know where I am and a message gets to me eventually.'

'Oh, and that's so very reassuring.'

She rolled her eyes. 'I'm here now so you can stop panicking.'

Indignation rolled through him. 'I. Do. Not. Panic.'

'I'm sure you don't when you're in your beloved operating theatre, but this isn't your area of expertise and it's normal to be nervous when you're out of your comfort zone.'

Her expression was devoid of any judgement. In fact, all he could read on her face was understanding and that confused him. Made him suspicious. If surgery had taught him anything it was that life was a competition. Any sign of weakness would and could be used to further someone else's career. He'd expected her to take this as another opportunity to show him up. Highlight his failings, as she'd done so succinctly yesterday. He'd never expected her to be empathetic.

As she pulled on a disposable plastic apron she flicked her braid to one side, exposing her long, creamy neck. He was suddenly engulfed by the scent of apples, cherries and mangoes, which took him straight back to the memories of long-past summers growing up and fruit salad and ice cream.

Regret that midwives no longer wore gowns slugged him hard. Back in the day he would have needed to tie her gown and his fingers would have brushed against that warm, smooth skin. His heart kicked up at the thought, pumping heat through him.

What are you doing? She's so not your type and you don't even like her.

That was true on all fronts. He limited his dating to women who were fun, flirty and only interested in a good time. A good time that ended the moment they planned beyond two weeks in advance. Somehow he got the feeling that Lilia wasn't that type of woman.

With the apron tied, she lifted her head and caught him staring at her. Her fingers immediately brushed her cheeks. 'What? Do I have jam or cream on my mouth from morning tea?'

'No.' Embarrassment made the word sound curt and sharp and she tensed. He instantly regretted his tone and sighed. 'Sorry. Can I please tell you about your patient?'

'Yes.' She sounded as relieved as him. 'Fill me in.'

Happy to be back in familiar territory, he commenced a detailed patient history. 'Jade Riccardo, primigravida, thirty-seven weeks pregnant. She's been visiting relatives in town and arrived here an hour ago in established labour. Foetal heart rate's strong and, going on my rusty palpation skills, the baby's in an anterior position. Her husband's with her but they're both understandably anxious because they're booked in to have the baby in Melbourne.'

A long, loud groan came from the other side of the door. 'Sounds like she's going to have it in Turraburra and very soon.' Lilia grinned up at him, her dimples diving deep into her cheeks and her eyes as bright as a summer's day. She was full of enthusiastic anticipation while he was filled with dread. She tugged on his arm. 'Come on, then. Let's go deliver a baby.'

The heat of her hand warmed him and he missed it when she pulled it away. He followed her into the room and introduced her. 'Jade, Paul, this is Lilia Cartwright, Turraburra's midwife.'

Jade, who was fully in the transition zone, didn't respond. She was on all fours, rocking back and forth and sucking on nitrous oxide like it was oxygen.

Paul was rubbing Jade's back and he threw a grateful look to both of them. 'Are you sure everything's okay? She's doing a lot of grunting.'

Lilia smiled. 'That's great. It means she's working with her body and getting ready to push the baby out.' She rested her hand on Jade's shoulder. 'Hi, Jade. I know this is all moving faster than you expected and it's not happening where you expected, but lots of babies have been born in Turraburra, haven't they, Noah?'

'Yes.'

She rolled her eyes.

Beads of sweat pooled on Noah's brow. Her resigned look spoke volumes, telling him he was failing at something. He looked at the husband, whose face was tight with worry. 'Lots of babies,' he echoed Lilia, practising how to be reassuring and hoping he could pull it off. 'It might not be Melbourne but you're in good hands.' *Lilia's hands.*

Paul visibly relaxed. 'That's good to know.'

Lilia placed one hand on Jade's abdomen and her

other on her buttocks. 'With the next contraction, Jade, I want you to push down here.'

Jade groaned.

'Your tummy's tightening. I can feel one coming now.'

Jade sucked on the nitrous oxide and then pushed, making a low guttural sound.

Lilia pulled on gloves. 'You're doing great, Jade. I can see some black hair.'

Paul stroked Jade's hair, his face excited. 'Did you hear that, honey?'

Contraction over, Jade slumped down onto the pillows. 'I can't do this.'

'You're already doing it, Jade,' Lilia said calmly. 'Every contraction takes you closer to holding your baby in your arms.'

Noah, feeling as useless as a bike without wheels, did what he knew best—busied himself with the surgical instruments. He snapped on gloves, unwrapped the sterilised delivery pack, set out the bowl, the forceps and scissors, and added the cord clamps, all the while listening to Lilia's soothing voice giving instructions and praising Jade.

They developed a rhythm, with Paul encouraging Jade, Lilia focusing on the baby's descent and Noah checking the baby's heartbeat after each contraction. Each time the rushing sound of horses' hooves sounded, Paul would grin at him and he found himself smiling back. With each contraction, the baby's head moved down a little further until twenty minutes later it sat bulging on the perineum, ready to be born.

'I think you're going to have your baby with the

next contraction,' Lilia said as her fingers controlled the baby's head. 'Pant, Jade, pant.'

Jade tried to pant and then groaned. 'Can't.' With a loud grunt, she pushed. A gush of fluid heralded the baby's head, which appeared a moment later, its face scrunched and surprised.

'The baby's head is born. Well done,' Lilia said.

'Our baby's nearly here, honey,' Paul's voice cracked with emotion. 'I can see the head.

'I want it to stop,' Jade sobbed. 'It's too hard.'

Noah looked at the sweaty and exhausted woman who'd endured an incredibly fast and intense labour. She was so very close to finishing and he recalled how once he'd almost stopped running in a marathon because his body had felt like it had been melting in pain. A volunteer had called out to him, 'You've done the hard yards, mate, keep going, the prize is in sight.' It was exactly what he'd needed to hear and it had carried him home.

'The hard work's over, Jade,' he said quietly. 'You can do this. One more push.' He caught Lilia's combined look of surprise and approval streak across her face and he had a ridiculous urge to high-five someone.

Jade's hand shot out and gripped Noah's shoulder, her wild eyes fixed on his. 'Promise?'

'Promise.'

'Noah's right, Jade,' Lilia confirmed. 'With the next contraction, I'll deliver the baby's shoulders and the rest of him or her will follow.'

'Okay. I can feel a contraction *noooooow*.' Jade pushed.

A dusky baby slithered into Lilia's arms and something deep down inside Noah moved. It had been years since he'd been present at a birth and he'd forgotten how amazing it was to witness the arrival of new life into the world.

Lilia clamped the umbilical cord before asking the stunned father, 'Do you want to cut the cord, Paul?'

'Yes.' With shaking hands, Paul cut where Lilia indicated and then said, with wonder in his voice, 'It's a little girl, Jade.'

Noah rubbed the baby with a towel and took note of her breathing and colour and muscle tone so he could give an Apgar score for the first minute of life. The baby hadn't cried but her dark eyes were bright and gazing around, taking in this new world. A lump formed in his throat and he immediately tried to get rid of it because emotion opened a guy up to being weak and vulnerable.

'I'm going to pass the baby between your legs, Jade,' Lilia said. 'Are you ready?'

'My arms are shaking and I'm getting another contraction.'

Paul took the baby, cradling her in his arms while Lilia delivered the placenta. As she examined it, Noah helped Jade roll over. 'In an hour we can transfer you to the midwifery unit. You'll be a lot more comfortable there.'

Paul reverently passed his daughter to his wife. 'Meet Jasmine.'

Silent tears rolled down Jade's cheeks as she unwrapped the baby and counted her fingers and toes. 'Hey, sweetie, I'm your mummy.'

Noah stepped back, moving to the corner of the room and standing next to Lilia, who was breathing deeply. He glanced at her. Her beautiful blue eyes shone with unshed tears but her face was wreathed in a smile. She was luminous with joy and it radiated from her like white light.

With a jolt, he realised this was the first time he'd ever seen her look truly happy. It called out to him so strongly that his body leaned in of its own accord until his head was close to hers and her fresh, fruity perfume filled his nostrils. He wanted to wrap his arms around her, kiss her long and slow and harvest her jubilation. Keep it safe.

Get a grip. You're at work and this is Lilia, remember? The ice queen and dragon rolled into one.

Shocked at what he'd almost done, he covered by saying quietly so only she could hear, 'You did an amazing job. It was very impressive.' The words came out rough and gruff and he jerked his head back, putting much-needed distance between them.

'Thanks.' She blew her nose. 'Sorry. I'm a bit of a sook and it gets to me every time.'

He took in the new family—their love and awe swirling around them in a life-affirming way. It both warmed and scared him. 'I guess I can understand that.'

She tilted her head and gave him a long, considering look. 'I'm glad. You did okay yourself.'

In his world, okay didn't come close to being good enough. 'Just okay?'

She laughed. 'Fishing for compliments, Noah?'

He found himself smiling at her directness. 'I might be.'

'Then let me put it this way. You did better today than you did yesterday.'

That didn't tell him very much at all. 'And?'

'And empathy doesn't come easily to you.'

She walked back to the bed to do a mother and baby check and he let his gaze drop to admire the swing of her hips. Part of him hated that she'd worked out he struggled to be naturally sympathetic and another part of him was glad. All of it added together discombobulated him, especially his response to her. How could he be driven to madness by her one minute and want to kiss her senseless the next?

Suddenly surviving four weeks in Turraburra just got harder for a whole different set of reasons.

Two days later Lilia waved goodbye to the Riccardos, who were keen to get back to Melbourne with Jasmine. She'd arranged for the district nurse to visit them so they'd have help when Jade's milk came in and to cover the days before the maternal and child health nurse visited. As she closed off the file, an unusual wistfulness filled her. She was used to farewelling couples but usually she knew she'd see them again around town and she'd be able to watch the baby grow. She hoped the Riccardos would call in the next time they were in town and visiting relatives, so she could get her little Jasmine fix. She really was a cute baby.

Lily had been beyond surprised when Noah had called in first thing this morning, insisting on doing a discharge check. She'd assumed he'd handed Jade and Jasmine's care over to her the moment she'd stepped into Emergency and he'd said, 'Can I tell you about *your* patient?' Even though she'd seen him try really hard to connect with Jade and Paul during the fast labour, she'd thought he probably much preferred to be far away from such patient intimacy.

Apparently, she'd been wrong.

He'd spent ten minutes with the Riccardos but in reality it had been way more of a cuddle of Jasmine than a discharge check. Always taut with tension, as if he needed to be alert and ready for anything, Noah had seemed almost relaxed as he'd cradled the swaddled baby—well, relaxed for him anyway. She'd been transfixed by the image of the tiny newborn snuggled up against his broad chest and held safely in his strong arms—his sun-kissed skin a honey brown against the white baby shawl.

The idea of arms providing shelter instead of harm burrowed into her mind and tried to set up residence. For a tempting moment she allowed it to. She even let herself feel and enjoy the tingling warmth spinning through her at the thought of Noah's arms wrapped around her, before she rejected all of it firmly and irrevocably. Entertaining ideas like that only led her down a dangerous path—one she'd vowed never to hike along again. It was one thing for other people to take a risk on a relationship but after what had happened with Trent she wasn't ever trusting her judgement with men again.

At almost the same time as she'd locked down her wayward body and thoughts Noah had quickly handed the baby back to Jade, stood abruptly, and with a brisk and brief goodbye had left the room. Paul had commented in a puzzled voice, 'I guess he needs to see a patient.'

Lily, who'd been busy getting her own emotions back under control, had suspected Noah had experienced a rush of affection for the baby and hadn't known how to process it. Like her, he probably had his reasons for avoiding feeling too much of anything and running from it when it caught him unawares.

Time to stop thinking about Noah Jackson.

Shaking her shoulders to slough off the unwanted thoughts, she set about preparing for her new mothers' group that was meeting straight after lunch. She was talking to them, amongst other things, about immunisation. Too many people took for granted the good health that life in Australia afforded them and didn't understand that whooping cough could still kill a young child.

'Ah, Lily?'

She glanced up to see Karen standing in the doorway. Karen rarely walked all the way back here to the annexe, preferring instead to use the intercom. The medical secretary ran the practice her way and she liked to have all the 'i's dotted and the 't's crossed.

Lily racked her brain to think if she'd forgotten some vital piece of paperwork but came up blank. 'Hi, Karen. Whatever I did wrong, I'm sorry,' she said with a laugh. 'Tell me how to fix it.'

Karen shook her head. 'It's not about work, Lily. The hospital just called and your grandfather's in Emergency.'

Gramps! No. Her hand gripped the edge of her desk as a thousand terrifying thoughts closed in on her. At eighty-five, any number of things could have happened to him—stroke, heart attack, a fall. She didn't want to consider any of them.

Karen shoved Lily's handbag into her arms and pushed her towards the door. 'You go to the hospital and don't worry about work. I'll call all the new mums and cancel this afternoon's session.'

'Thanks, Karen, you're the best.' She was already out the door and running down the disabled entry ramp. She crossed the courtyard gardens and entered the emergency department via the back entrance, all the while frantically praying that Gramps was going to be okay.

Panting, she stopped at the desk. 'Where is he?'

'Room one,' Bronwyn Patterson, the emergency nurse manager, said kindly, and pointed the direction.

'Thanks.' Not stopping to chat, she tugged open the door of the resus room and almost fell through the doorway. Her grandfather lay on a narrow trolley propped up on pillows and looking as pale as the sheet that covered him. 'Gramps? What happened?'

He took in her heaving chest and what was probably a panicked look on her face and raised his thin, bony arm. 'Calm down, Lily. I'm fine.'

She caught a flicker of movement in the corner of her eye and realised Noah was in the room. He raised his head from studying an ECG tracing and his thoughtful gaze sought hers.

'Hello, Lilia.'

There was a slight trace of censuring amusement in his tone that she'd just barged into the room and completely ignored him. She knew if he'd done that to her, she'd have been critical of him. 'Hello, Noah. How's my grandfather?'

'He fainted.'

The succinct words made her swing her attention back to her grandfather. 'Did you eat breakfast?' Her fear and concern came out as interrogation.

'Of course I ate my breakfast and I had morning tea,' he said grumpily, responding to her tone. 'When have you ever known me to be off my tucker? And before you ask, I took all my tablets too. I just stood up too quickly at exercise class.'

You're lucky you didn't break a hip. She noticed a wad of gauze taped to his arm and a tell-tale red stain in the centre. 'What happened to your arm?'

'Just a superficial cut. Don't get all het up.' He wriggled up the pillows and glared at her in a very un-Gramps way. 'Isn't there a baby you need to go and deliver?'

She sat down hard on the chair next to him, pressing her handbag into her thighs. 'I'm not going anywhere until I know you're okay.'

'Fine, but don't fuss.' Her usually easygoing grandfather crossed his arms and pouted.

'Let me know when both of you want my opinion,' Noah said drily.

Her grandfather laughed, his bad mood fading. 'You didn't tell me this one's got a sense of humour, Lily.'

I didn't know he did. She wanted to deny she'd ever spoken about Noah at home but there'd be no point given it was obvious she'd discussed him with her grandfather. Embarrassment raced through her and she could feel the heat on her face and knew she was blushing bright pink.

Noah shot her a challenging look. 'I'm not sure your granddaughter would agree with your assessment of my sense of humour, Mr Cartwright.'

'Call me Bruce, Doc. Now, why did I faint?'

'Your heart rate's very slow.'

'That's good, isn't it? Means I'm fit for my age?'

Lily put her hand on Gramps's and waited for Noah to explain. She hoped he was able to do it using words her grandfather could understand and do it without scaring him.

Noah held up the tracing strip. 'The ECG tells me there's a block in the electrical circuitry of your heart, in the part that controls how fast it beats. When the message doesn't get through, your heart beats too slowly and not enough blood is pumped out. That makes you faint.'

Bruce looked thoughtful. 'Sounds like I need some rewiring.'

This time Noah laughed. 'More like a new starter motor but, yes, some wires are involved. It's called a pacemaker and it's a small procedure done by an elec-trophysiologist at a day-stay cardiac unit. I can refer you to the pacemaker clinic in Melbourne.'

'Is there anywhere closer?' Bruce asked.

Lily expected Noah to give his usual grunt of an-noyance that a country person would want to use a country hospital.

Noah rubbed the back of his neck. 'There's a clinic at Dandenong, which is closer to Turraburra. I could refer you there if you don't want to go all the way to the centre of the city.'

She blinked. Was this the same doctor from the start of the week?

'Well, that all sounds reasonable,' Bruce said, squeezing her hand. 'What do you think, Lily? It will be easier for you if I don't go to Melbourne, won't it?'

Her throat thickened with emotion. Even when her grandfather was sick, he was still putting her first. 'It's your choice, Gramps.'

'Dandenong it is, then.'

'Can I get you anything?' she asked, wanting to

focus on practical things rather than the surging relief that she wouldn't have to take him to Melbourne.

'A cup of tea and some sandwiches would be lovely, sweetpea.'

She felt Noah's gaze on her and a tingle of awareness whooshed across her skin. Looking up, she found his dark, inscrutable eyes studying her in the same intense way she'd noticed on other occasions. As usual, with him, she couldn't tell if it was a critical or a complimentary gaze, but its effect made her feel hot and cold, excited and apprehensive, and it left her jittery. She didn't like jittery. It reminded her far too much of the early days with Trent when lust had drained her brain of all common sense. She wasn't allowing that to happen ever again.

'Is it okay for Gramps to have some food?'

Noah seemed to snap out of his trance. 'Sure, if you can call what the kitchen here serves up food,' he said abruptly. He scrawled an order on the chart and left the room.

'See what I have to put up with, Gramps?' she said, feeling baffled that Noah could go from reasonable to rude in a heartbeat.

'He seems like an okay bloke to me. Now, go get me those sandwiches and some cake. A man could starve to death here.'

CHAPTER FOUR

Noah found Lily sitting in the staff tearoom in the emergency department. *Her name is Lilia*, he reminded himself sharply.

When his phone had woken him at three that morning with an emergency call, it had pulled him out of a delicious dream where he'd been kissing her long, delectable and creamy neck. He'd woken hard, hot and horrified. Right then he'd vowed he was only ever using her formal and full name. It wasn't as pretty or as soft as Lily and that made it easier to think of her as a one-sided equation—defensive and critical with hard edges. He didn't want to spend any time thinking about the talented midwife, the caring granddaughter and the very attractive woman.

Doing that was fraught with complications given they sparked like jumper leads if they got within a metre of each other. Hell, they had enough electricity running between them to power Bruce Cartwright's heart. Working in Turraburra was complication enough given the closeness of his exams. He wasn't adding chasing a woman who had no qualms speaking her mind, frequently found him lacking and gave no sign he was anything more to her than a doctor she had to put up with for four long weeks.

She intrigues you.

No, she annoys me and I'm not pursuing this. Hell, he didn't pursue women any more, full stop—he didn't have to. Since qualifying as a doctor, women had taken to pursuing him and he picked and chose as he pleased, always making sure he could walk away.

Seriously, can you hear yourself?

Shut up.

Needing coffee, he strode to the coffee-machine and immediately swore softly. The pod container was empty.

'Do you need to attend a meeting for your coffee addiction?' Lilia asked with a hint of a smile on her bee-stung lips as she handed him a teabag.

'Probably.' He filled a mug with boiling water. 'I suppose I should be happy you didn't tell me to put money in a swear jar.'

Her eyes sparkled. 'Oh, now, there's an idea. With you here filling it ten times a day, I could probably go on a cruise at the end of the month.'

He raised his brows at her comment. 'And if I instigated a sarcasm jar, so could I.'

'Touché.' She raised her mug to her mouth and sipped her tea, her brow furrowed in thought. 'Thanks for picking up Gramps's heart block so fast.'

He shrugged, unnerved by this almost conciliatory Lilia. 'It's what I'm paid to do.'

She rolled her eyes. 'And he takes a compliment so well.'

He wasn't touching that. 'Your grandfather's not doing too badly for eighty-five.'

Shadows darkened the sky blue of her eyes. 'He's not doing as well as he has been. I've noticed a definite slowing down recently, which he isn't happy about. As you saw, he's an independent old coot.'

He jiggled his teabag. 'Does he live alone?'

She shook her head. 'No. I live with him.'

He thought about the two long years he'd been tied to home, living and caring for his sick mother. Eight years may have passed since then, but the memories of how he'd constantly lurched between resentment that his life was on hold and guilt that he dared feel that way remained vivid. It still haunted him—the self-reproach, the isolation, the feelings of uselessness, the overwhelming responsibility. 'Doesn't living with your grandfather cramp your style?'

She gave him a bewildered look and then burst into peals of laughter, the sound as joyous as the ringing bells of a carillon. 'I don't have any style to cramp. Besides, I've been living with him since I was four. My parents died fighting the bush fires that razed the district twenty-seven years ago.'

'That must have been tough for you.'

She shrugged. 'I was two when it happened and, sure, there were times growing up when I wondered if my life might have been different if my parents had lived, but I never lacked for love. Somehow Gramps not only coped with his own grief at losing his son and daughter-in-law but he did a great job raising me.'

She sounded very together for someone who'd lost both parents. 'He's a remarkable man.'

'He is.' She gave a self-deprecating grimace. 'Even more so for not dispatching me off to boarding school when I was fifteen, running wild and being particularly difficult.'

'One of those times you were wondering about what life would have been like if your parents were still alive?'

She tilted her head and her gaze was thoughtful. 'You know, you may be right. I never thought about it that way. All I remember is playing up and testing Gramps.'

He found himself smiling. 'I can't imagine you being difficult.'

Her pretty mouth curved upwards, its expression ironic. 'Perhaps we both need a sarcasm jar.'

Her smile made him want to lean in close so he could feel her breath on his face and inhale her scent. He immediately leaned back, desperate to cool the simmering attraction he couldn't seem to totally shut down, no matter what he did.

Stick to the topic of work. 'The insertion of the pacemaker should be straightforward but, even so, you need to give some thought to what happens if he continues to go downhill.'

Her plump lips pursed as her shoulders straightened. 'There's nothing to think about. He cared for me so I'll care for him.'

He drummed his fingers against the tabletop, remembering his own similarly worded and heartfelt declaration, and the inevitable fallout that had followed because he'd not thought any of it through. His life had become hijacked by good intentions. 'How will you work the unpredictable hours you do and still manage to care for him?'

Her chin tilted up. 'I'll find a way.'

'Really?' Memories of feeling trapped pushed down on him. 'What happens when you're called out to deliver a baby in the middle of the night and Bruce can't be left home alone? What happens when you have a woman in labour for longer than a few hours? You could be gone for two days at a time and what happens then? You haven't fully thought it through.'

Lily watched Noah become increasingly tense and fervent and she couldn't fathom where his vehemence was coming from. Despite his slight improvement with patients, this was a man who generally saw people in terms of disconnected body parts, not as whole people with thoughts and feelings and a place in a family and community. Why was he suddenly stressing about something that didn't remotely concern him.

'I live in a community that cares, Noah. People will help.'

'Good luck with that,' he muttered almost bitterly, his cheekbones suddenly stark and bladed.

His chocolate-brown eyes, which for the last few minutes had swirled with unreadable emotions, suddenly cleared like a whiteboard wiped clean. His face quickly returned to its set professional mask—unemotional. With his trademark abruptness, he pushed back his chair and stood.

'I have to get back to work. I'll call Monash and try and get your grandfather transported down there this afternoon for the procedure tomorrow morning. Hopefully, he'll be home by five tomorrow night.'

'Thanks, Noah.'

'Yeah.'

The terse and brooding doctor was back, front and

centre, and she had the distinct feeling he'd just returned from a very dark place. 'Is everything okay?'

'Everything's just peachy,' he said sarcastically as he tossed a two-dollar coin in her direction. 'Choose a charity for the S jar.'

One side of his wide mouth pulled up wryly and she found herself wishing he'd smile again, like he had when he'd teased her about being difficult. Those rare moments of lightness were like treasured shafts of sunshine breaking through cloud on a dark and stormy day. They lit him up—a dark and damaged angel— promising the hope of redemption. His smiles made her smile. Made her feel flushed and giddy and alive. They reminded her that, despite everything, she was still a woman.

No man is who he seems. Remember Trent? He hid something so dark and dangerous from you that it exploded without warning...

And she knew that as intimately as the scars on her back and shoulder. She'd been sensible and celibate for three years without a single moment of temptation. Now wasn't the time to start craving normality—craving the touch of a man, especially not a cantankerous and melancholy guy who did little to hide his dark side.

She reminded herself very firmly that Noah would be gone in three weeks and all she had to do to stay safe and sane was to keep out of his way. He was general practice, she was midwifery. As unusual as this week had been for them to be intersecting so often at work, it was thankfully unlikely to continue.

He spun around to leave and then turned back, slapping his palm to the architrave as he often did when a thought struck him. Again, the muscles of his upper arms bulged. 'Lilia.'

A rush of tingling warmth thrummed through her. Somehow, despite his usual taciturn tone, he managed to make her full name sound soft, sweet and, oh, so feminine. 'Ye—' Her voice caught on the word, deeply husky. She cleared her throat, trying to sound in complete control instead of battling delicious but dangerous waves of arousal. 'Yes?'

'You got the agenda for the quarterly meeting at the Victoria?'

It had pinged into her inbox earlier in the day and she'd done what she always did when it arrived. Ignored it until she couldn't ignore it any longer. 'I did.'

'So you're going?'

She sighed. 'Yes. It ticks me off, though. The secretary who sets the agenda is utterly Melbourne-centric and has no clue of what's involved for people who have to travel. She always sets the meetings to start at nine in the morning, making me battle peak-hour traffic on top of a pre-dawn start.'

'So go up to Melbourne the night before,' he said reasonably.

'No.' She heard the horror in her voice and saw a flash of recognition on his face that he'd heard it too. She backpedalled fast. 'I've got a prenatal class the night before.'

'Fair enough. I'll pick you up at five, then.'

'I beg your pardon?'

He sighed. 'I can't get away early either so there's no point in both of us driving up independently. Carbon footprint, parking issues and all that.'

Panic simmered in her veins. 'I might not be able to go after all. Gramps might need me.'

He folded his arms. 'You just finished telling me there were plenty of people you can call on to keep an eye on him and this is one of those times. You know you can't miss the meeting and that it makes perfect sense for us to drive up together.'

No, no, no, no, no. She wanted to refuse his offer but she would look deranged if she insisted on driving up herself. The urge to go and rock in a corner almost overwhelmed her. She didn't know which was worse—spending two four-hour stretches in Noah's luxury but small European sports car—where there'd be no escape from his woodsy scent, his penetrating gaze and all that toned and fit masculinity—or the fact the first leg of the journey was taking her back to Melbourne, the place of her worst folly. A place full of shadows and fears where her past could appear at any moment and suck her back down into the black morass she'd fought so hard to leave.

Either way, no matter how she came at it, all of it totally sucked.

Noah opened the car door and slid back inside the warmth, surprised to find Lilia still asleep. They'd left Turraburra two hours ago in the dark, the cold and spring fog, when the only other people likely to be awake had been insomniacs and dairy farmers.

She'd greeted him with a tight and tired smile and had immediately closed her eyes and slept. At first he'd spent far too much time glancing at her in the predawn light. Asleep, she'd lost the wary look she often wore and instead she'd looked soft and serene. And kissable. Far too kissable.

To distract himself, he'd connected his MP3 player and listened to a surgical podcast. The pressure of the looming exams was a permanent part of him and the time in the car was welcome revision time. Turraburra had kept him so busy that he hadn't found much time for study since he'd arrived, adding to his dislike of the place.

Lilia stirred, her eyes fluttering open and a sleep crease from the seat belt marking her cheek. 'What time is it?'

'Seven. I've got coffee, fruit and something the bakery calls a bear claw.'

'Yum. Thanks, that was thoughtful.'

'It's who I am,' he said, teasing her and wanting to see her smile.

'And there's another two dollars for the children's leukaemia fund,' she said with a laugh. Her usually neat braided hair was out today, flowing wildly over her shoulders. She tucked it behind her ears before accepting the coffee. 'Where are we?'

'Cranbourne.' He clicked his seat belt into place, feeling the buzz of excitement flicker into life as he pulled onto the highway and saw the sign that read 'Melbourne 60km'.

'We'll be in East Melbourne by eight-thirty with time to park and make it to the meeting by nine.'

'Great.'

The tone of her voice made him look at her. 'You just matched my donation to the sarcasm jar.'

'Who knew we were both so philanthropic,' she said caustically, before biting into her bear claw.

'Do you always wake up grumpy?'

She wiped icing sugar from her lips. 'Only when the smell of Melbourne's smog hits my nostrils.'

'Well, your bad mood isn't going to dent my enthusiasm,' he said as he changed lanes. 'I can't wait to step inside the Victoria.'

'What about sitting in snarled traffic just to get there?'

'You really are Ms Snark, aren't you?' He grinned at her, perversely enjoying the fact that their individual happiness was proportional to the proximity of their respective homes. Using it as much-needed protection and reminding himself that no matter how much his body craved her, they were a total mismatch.

'We won't be sitting in a traffic jam. I know every side street within a five-kilometre radius of the hospital. My favourite way is through Richmond.'

'That's ridiculous,' she said, her fingers suddenly shredding the white paper bag that had contained the pastry. 'That way you've got traffic lights and trams.'

He rolled his eyes. 'You've just described most of the inner city.'

'Exactly. Just *stay* on the toll road and use the tunnel,' she said tightly, her words lashing him. 'It will get us there just as fast.'

A bristle of indignation ran up his spine. 'And suddenly the country girl's an expert on Melbourne?'

Her eyes flashed silver blue. 'On your first day I told you I did my Master's in midwifery here but you were too busy being cross to listen.'

He ignored her jibe. 'So how long did you live here?'

'Two years.' Her bitter tone clashed with the love he knew she had for midwifery and this time he did more than just glance at her. Her face had paled to the colour of the alabaster statue of mother and child that graced the foyer of MMU and her usually lush mouth had thinned to a rigid and critical line. The paper bag in her lap was now a series of narrow strips. What the hell was going on?

Don't ask. Don't get involved, remember? No emotions means no pain. Whatever's upsetting her is her thing. Let it be. It's nothing to do with you.

Her hand shot from her lap and she turned on the radio as if she too wanted to change the subject. The raucous laughter of the breakfast show announcers filled the silence between them and both of them allowed it.

Noah couldn't stop smiling as the reassuring familiarity of the Melbourne Victoria hospital wrapped around him like a child's blankie. He loved it all, from the mediocre coffee in the staff lounge to the buzz of the floor polisher being wielded by a cleaner.

The moment he'd pulled into his car space he'd been suffused with such a feeling of freedom he'd wanted to sing. Lilia, on the other hand, had looked as if she'd seen a ghost but once inside the hospital she'd perked up. They had different schedules across the day and had agreed to meet at six o'clock in the foyer. He'd gone direct to the doctors' lounge in the theatre suite like a puppy panting for a treat.

Unluckily for him, the first person he saw was Oliver Evans.

'Noah.' The surgeon greeted him coolly. 'How's Turraburra?'

It's purgatory. Certain that Oliver had been a big

part of the reason he'd been sent to the small country town, he kept his temper leashed, drawing on will-power born from his sheer determination to succeed. He was half ticked off and half grateful to the guy but, even so, he still thought that with his exams so close he could have worked on his communication skills here at the Victoria, instead of being shunted so far south.

'It's coastal. The beach is okay.'

'And the people? Emily introduced me to the mid-wife down there once. She seemed great.'

'She's certainly good at her job but she's seriously opinionated.'

'Not something you're known for,' Oliver said, with an accompanying eye-roll. 'She sounds like the per-fect match for you.'

It was a typical comment from a happily married family man and it irked him. 'I've got exams looming, a private surgical practice to start and no interest in being matched up with anyone.'

'Shame. I remember her as intelligent, entertain-ing and with a good sense of humour, but then again I don't have to work with her.' He picked up a file. 'Talk-ing about work, I imagine you're missing operating. I've got a fascinating case today if you want to scrub in and observe.'

Interest sparked. 'What is it?'

'Jeremy Watson, the paediatric cardiologist from The Deakin is inserting a stent into the heart of Flick Lawrence and Tristan Hamilton's baby. Are you in?'

Eagerness and exhilaration tumbled through him at the chance to be part of such intricate and delicate in utero surgery. He almost said, 'Hell, yeah,' but memo-ries stopped him. Oliver standing in front of an open lift. Oliver yelling at him about a little girl with Down's syndrome. Oliver telling him to get some people skills.

This surgery wasn't taking place on just any baby— it was the unborn child of Melbourne Victoria's paediatric cardiologist. If Noah failed to acknowledge that, he knew he'd be kicked to the kerb, and fast. 'This is a pretty personal case, Oliver. Tristan and Flick are staff. How will they feel about me scrubbing in?'

Oliver gave him a long, assessing look before his stern mouth softened. 'They'll be happy to know they're in the hands of talented doctors.' He shoved papers at Noah's chest. 'Read up on the procedure so you know exactly what's required of you. We don't want Jeremy taking any stories back to The Deakin about our team not being up to scratch. I'll see you in Theatre Five at one.'

Lily's head spun after a morning of meetings. She craved to feel fresh air and sunshine on her skin instead of artificial lighting and to feel earth underneath her feet instead of being six floors up in the air. A sandwich in the park across the road from the hospital was the perfect solution.

Are you sure? What if Trent walks past?

Stop it! You're being irrational. A. Melbourne is a city of four million people. B. Trent doesn't work at the Melbourne Victoria. C. Richmond is far enough away for this not to be his local park. D. He doesn't even know you're in Melbourne and, for all you know, he might have left for Queensland, like he always said he would.

She hauled in deep breaths, trying desperately to hold onto all the logic and reason that half her brain quietly told her, while ignoring the crazy la-la her para-noia had going on. She hated that she had the same conversation with herself every time she came to Mel-bourne. It was one of the reasons why she limited her visits to the city to the bare minimum.

It's been three years and this has to stop. Lunch in the park will be good for you. It's the same as when you have lunch at the beach in Turraburra. You need the natural light—it will boost your serotonin and it's good for your mental health.

Still feeling jittery, she decided to take the service elevator. It gave her the best chance of making it down to the ground floor without running into anyone she knew. People who would implore her to join them for lunch in the cafeteria. She pressed the 'down' button and waited, watching the light linger on level one, the operating theatre suite.

'Lily?' Isla Delamere, looking about seven months pregnant, walked easily towards her *sans* waddle and leaned in to kiss her on the cheek. 'I thought it was you.'

Lily hugged her friend. 'Look at you. You look fan-tastic.'

'Thanks.' Isla rubbed her belly with a slightly dis-tracted air. 'I'm just starting to feel a bit tired by the end of the day and Alessi has gone from dropping occasional hints that I should be giving up work to getting all macho and protective.' She laughed. 'But in a good way, you know, not a creepy way.'

Sadly, Lily understood the difference only too well. 'When do you start mat leave?'

'Next month.' A smile wreathed her face. 'I can't wait to set up the nursery and get organised.'

'That sounds like fun,' Lily said sincerely. She was shocked then to feel a flutter of something she didn't want to acknowledge as a tinge of jealousy.

The sound of voices floated out from the office—the crisp and precise tones of a female British accent contrasting sharply with a deeply male and laconic Aussie drawl. Neither voice sounded happy.

Emergencies excepted, Lily was used to the MMU being a relatively tranquil place. 'What's going on?'

'Darcie and Lucas. Again.' Isla's brows shot skyward. 'They spit and hiss like territorial cats when they get within five metres of each other. All of us are over it.' She laughed. 'We think they should just get on with it and have sex. You know, combust some of that tension so the MMU can go back to the calm place it's known for.'

Lily thought about the tension that shimmered between her and Noah and immediately felt the hot, addictive heaviness between her legs. 'You really think having sex would work?'

'I have no clue but if it means Darcie and Lucas could work together in harmony, I'd say do it. They'd make an amazing obstetric team.'

Working in harmony...

Stop it! Now you're totally losing your mind. Don't even go there.

'You okay, Lily?' Isla asked, clicking her fingers. 'You've vagued out on me.'

She forced a laugh. 'Sorry, I was thinking about sex and the occupational health and safety implications.'

'As long as no ladders are involved, it's probably fine,' Isla quipped, then her face sobered. 'Lily, if you're not busy, can you do me a favour?'

You really need ten minutes in the park out of this artificial light so you can get through the rest of the day. The thought of being in the park and Trent finding her there sent her heart into panicky overdrive. 'I'm not busy, Isla. How can I help?'

'I hate this so much, Lily.' Tristan Hamilton leaned his head against the glass that separated them from Theatre Five, gazing down at his wife's draped and prostrate form on the operating table. The only thing not covered in green was Flick's pregnant belly.

'It must be so hard.' Lily put her hand on the Melbourne Victoria's neonatal cardiothoracic surgeon's shoulder, struck by the sobering thought that today he wasn't a doctor, just a scared and anxious father-to-be. 'It's especially difficult when you're the one used to being in charge and in control so let's look at the positives. Oliver's an expert in utero surgeon and you and Jeremy Watson share that award for the groundbreaking surgery the two of you did on the conjoined twins. Just like you, he's one of the best. Flick and the baby are in great hands.'

Isla had explained to Lily how she'd desperately wanted to support both Tristan and Flick by being here and how she and Alessi had discussed it. They'd both felt strongly that it would be difficult enough to cope with the fact their baby was undergoing life-threatening surgery without their support person being heavily pregnant with a healthy baby. Isla had asked Lily to stay with Tristan throughout the operation, saying, 'He says he doesn't need anyone with him but he does, and you're perfect because you're always so calm.'

Lily had immediately thought about her chaotic reactions to Noah, which were the antithesis of calm, but she hadn't voiced them because it hadn't been the time or place. People needed her. They needed her to be the person they thought she was—serene and unflappable. No one knew how hard she'd worked to cultivate that aura of tranquillity for her own protection.

Now she was doing as Isla asked, staying with Tristan during the surgery, and she was glad. The guy was understandably stressed and she was more than happy to help.

The operating theatre was full of people scrubbed and wearing green gowns, unflattering blue paper hats and pale blue-green masks. Their only visible distinguishing features were their eyes and stance. She recognised Ed Yang, the anaesthetist, by his almond-shaped eyes, Oliver Evans's by his wide-legged stance, and Jeremy Watson by his short stature and nimble movments, but she didn't recognise the back of the taller doctor standing next to him.

'Oliver is using ultrasound to guide Jeremy's large-gauge needle into Flick's abdomen. It will pierce the uterus before going directly into the baby's heart,' Tristan said, as if he was conducting a teaching session for the interns.

If talking was going to help him get through this then Lily was more than happy to listen.

'Of course the risks are,' he continued in a low voice, 'rupture of the amniotic sac, bleeding through the insertion site, the baby's heart bleeding into the pericardial sac and compressing the heart.' His voice cracked. 'And death.'

Lily slid her hand into his and squeezed it hard. 'And

the best-case scenario is the successful insertion of the stent and a healthy baby born at term.'

'Who will still need more surgery.'

Lily heard the guilt and sadness in his voice. 'But the baby will be strong enough to cope with it. Most importantly, unlike you, he or she is unlikely to need a heart transplant. You know it's a different world now from when you were born and your baby is extremely fortunate to have the best doctors in the country.'

'You're right. She is.' He gave her a grateful smile. 'We're having a little girl. We found out during the tests.'

'That's so exciting.'

'It is.' A slow smile wove across his face. 'I thought I didn't need anyone here with me today but I was wrong. Thanks for being here, Lily.'

'Oh, Tris, it's an honour. All I ask is for a big cuddle when she's born.'

'It's a deal.' He suddenly muttered something that sounded like, 'Thank God.'

'Tris?'

He grinned at her. 'The stent's in. Both my girls have come through the surgery with flying colours.'

'Fantastic.' She noticed the assistant surgeon suddenly raising both of his arms away from the surgical field as if he were a victim of an armed hold-up. He stepped back from the table. 'What's happening?'

'That's the surgical registrar. The operation's almost over and he's not required any more.'

As the unknown surgeon walked around, he glanced up at the glass. A set of very familiar brown eyes locked with hers. She stifled a gasp. *Noah.*

The Swiss chocolate colour of his eyes was familiar but she didn't recognise anything else about them. Gone was the serious, slightly mocking expression that normally resided there and in its place was unadulterated joy. His eyes positively sparkled, like fireworks on New Year's Eve.

Her heart kicked up, her knees sagged and lust wound down into every part of her, urging her dormant body to wake up. Wake up and dare to take a risk—live on the wild side and embrace it—like she'd often done before life with Trent had extinguished that part of her.

No. Not safe. You must stay safe.

Panic closed her eyes but the vision of his elation stayed with her—vibrant and full of life—permanently fused to her mind like a brand.

It scared the hell out of her.

CHAPTER FIVE

'MAN, THAT WAS a great day,' Noah said, smoothly changing through the gears as he took yet another bend on the narrow, winding and wet road back to Turraburra.

'I'm glad,' Lilia said with a quiet smile in her voice.

'Why?'

She sighed. 'Are you always so suspicious of someone being happy for you?'

He glanced at her quickly before returning his gaze to the rainy night, the windscreen wipers working overtime to keep the windshield clear. 'Sorry, but you have to admit we don't exactly get along.'

'That's true, I guess, but today I saw you in a new light.'

'Should I be worried?' he said, half teasing, half concerned.

'I guess I saw you on your home turf and I've never seen you look like that before. You looked happy.' Her fingers tangled with each other on her lap. 'You've really missed the Victoria and surgery, haven't you?

'Like an amputee misses his leg.' He shot her an appreciative glance, one part of him both happy and surprised that she'd drawn the connections. 'Couldn't you feel the vibe of the place? Being part of world-class surgery is my adrenalin rush.

'It bubbles in my veins and I love it. What you saw today, when Jeremy inserted that stent into the Hamilton-Lawrence baby's heart, is cutting-edge stuff. It's an honour and a privilege to be part of it and I want to be part of it. I didn't work this hard for this long to spend my life stuck in a backwater.'

'Let me take a wild stab in the dark that you're talking about a place like Turraburra.'

'Exactly. By the way, you owe another two dollars to the S jar,' he said lightly, then he sobered. 'But, seriously, doesn't it frustrate you on some level that you're so far away from the centre of things?'

'Not at all,' she said emphatically, the truth in her voice ringing out loud and clear in the darkness of the car.

'I can't believe you didn't even have to think about that for a second.'

'How is it any different from me asking you if being in Melbourne frustrates you on any level?'

He nodded thoughtfully. 'Fair point.'

'Noah, babies have been coming into the world in pretty much the same way for thousands of years so, for me, the joy comes from helping women, not from feeling the need to be constantly chasing new and exciting ways of doing things.'

He thought of his mother. 'There's nothing wrong with wanting to discover new techniques and new ways of doing things. It's how we progress, find cures for diseases, better ways of treating people.'

'I never said there was anything wrong with it.' She

suddenly pointed out the window and yelled, 'Wombat! Look out.'

His headlights picked up the solid black shape in the rain, standing stock-still on the road, right in the path of the car. He pulled the steering-wheel hard, swerving to avoid hitting and instantly killing the marsupial. Lilia's hands gripped the dash, stark white in the dark as the car heaved left. The tyres hit the gravel edge of the road and the car fishtailed wildly.

Don't do this. He braked, trying to pull the car back under control, but in the wet it had taken on its own unstoppable trajectory. The back wheels, unable to grip the gravel, skidded and the next moment the car pulled right, sliding across the white lines to the wrong side of the road. White posts and trees came at them fast and he hauled the wheel the other way, driving on instinct, adrenalin and fear.

The car suddenly spun one hundred and eighty degrees and stopped, coming to an abrupt halt and facing in the opposite direction from where they were headed. The headlights picked up shadows, the trees and the incessant rain, tumbling down from the sky like a wall of water. The wombat ambled in front of the car and disappeared into the bushes.

Noah barely dared to breathe while he did a mental checklist that all his body parts still moved and that he was indeed, alive. When reality pierced his terror, his half-numb fingers clumsily released his seat belt and he leaned towards Lilia, grabbing her shoulder. 'Are you okay?'

'I…I…' Her voice wobbled in the darkness. 'I thought for sure we'd slam into the trees. I thought we were dead.'

'So did I.' He flicked on the map reading light, needing to see her.

Her eyes stared back at him, wide and enormous, their blue depths obliterated by huge black discs. 'But we're not.'

'No.' He raised his right hand to her cheek, needing to touch her, needing to feel that she was in one piece. 'We're safe.'

'Safe.' She breathed out the word before wrapping her left hand tightly around his forearm as if she needed to hold onto something.

Her heat and sheer relief collided with his, calling to him, and he dropped his head close in to hers, capturing her lips in a kiss of reassurance. A kiss of mutual comfort that they'd survived unscathed. That they were fine and here to live another day.

Her lips were warm, pliant and, oh, so gloriously soft. As he brushed his lips gently against them, he tasted salt and sugar. God, he wanted to delve deep and taste more. Feel more.

He suddenly became aware she'd stilled. She was neither leaning into the kiss nor leaning back. She was perfectly motionless and for a brief moment he thought he should pull away—that his kiss was unwelcome— but then she made a raw sound in the back of her throat. Half moan, half groan, it tore through him like a primal force, igniting ten long days of suppressed desire.

He slid one hand gently around her neck, cupping the back of it and tilting her head. He deepened the kiss while he used his other hand to release her seat belt. Her arms immediately slid up around his neck and she met his kiss with one of her own.

If he'd expected hesitation and uncertainty, he'd

been wrong. Her tongue frantically explored his mouth as if she had only one chance to do so, branding him with her heat and her taste, and setting him alight in a way he'd never known. His blood pounded need and desire through him hot and fast, and his breathing came short and ragged. He wanted to touch her and feel her, wanted her to touch and feel him. Hell, he just wanted her.

His talented surgical fingers, usually so nimble and controlled, fumbled with the buttons on her blouse. Lilia didn't even try to undo his buttons—she just ripped. Designer buttons flew everywhere and then her palms pressed against his skin, searing him. Her lips followed, tracing a direct line along his chest to his nipples. Her tongue flicked. Silver spots danced before his eyes.

Somehow he managed to rasp out, 'Need more room.' Shooting his seat back, he hauled her over him. As she straddled him, her thighs pressed against his legs and she leaned forward, lowering her mouth to his again. Her hair swung, forming a curtain around their heads, encasing them in a blonde cocoon and isolating them from the real world. It was wild and crazy as elbows and knees collided with windows, the steering-wheel and the handbrake. A small part of him expected her to jolt back to sanity, pull back and scramble off him.

Thank God, it didn't happen.

He'd never been kissed like it. She lurched from ingénue to moments of total control. Her mouth burned hot on his and her body quivered against him, driving him upward to breaking point. She matched his every move with one of her own, and when he finally managed to unhook her bra she whipped off his belt. When he slid his hand under her skirt, caressing the skin of her inner thighs, she undid his fly. When he cupped her, she gripped him.

She rose above him a glorious Amazon—face flushed, eyes huge, full breasts heaving—and he wanted nothing more than to watch her fly. 'God, you're amazing.'

'Shush.' Lilia managed to sound the warning. She didn't want compliments, she didn't want conversation—she didn't want to risk anything being said that might make her think beyond this moment. She'd spent years living a safe and bland life and tonight she could have died. In this moment she needed to feel alive in a way she hadn't felt in years. The woman she'd once been—the one life had subjugated—broke through, demanding to be heard. She had Noah under her, his hands on her, and she was taking everything he offered.

'No condoms,' he said huskily. 'Sorry. Hope this will do.' His thumb rotated gently on her clitoris as his fingers slid inside her, moving back and forth with delicious and mind-blowing pressure.

She swayed against him, her hands moving on him trying to return the favour, but under his deft and targeted ministrations they fell away. Sensations built inside her, drowning out everything until nothing existed at all except pleasure. Sheer, glorious, pleasure. It caught her, pushing her upwards, pulling her forward, and spinning her out on an axis of wonder until she exploded in a shower of light far, far away from everything that tied her to her life.

As she drifted back to earth, muscles twitching,

chest panting, she caught his sparkling eyes and deliciously self-satisfied grin.

What have you done?

The enormity of what had just happened hit her like a truck, sucking the breath from her lungs and scaring her rigid.

If Lily hadn't known better she would have said she'd drunk a lot of tequila and today's headache was the result of a hangover. Only she knew she hadn't touched a drop of alcohol yesterday or today. All she wanted was to desperately forget everything about last night's drive home from Melbourne, but sadly it was all vividly crystal clear, including her screaming Noah's name when she'd come.

She ruffled her dog's ears. 'Oh, Chippy, I've been so sensible and restrained for so long, why did I have to break last night? Break with Noah?'

But break she had—spectacularly. How could she have put herself at risk like that? Left herself open to so many awful possibilities?

It was Noah, not a mass murderer.

We don't know that.

Oh, come on!

She blamed Isla's suggestion that people should have sex to defuse tension, Noah's look of utter joy in the operating theatre, which had reached out and deliciously wrapped around her, and finally, to cap it all off, their near-death experience. All of it had combined, making her throw caution to the wind. But despite how she was trying to justify her actions, the only person she could blame was herself. She'd spent all night wide awake, doing exactly that.

Gramps had even commented at breakfast that she looked in worse shape than he did. Since the insertion of his pacemaker he was doing really well and had a lot more energy than he'd had in a long time. For that she was grateful. She was also grateful that she hadn't seen Noah all morning.

Last night, after she'd scrambled off his lap in a blind panic and had said, 'Don't say a word, just drive,' he'd done exactly that. When he'd pulled up at the house just before eleven, he'd leaned in to kiss her on the cheek. She'd managed to duck him and had hopped out of the car fast. Using the door as a barrier between them, she'd thanked him for the ride and had tried to walk normally to the front door when every part of her had wanted to run. Run from the fact she'd just had sex in a car.

Dear God, she was twenty-nine years old and old enough to know better. She'd kept the wild side of herself boxed up for years and she still couldn't believe she'd allowed it to surface. Not when she had the physical evidence on her body constantly reminding her of the danger it put her in.

She lined her pens up in a row on her desk and straightened the files in her in-box. Yesterday was just a bump in the road of her life and today everything went back to normal. Normal, just like it had been for the last three years. Like she needed it to be. Safe. Controlled. Restrained. Absolutely drama-free.

A hysterical laugh rose in her throat. She should probably text Isla, telling her that sex didn't reduce tension at all. If anything, it made things ten times worse.

She dropped her head in her hands. She had to work with Noah for the next two and a half weeks and all the time he would know that if he tried, it barely took any time at all for him to strip away her reserve and reduce her to a primal mess of quivering and whimpering need. She'd unwittingly given him power over her—power she'd vowed no man would ever have over her again. Somehow she had to get through seventeen days before she could breathe easily again.

To keep her chaotic thoughts from ricocheting all over her brain, she decided to check her inventory for expired sterilised equipment and drugs nearing their use-by dates. There was nothing like order and routine to induce calm.

She was halfway through the job when a knock on her door made her turn.

'May I come in?'

Noah stood in the doorway in his characteristic pose of one hand pressed against the doorjamb, only this time he looked very different. Gone was the suit and tie he'd worn during his first week and a half in Turraburra. Today his long legs were clad in chinos and his chest, which she now knew was rock-hard muscle, was covered in a green, pink, blue and orange striped casual shirt. His brown curls bounced and his eyes danced. He looked…relaxed.

Her heart leaped, her blood pounded and tingles of desire slammed through her, making her shimmer from top to toe. If her body had been traitorously attracted to the strung-out Noah, it was nothing compared to its reaction to the relaxed Noah.

Distance. Keep your distance. 'I'm pretty busy, Noah. Did you need something?'

His mouth curved up in a genuine smile that raced to his eyes. 'I figured, seeing as we've done things back to front and had sex first, we should probably go out to dinner.'

'I...I don't think that's a good idea,' she said hurriedly, before her quivering body overrode her common sense and she accepted the unexpected invitation. 'And we didn't actually have sex,' she said, feeling mortified that she'd been the one to have the orgasm while he'd been left hanging.

His brows rose. 'I'm pretty certain what we did comes under the banner of sex.'

The irony of what she'd said wasn't lost on her, given she always put a lot of emphasis in sex ed classes with the local teenagers on the fact that sex wasn't just penetration. 'Either way, it was a mistake so why compound it by going on a date?'

'A mistake?' The words came out tinged with offence and a flare of hurt momentarily sparked in his eyes before fading fast. 'If it was a mistake, why did you have sex with me?'

She didn't meet his gaze. 'I panicked.'

'You panicked?'

She heard the incredulity in his voice and it added to the flash of hurt she'd seen. She felt bad and it made her tell him the truth. 'I'd just had a near-death experience and I hadn't had sex in a very long time.'

'So you used me?'

Her head jerked up at the slight edge in his voice. 'Oh, and you didn't use me?'

A look of distaste and utter indignation slid across his face and two red spots appeared on his cheeks as if she'd slapped him. 'No! I don't use women. What the hell sort of a man do you think I am?'

A kernel of guilt burrowed into her that because

of Trent's role in her life she'd offended him, but she wasn't about to explain to him why. 'Look, we're adults. You don't need to appease your conscience by buying me dinner. What happened happened and now we can just forget about it and move on.'

'I don't want to forget about it,' he said softly, as he moved towards her.

Panic had her pulling a linen skip between them but he put his hands on either side of it and leaned in close. 'Do you?'

His soft words wound down into her, taunting her resolve. *I have to forget.*

He suddenly straightened up and opened his hands out palms upward in supplication. 'Come to dinner, Lily. You never know, we might actually enjoy each other's company.'

'I really don't think—'

'I promise you it will just be dinner.' He gave a wry smile. 'Sex is an optional extra and totally your choice. I'm not here to talk you into or out of it.'

She stared at him, trying desperately hard to read him and coming up blank. Why was he was doing this? Why was he being so nice? She sought signs of calculation but all she could see was genuineness. It clashed with everything she wanted to believe about him—about all men—only she got a sense that if she said no, she'd offend him. Again. 'Okay, but I'm paying.'

His jaw stiffened. 'I'm not an escort service. We'll go Dutch.'

The memory of him stroking her until she'd come made her cheeks burn hotly. 'I guess…um…that's fair.'

Shoving his hands in his pockets, he said, 'I'd offer to pick you up but that would probably upset your in-

dependent sensibilities. Emergencies and babies excepted, how does seven at Casuarina sound?'

She was so rusty at accepting invitations that her
voice came out all scratchy. 'Seven sounds good.'

He shot her a wary smile. 'Cheer up. You never
know, you might just enjoy yourself.'

Before she could say another word, he'd turned and
left.

Please, let a baby be born tonight. Please.

But, given her luck with men, that was probably not
going to happen.

CHAPTER SIX

NOAH FULLY EXPECTED Lily to cancel. Every email and text that had hit his phone during the afternoon he'd opened with that thought first and foremost in his mind. Now, as he sat alone in the small restaurant, he fingered his phone, turning it over and over, still waiting for the call to come. He caught sight of his countdown app and opened it. Four hundred and fifty-six hours left in Turraburra. Almost halfway.

Why are you even here in this restaurant? That thought had been running concurrently with *She will cancel.* He had no clue why he'd insisted they have dinner. It wasn't like he'd never taken the gift of casual sex before and walked away without a second glance. Granted, he'd not actually hit the end zone last night, but watching Lilia shatter above him had brought him pretty damn close. And it had felt good in a way he hadn't experienced in a long time.

Something about her—the wildness in the way she'd kissed him, the desperation in the way she'd come and then her rapid retreat into herself afterwards had kick-started something in him. A desire to get to know her more. A vague caring—something he'd put on ice years ago.

It confused him and dinner had seemed a way of exorcising both the confusion and the caring. Hell, her reaction to his dinner invitation had almost nuked the caring on the spot. He'd never had a woman so reluctant to accept his invitation and it had fast become a challenge to get her to accept. He refused to be relegated to the category of *a mistake*. He checked his watch. Seven-ten p.m.

'Would you like a drink, Dr Jackson?' Georgia Brady asked, as she extended the black-bound wine list towards him.

Noah had recently prescribed the contraceptive pill for the young woman and had conducted the examination that went along with that. He was slightly taken aback to find she was now his waitress. 'I think I'll wait, thanks.'

'Who are you waiting for?'

'Lilia Cartwright,' he answered, before he realised the inappropriateness of the question. Small towns with their intense curiosity were so not his thing. 'Aren't there other customers needing your attention?'

Georgia laughed as she indicated the virtually empty restaurant. 'Thursday nights in Turraburra are pretty quiet. Are you sure Lily's coming? It's just she never dates.'

'It's a work dinner,' he said quickly, as a crazy need to protect Lilia from small-town gossip slugged him.

Georgia nodded. 'That makes more sense. Oh, here she is. Hi, Lily.'

Lily stood in the entrance of the restaurant and slipped off her coat, wondering for the thousandth time why she was there. Why she hadn't created an excuse to cancel. That was the one drawback of a small town. Without a cast-iron reason it was, oh, so easy to be caught out in a lie because everybody knew what everyone was doing and when they were doing it. So, here she was. She'd eat and leave. An hour, max.

Plastering on a smile, she walked forward and said, 'Hi, Georgia,' as she took her seat opposite Noah, who'd jumped to his feet on her arrival. 'Noah.'

He gave her a nod and she thought he looked as nervous as she felt.

'If this is a work dinner, will you want wine?' Georgia asked.

'Yes.'

Noah spoke at exactly the same moment as she did, his deep 'Yes' rolling over hers.

They both laughed tightly and Georgia gave them an odd look before going to fetch the bottle of Pinot Gris Noah ordered.

Lily fiddled with her napkin. 'This is a work dinner?'

Noah grimaced. 'Georgia was giving me the third degree about my date and as the town believes you're married to your job, I thought it best not to disabuse them.'

She stared at him, stunned. 'How do you know the town thinks I'm married to my job?'

'Linda Sampson told me on my first day,' he said matter-of-factly, before sipping some water. 'So are you?'

She didn't reply until Georgia had finished pouring the wine, placed the bottle in an ice bucket by the side of the table and left. 'I love my job but I also love Gramps, Chippy and bushwalking. Plus, I'm involved as a volunteer with Coastcare so I live a very balanced life,' she said, almost too emphatically. 'It's just that Linda wants to marry off every single woman in town.'

'And man,' Noah said, with a shake of his head. 'The first day I was here she ran through a list of possible candidates for me, despite the fact I'd told her I wasn't looking.'

'Why aren't you looking?' The question came out before she'd censored it.

His perceptive gaze hooked hers. 'Why aren't you?'

So not going there. She dropped her gaze and sipped the wine, savouring the flavours of pear and apple as they zipped along her tongue. 'This is lovely.'

'I like it. The Bellarine Peninsula has some great wineries.'

'You mean there are times you actually leave Melbourne voluntarily?' she teased.

He grinned. 'I've been known to when wine's involved.'

'There's a winery an hour away from here.'

'This far south?'

She smiled at his scepticism. 'They only make reds but the flavours are really intense. You should visit. You get great wine, amazing views across Wilson's Prom and wedge-tailed eagles.'

His eyes, always so serious, lightened in self-deprecation. 'I guess I should have read the tourist information they sent me after all.'

She raised her glass. 'To the hidden gems of Turraburra.'

'And to finding them.' He clinked her glass with his, his gaze skimming her from the top of her forehead, across her face and down to her breasts and back again.

A shiver of need thundered through her and she hastily crossed her legs against the intense throb, trying to quash it. She gulped her wine, quickly draining the glass and then regretting it as the alcohol hit her veins.

Stick to pleasantries. 'The eye fillet here is locally grown and so tender it melts in your mouth.'

'Sounds good to me,' he said, as he instructed Georgia that he wanted his with the blood stopped. When the waitress had refilled their glasses, removed the menus and departed for the kitchen, he said, 'I saw your grandfather this morning for his check-up. He's a new man.'

'He is. Thanks.'

He gave a wry smile. 'Don't thank me. Thank the surgeon who inserted the pacemaker and fixed the problem.'

'A typical surgeon's response. Noah, you made the diagnosis so please accept the thanks.' She fiddled with the base of her glass and sought desperately for something to say that was neutral. 'So you know I grew up in Turraburra, what about you?'

He took a long drink of his wine.

Her curiosity ramped up three notches. 'Is it a secret?'

'No. It's just not very interesting.'

'Try me.'

'West of Sydney.'

She thought about his reaction to Turraburra and wondered if he'd grown up in a small town. 'How west? Orange? Cowra?'

'Thankfully, not that far west.' He ran his hand through his curls as if her questions hurt. 'I grew up in a poverty-stricken, gossip-ridden town on the edge of Sydney. Not really country but too far away to be city. I hated it and I spent most of my teenage years plotting to get out and stay out.'

She thought about her own childhood—of the freedom of the beach, of the love of her grandfather and the circle of care from the town—and she felt sad for him. 'Do your parents still live there?'

He shook his head. 'I was a change-of-life baby. Totally unexpected and my mother was forty-four when she had me. They're both dead now.'

She knew all about that. 'I'm sorry.'

'Don't be.'

The harshness of his reply shocked her. 'You're glad your parents are dead?'

A long sigh shuddered out of him and he suddenly looked haggard and tired. 'Of course not, but I'm glad they're no longer suffering.'

'So they didn't die from old age?'

'Not exactly.' He cut through the steak Georgia had quietly placed in front of him. 'My father died breathless and drowning in heart failure and my mother...' He bit harshly into the meat.

His pain washed over Lily and she silently reached out her hand, resting it on top of his. He stared at it for a moment before swallowing. 'She died a long and protracted death from amyotrophic lateral sclerosis.'

Motor neurone disease. 'Oh, God, that must have been awful.' She caught a flash of gratitude in his eyes that she understood. 'Did you have a good nursing home?'

'At the very end we did but for the bulk of two years I cared for her at home.' His thumb moved slowly against her hand, almost unconsciously, caressing her skin in small circular motions.

Delicious sensations wove through her, making her mind cloud at the edges. She forced herself to concentrate, working hard to hear him rather than allowing herself to follow the bliss. 'That's…that's a long time to care for someone.'

His mouth flattened into a grim line as he nodded his agreement. 'It is and, to be honest, when I took the job on we didn't have a diagnosis. I just assumed she'd need a bit of help for a while until she got stronger. I had no clue it would play out like it did, and had I known I might have…'

She waited a beat but he didn't say anything so she waded right on in. 'When did she get sick?'

'When I was nineteen. With illness, no timing is ever good but this totally sucked. I was living in Coogee by the beach, doing first-year medicine at UNSW and loving my life. It was step one of my plan to get out and stay out of Penrington.'

She thought of what he'd said about growing up in a poverty-stricken town. 'Because doctors are rarely unemployed?'

'That and the fact I was sixteen when my father died. I guess it's an impressionable age and I used to daydream that if I'd been a doctor I could have saved him.' He gave a snort of harsh laughter. 'Of course, I now know that no doctor could have changed the outcome, but at the time it was a driving force for me to choose medicine as a career.'

A stab of guilt pierced her under the ribs. She'd so easily assigned him the role of arrogant surgeon—a guy who'd chosen the prestigious speciality for the money—that she'd missed his altruism. 'You must have needed a lot of help to balance the demands of your study with helping your mum.'

He shook his head. 'My parents never had a lot of money and Mum gave up work to care for Dad in his last weeks of life. By the time she got sick, there wasn't any spare cash for a paid carer and there wasn't a lot of choice.'

'What did you do?'

He pulled his hand away from hers and ripped open the bread roll, jerkily applying butter. 'I deferred uni at the end of first year and took care of her.'

She thought about her own egocentric student days. 'That would have been a huge life change.'

His breath came out in a hiss. 'Tell me about it. I went from the freedom of uni where life consisted of lectures and parties to being stuck back in Penrington, which I'd thought I'd escaped. Only this time I was basically confined to the house. I spent a lot of time being angry and the rest of it feeling hellishly guilty as I watched my strong and capable mother fade in front of me.'

There weren't many nineteen-year-olds who'd take on full-time care like that and this was Noah. Noah, who seemed so detached and closed off from people. She struggled to wrap her head around it. 'But surely you had some help?'

He shrugged. 'The council sent a cleaner every couple of weeks and a nurse would visit three times a week, you know the drill, but the bulk of her care fell to me.' He took a gulp of the wine before looking at her, his eyes filled with anguish. 'Every day I was haunted by a thousand thoughts. Would she choke on dinner? Would she aspirate food into her lungs? Would she fall? Would she wake up in the morning?'

Lily heard the misery and grief in his voice and her heart wept. This brisk, no-nonsense, shoot-from-the-hip doctor—the man who seemed to have great difficulty empathising with patients—had nursed his mother. 'I… That's… It…'

'Shocks you, doesn't it?' he said drily, accurately gauging her reaction. 'Part of it shocks me too but life has a way of taking you to places you never expected to go.'

He returned to eating his meal and she ate some of hers, giving him a chance to take a break from his harrowing story. She was certain he'd use the opportunity to change the subject and she knew she'd let him. She was familiar with how hard it was to revisit traumatic memories, so it came as a surprise when he continued.

'You really don't learn a lot more than anatomy and some physiology in first-year medicine and I truly believed we'd find a doctor who could help Mum.' His hand sneaked back to hers, covering it with his warmth. 'We went from clinic to clinic, saw specialist after specialist, tried three different drug trials and nothing changed except that Mum continued to deteriorate. In all those months, not one person ever said it was hopeless and that there was no cure.' His mouth curled. 'I've never forgiven them for that.'

'And yet you still had enough faith to return to your studies and qualify as a doctor?'

'I became a surgeon,' he said quietly but vehemently. 'Surgery's black and white. I see a problem and I can either fix it or I can't. And that's what I tell my patients. I give it to them straight and I *never* give them false hope.'

And there it was—the reason he was so direct. She'd been totally wrong about him. It wasn't deliberate rudeness—it came from a heartfelt place, only the message got lost in translation and came out harsh and uncaring. 'There's a middle line between false hope and stark truth, Noah,' she said quietly, hoping he'd actually hear her message.

He pulled his hand away. 'Apparently so.'

Her hand felt sadly cool and she struggled not to acknowledge how much she missed his touch.

Noah helped Lily into her coat, taking advantage of the moment to breathe in deeply and inhale her perfume. All too soon, her coat was on and it was time for him to open the front door of Casuarina and follow her outside onto the esplanade. The rhythmic boom of the waves against the sand enveloped them and he had to admit it had a soothing quality. He glanced along the street. 'Where's your car?'

She thrust her hands into her coat pockets, protecting them against the spring chill. 'I walked.'

'I've got mine. I can drive you home.'

Her eyes widened for a second and he caught the moment she recalled exactly what had happened the last time they had been in his car. Sex. The topic they'd both gone to great lengths to avoid talking about tonight. The one thing he'd told her was her choice.

He didn't want her to bolt home alone so he hastily amended his offer. 'Or I can walk you home, if you prefer.'

She tilted her head and studied him as if she couldn't

quite work him out and then she gave him a smile full of gratitude. 'Thanks. A walk would be great.'

'A walk it is, then.' She could go from guardedly cautious to sexy in a heartbeat and it disarmed him, leaving him wondering and confused. With one of her hands on her hip, he took advantage of an opportunity to touch her and slid his arm through hers. 'Which way?'

She glanced at his arm as if she was considering if she should allow it to remain there but she didn't pull away. 'Straight ahead.'

The darkness enveloped them as they strolled out of the pool of light cast by the streetlamp. Unlike Melbourne, there weren't streetlights every few houses—in fact, once you left the main street and the cluster of shops on the esplanade there were very few lights. He glanced up into the bright and cluttered Milky Way. 'The stars are amazing here.'

'The benefits of barely any light pollution. Are you interested in astronomy?'

He mused over the question. 'I'm not saying I'm not interested, it's just I've never really given it much thought.'

'Too busy working and studying?'

'You got it.'

She directed them across the street and produced a torch from her pocket as they turned into an unpaved road. 'How far away are you from taking your final exams?'

'Six months,' he said, trying really hard to sound neutral instead of bitter and avoid yet another city-ver-sus-country argument.

She stopped walking so suddenly that his continued

motion pulled her into his chest and her torch blinded him. 'What's wrong? Did you leave something at the restaurant?' he asked, seeing floaters as he turned off the torch.

'Six months?' Her voice rose incredulously. 'That close?' Her hands gripped his forearms. 'Noah, you should be in Melbourne.'

Her unexpected support flowed into him. 'You won't get an argument from me.'

'So why are you here?'

Her voice came out of the dark, asking the same question she'd posed almost two weeks ago. Back then he'd dodged it, not wanting to tell her the truth. Admitting to frailties wasn't something he enjoyed doing. Then again, he hadn't told anyone in a very long time about the dark days of caring for his mother and although he'd initially been reluctant, telling Lily the story at dinner hadn't been the nightmare he'd thought it would be.

Don't expose weakness.

She'll understand.

Hell, she'd hinted at dinner that she suspected so what was the point in avoiding the question? He sucked in a deep breath of sea air and found his fingers playing with strands of her hair. 'The chief of surgery believes if I sat the communication component of my exams now, I'd fail. He sent me down here for a massive increase in patient contact when they're awake.'

Her fingers ran along the lapel of his jacket and then she took the torch back from him, turning it on. Light spilled around them. 'Do you think you're improving?'

God, he hoped so. He'd been trying harder than he

ever had before but it didn't come easily. 'What do you think?'

She worried her bottom lip.

He groaned as his blood pounded south. 'Lily, please don't do that unless you want me to kiss you.'

'Sorry.'

Her voice held an unusual trace of anxious apology, which immediately snagged him. 'Don't be sorry. But, seriously, do you think I'd pass now?'

She sighed. 'Do you promise not to yell?'

'Come on, Lily,' he said bewildered, 'I'm asking for your opinion. Why would I yell?'

She gave a strangled laugh. 'Because what I'm about to say may not be what you want to hear.'

He gently tucked her hair behind her ears, wanting to reassure her. 'I've been watching you for a week and a half and you have a natural gift with people. I want and need your opinion.'

She was quiet for a moment and when she spoke her voice was soft and low. 'I think you're doing better than when you arrived.'

Her tone did little to reassure him. 'But?'

'But you're not quite there yet.'

Damn it. Every part of him tightened in despair and he ploughed his hands through his hair. He'd thought what he was doing was enough and now that he knew it wasn't, he had no clue what else he could try.

She reached up, her hand touching his cheek. 'I can help, Noah.'

The warmth of her hand dived into him, only this time, along with arousal, came something else entirely. He didn't know how to describe it but hope was tangled up in it. 'How?'

Her hand dropped away and she recommenced walking as if she'd regretted the intimate touch. 'It's no different from surgery.'

'It's hugely different from surgery,' he said, non-plussed.

'I meant,' she said kindly, 'it's a skill you can learn.'

'And you're willing to teach me? Why?'

She paused outside a house whose veranda lamp threw out a warm, golden glow. When she looked up at him he caught a war of emotions in her eyes and on her pursed lips. 'Because, Noah, despite not wanting to and despite all logic, I like you.'

He should be affronted but the words made him smile. 'Aw, you're such a sweet talker,' he teased. 'Does this mean I'm no longer a mistake?'

She tensed. 'Goodnight, Noah.'

Crazy disappointment filled him that she was going to turn and disappear inside. He wasn't ready to let her go just yet. 'Lily, wait. I'm sorry.' He wanted her back in his arms and to kiss her goodnight but he had the distinct impression that if he pulled her towards him she'd pull right back. The woman who'd thrown caution to the wind last night had vanished like a desert mirage.

He shot for honesty. 'I had a good time tonight.'

She fiddled with her house key. 'So did I. Thanks.'

'You're welcome.' He suddenly gave in to an overwhelming urge to laugh.

Her chin instantly jutted. 'What's so funny?'

'This.' He threw out his arms, indicating the space between them. 'A first date after we've touched each other in amazing places and I've almost come just watching you fall apart over me. Yet I'm standing here on your grandfather's veranda like an inexperienced teenager, wondering if I'm allowed to kiss you good-night.'

Her feet shuffled, her heels tapping on the wooden boards. 'You still want to kiss me, even though you know nothing else is going to happen?'

Something in her quiet voice made goose-bumps rise on his arms. 'Lily, what's going on?'

'Nothing. Just checking.'

The words came out so sharply they whipped him. The last thing he expected was for her to step in close, wrap her arms around him, rise up on her toes and press her lips to his.

But he wasn't complaining. His arms tightened around her as he opened his mouth under hers. Orange and dark chocolate rushed him, tempting him, addict-ing him, and he moaned softly as his blood thundered pure pleasure through his veins. It hit his legs and he sat heavily on the veranda ledge of the old Californian bungalow, pulling her in close, loving the feel of her breasts and belly pressing against him.

She explored his mouth like a sailor in uncharted waters—flicking and probing, marking territory—each touch setting fire to a new part of him until he was one united blaze, existing only for her. The fren-zied exploration slowly faded and with one deep kiss she stole the breath from his lungs.

A moment later, wild-eyed and panting, she swung out of his arms and opened the front door.

'Lily,' he croaked, barely able to see straight and struggling to construct a coherent sentence, 'not that I'm complaining, but somehow I think I still owe you a kiss.'

A wan smile lifted the edge of her mouth. 'Not at all. Goodnight, Noah.'

As the door clicked shut softly, he had the craziest impression that he'd just passed some sort of a test.

CHAPTER SEVEN

LILY CLOSED THE DOOR behind her and sagged back against it.

What on earth were you thinking?

I wasn't thinking at all.

And that was the problem. What had started out as a kiss to test if what Noah had said about sex being her choice was really true had almost culminated in something else entirely. Thank goodness they'd been on Gramps's front veranda—that had totally saved her.

She pushed off the door and headed to the bathroom to splash her burning face and body with cold, cold water. Damn it, she should never have agreed to dinner. She could rationalise her reaction in the car last night as a response to trauma. She had no such luxury tonight. Dinner had been a huge mistake. If she hadn't gone to dinner she wouldn't have seen a vulnerable side to a guy she'd pegged as irritable and difficult. She desperately needed to see him as arrogant, irascible, opinionated, unfeeling and short-sighted, because that gave her a buffer of safety. Only he really wasn't any of those things without good reason and *that* had decimated her safety barrier as easily as enemy tanks rolling relentlessly into a demilitarised zone.

At dinner he'd been the perfect gentleman and he'd walked her home, and—this still stunned her—he'd asked her permission to kiss her goodnight. He was all restraint while she… *Oh, God.* She groaned at the memory and studied herself in the bathroom mirror.

Face flushed pink, pupils so large and black they almost obliterated the blue of her irises, and her hair wild and untamed, framing her cheeks. She looked like an animal on heat. One kiss and she'd been toast. Toast on fire, burning brightly with flames leaping high into the air. Feeling alive for the first time in, oh, so long, and she both loved and feared the feeling.

Why fear it? He kept his word.

And that scared her most because it tempted her to trust again.

'You're looking tired,' Lily said to Kylie Ambrose as she took her blood pressure. 'Are you getting any rest?'

'With three kids? What do you think?'

Lily wrapped up the blood-pressure cuff. 'I think that as tomorrow's Saturday you need to get Shane to take the kids out for the day and you need to sleep.'

'Shane's working really hard at the moment, Lily. He needs to rest too.'

Lily's pen paused on the observation chart and she set it down. 'Shane's not six months pregnant, Kylie.'

'Can you imagine if guys got pregnant? They'd have to lie down for the whole nine months.' Kylie's laugh sounded forced. 'You know tomorrow's the footy so he can't mind them.'

'Sunday, then,' Lily suggested, with a futility she didn't want to acknowledge.

Despite the fact she was both taller and fitter than

Shane Ambrose, he was the sort of man she avoided. He reminded her too much of Trent—the life of the party, charming and able to hold a crowd in the palm of his hand, flirting shamelessly with all the women of the town while Kylie, so often pregnant, stood on the sidelines and watched.

'Shane insists that Sunday's family day,' Kylie said in a tone that brooked no further comment. 'I promise I'll catch up on some sleep next week.'

'Great,' Lily said, stifling a sigh and knowing it was unlikely to happen. 'Your ankles are a little puffy so I want to see you next week too.'

'Shane's not going to like that.'

Memories of Trent trying to control her made Lily snap. 'Tell Shane if he has a problem with the care you're receiving, he can come and talk to me and Dr Jackson.' And she'd tell Noah that Shane Ambrose was the one person he didn't have to be polite with. In fact, she'd love it if he gave the man some of his shoot-from-the-hip, brusquely no-nonsense medical advice.

Kylie immediately backpedalled. 'That's not necessary, Lily. Of course Shane wants the best for me and the kids.'

Lily wasn't at all sure Shane Ambrose wanted the best for his family but she felt bad for being short with Kylie. 'If it helps, bring the kids with you to the appointment. Karen and Chippy can keep them entertained while I see you.'

Kylie gave her a grateful look. 'Thanks, Lily. Not everyone understands.'

Lily understood only too well and that was the problem.

* * *

Noah heard the click-clack of claws on the floor and turned to see Chippy heading to his basket. 'Hey, boy, what are you doing here on a Saturday?'

The dog wandered over to him, presenting his head to be patted. It made Noah smile. When he'd arrived he'd thought the idea of a dog in a medical practice was ridiculous but two weeks down the track he had to agree that Chippy had a calming effect on a lot of the patients. 'Where's your owner, mate?'

'Right here.'

He spun around to see Lily wearing three-quarter-length navy pants, a cream and navy striped top and bright red ballet flats—chic, casual, weekend wear. She looked fresh and for Lily almost carefree. Almost. There was something about her that hovered permanently—a reserve. An air of extreme caution, except for the twice it had fallen away spectacularly and completely. Both times had involved lust. Both times he'd been wowed.

He hadn't seen her since Thursday night when she'd kissed him like he was the last man standing. He'd thought he'd died and gone to heaven. As a result, his concentration had been hopeless yesterday, to the point that one of the oldies in the nursing home had asked him if he was the one losing his memory.

With a start, he realised he was staring at her. 'You look good.' The words came out gruff and throaty. 'Very nautical.'

She shrugged as if the compliment unnerved her. 'It's the first sunny day we've had this season so I hauled out the spring clothes to salute the promise of summer.'

'As you're here on a Saturday, I guess that means you have a labouring woman coming in?'

'No. I'm here to help you, like I promised.'

Confusion skittered through him. 'But I got the book you left in my pigeonhole and I've read it.' It was a self-help guide that he'd forced himself to read and had been pleasantly surprised to find that, instead of navel-gazing mumbo-jumbo, it actually had some reasonable and practical suggestions. 'Is there more?'

'Yes.' Her mouth curved up into a smile. 'This is Noah's Practical Communication Class 102.'

'I guess that's better than 101,' he grumbled.

'That's the spirit, Pollyanna,' she said with a laugh, as her perfume wafted around him.

He wanted so badly to reach out and grab her around the waist, feel her against him and kiss those red, ruby lips. He almost did, but three things stopped him.

Number one: he was at work and a professional.

There's no one else here yet so it would be okay.

Shut up.

Number two: after two nights of broken sleep and reliving their exhilarating and intoxicating random hook-ups, he'd decided that the best way to proceed with Lily was with old-fashioned dating. Not that he really knew anything about that because his experience with women came more under the banner of hook-ups rather than dating, but his month in Turraburra was all about firsts.

Number three: Karen chose that moment to march through the door like the Pied Piper, with half a dozen patients trailing in behind her.

If he was brutally honest with himself, this was the *only* reason he didn't give in to his overwhelming desire to kiss Lily until she made that mewling sound in the back of her throat and sagged against him.

'No rest for the wicked, Doctor,' Karen said briskly, dumping her bag on the desk. 'Mrs Burke is up first.'

Smile, eye contact, greeting. He recalled the basics from the book. Smiling at the middle-aged woman, he said, 'Morning, Mrs Burke. Glorious day today.'

'For some perhaps,' she said snarkily as she stomped ahead of him down the hall.

'Deep breath, Noah,' Lily said quietly, giving his arm a squeeze before they followed their patient into the examination room.

His automatic response was to read Mrs Burke's history but as he turned towards the computer screen Lily cleared her throat. He stifled a sigh and fixed his gaze on his patient. 'How can I help you today, Mrs Burke?'

'You can't.' She folded her arms over her ample chest. 'Not unless you can pull any strings with the hospital waiting lists.'

'What procedure are you waiting for?'

'Gall bladder.'

'You're—' He stopped himself from saying, 'fair, fat and forty', which was the classic presentation for cholelithiasis. 'How many attacks have you had?'

'One. I thought I was having a heart attack but, according to the hospital in Berwick, one attack doesn't qualify as urgent so I'm on the waiting list. It's been three months and now on top of everything I have shocking heartburn. I feel lousy all the time.'

He tapped his pen, running through options in his

head. 'Is there any way you can afford to be a private patient?'

'Oh, right. I'm just waiting around for the hell of it.'

Frustration dripped from the words and he was tempted to suggest she donate to the sarcasm jar.

'I think Dr Jackson is just covering all the bases,' Lily said mildly.

Surprise rocked him. Had she just defended him? Or was she just worried he was going to be equally rude back to Mrs Burke? Ordinarily, he would have said what he always said to patients attending the out-patient clinic at the Melbourne Victoria, which was, 'You're just going to have to wait it out,' and then he'd exit the room quickly. Only that wasn't an option in Turraburra.

Try reflective listening. The self-help book had an entire chapter on it, but Noah wasn't totally convinced it worked. 'I understand how frustrating it must be—'

'Do you really?' Claire Burke's eyes threw daggers at him. 'With that car you drive and the salary you earn, I bet you have private health insurance.'

He wanted to yell, *I'm a surgical registrar. Plumbers earn more than I do at the moment and my student debt is enormous,* but he blew out a breath and tried something he'd never done before. He gave a tiny bit of himself. 'I grew up in a family who couldn't afford insurance, Claire,' he said, hoping that by using her first name it might help defuse some of her anger. 'I can treat your heartburn and I'll make a call on Monday to find out where you are on the surgical waiting list. I will try and see if I can move you along a bit.'

He knew the chance of getting her moved up the list was about ten thousand to one. It frustrated him because the crazy thing was that an elective cholecys-tectomy was routine laparoscopic surgery. He could have operated on her but in Turraburra he didn't have access to any operating facilities.

You will in two weeks. The thought cheered him. 'Would you be able to go to East Melbourne for surgery if that was the only option?'

'I'll go anywhere.' Claire's anger deflated like a balloon as she accepted the prescription for esome-prazole. 'Thanks, Doctor. I appreciate that you took the time to listen.'

He saw her out and then turned to face Lily. 'You have no idea how much I wanted to tell her she was rude and obnoxious.'

Lily laughed. 'We all want to do that. The important thing is that you didn't.' She raised her hand for a high-five. 'You managed empathy under fire.'

He grinned like a kid let loose in a fairground, ri-diculously buzzed by her praise. 'Empathy is damn hard work.'

'It will get easier.' She steepled her fingers, bounc-ing them gently off each other. 'I do have one sugges-tion for you, though. Get into the habit of giving the medical history a brief scan before you go and get the patient. That way you're not tempted to read it and ignore them when they first arrive.'

'First I have to show empathy and now you're asking me to take advice as well?' he said with a grin. 'It's a whole new world.'

'Sarcasm jar?' she said lightly.

'I'll pay up on behalf of Claire Burke.' He clicked on the computer, bringing up the next patient history. 'Mr Biscoli, seventy-three and severe arthritis.'

'He's a honey and will probably arrive with produce from his garden for you.'

'It says here he's on a waiting list for a hip replacement.' Noah frowned. 'How long since the Turraburra hospital closed its operating theatre?'

'Five years. It's crazy really because the population has grown so much since then. Now we have a lot of retirees from Melbourne who come down here to live just as they're at an age where they need a lot more health services. The birth centre had to fight hard to exist because we can't push through double doors for an emergency Caesarean section, which is why the selection criteria are so strict.'

Noah leaned over to the intercom. 'Karen, on Monday can you do an audit on how many clinic patients are on surgical waiting lists, please?'

'I can do that, Doctor,' Karen said, sounding slightly taken aback.

'Thanks.' He released the button and leaned back, watching Lily. He laughed at her expression. 'I've just surprised you, haven't I?'

'You do that continually, Noah,' she said wryly.

'I'm taking that as a good thing.'

'I never expected any less.' She laughed and smile lines crinkled the edges of her eyes. She almost looked relaxed.

God, she was gorgeous and he wanted time to explore this thing that burned so hotly between them. He checked his watch as an idea formed and firmed. 'Emergencies excepted, I should be out of here by twelve-thirty. Let's have lunch together. We can put together a picnic and you choose the place. Show me a bit of Turraburra I haven't seen.'

Somewhere quiet and secluded so we can finish what we started the other night.

Based on previous invitations, he expected protracted negotiations with accompanying caveats and he quickly prepared his own strategic arguments.

'Sounds great.'

He blinked at her, not certain he'd heard correctly. 'So you're up for a picnic?'

Her eyes danced. 'Yes, and I know the perfect place…'

He was already picturing a private stretch of beach or a patch of pristine rainforest in the surrounding hills, a picnic rug, a full-bodied red wine, gourmet cheeses from the local cheese factory, crunchy bread from the bakery and Lily. Delectable, sexy Lily.

'The oval. Turraburra's playing Yarram today in the footy finals.'

Her words broke into his daydream like a machete, splintering his thoughts like kindling. 'You're joking, right?'

'About football?' She shook her head vehemently. 'Never. Turraburra hasn't won against Yarram in nine years but today's the day.'

And that's when it hit him—why she'd so readily accepted his invitation. They weren't going to be alone at all. They'd be picnicking with the entire town.

Lily wrapped the black and yellow scarf around Noah's neck. 'There you go. Now you're a Tigers fan.'

He gave a good-natured grimace. 'This wasn't quite what I had in mind when I suggested a picnic. Tell me, are you truly a football fan or are we here because you don't want to be alone with me?' His face sobered to deadly serious. 'If you don't want to build on what's already gone down between us, please just tell me now so I know the score and I'll back off.'

This is your absolute out. Her heart quivered at the thought. It should be an easy decision—just say no— but it wasn't because nothing about Noah was as clear-cut as she'd previously thought.

Why are you being so nice, Noah?

Trent had been nice at the start—charming, gener-ous and, unbeknownst to her at the time, calculatingly thoughtful. She already knew Noah was a far better man than Trent. He had a base honesty to him. A man who put his studies on hold to care for his dying mother wasn't selfish or self-serving. A man who confessed to his guilt about finding it so much harder than he'd thought it would be and yet hadn't walked away from it was a thousand times a better man than Trent.

She tied a loose knot in the scarf for the sheer rea-son that it gave her an excuse to keep touching him. 'I'm a die-hard footy fan to the point that I'll probably embarrass you by yelling at the umpire. And...' She hauled in a fortifying breath and risked looking into those soulful brown eyes that often saw far too much. 'I like being alone with you. It's just that I don't trust myself.'

He caught her hand. 'We're both adults, Lily. Having sex doesn't mean a lifelong commitment. It can just be fun.'

Fun. It had been fun and good times that had landed her in the worst place she'd ever been in her life and she wasn't going back there. 'That's what scares me.'

'Fun scares you?' He frowned down at her and then pulled her into him, pressing a kiss to her hair.

He smelled of sunshine and his heart beat rhythmi-cally against her chest. She didn't want to move.

He stroked her back. 'Let's just enjoy the match, hey?'

He could have done a million things—told her she was being silly, urged her to tell him why, cajoled her to leave the game and go and have the sort of fun they both wanted, but he didn't do any of those things. She fought the tears that welled in her eyes at his under-standing. 'Sounds good to me.'

He kept his arm slung casually over her shoulder as they watched the second quarter and she enjoyed its light touch and accompanying warmth. It felt delight-fully normal and it had been for ever since she'd asso-ciated normal with a guy.

The aroma of onions and sausages wafted on the air from the sausage sizzle. Farm and tradies' utes were parked along the boundary of the oval and families sat in chairs while the older kids sat on the utes' cabs for a bird's-eye view. The younger ones scampered back and forth between their parents and the playground. She recognised the Ambrose girls playing on the slide and glanced around for Kylie, but she couldn't see her.

The red football arced back and forth across the length of the oval many times, with the Turraburra Tigers and the Yarram Demons fighting it out. When Matty Abrahams lost possession of the ball to a De-mons player, who then lined up for a set shot at goal, Noah yelled, 'Chewy on your boot!'

She laughed and nudged him with her hip. 'Look at you. Next you'll be eating a pie.'

He grinned down at her, his eyes dancing. 'I never said I didn't enjoy football. I may have grown up in

New South Wales in the land of rugby league, but since coming to Melbourne I've adopted AFL. I get to games when I can.'

The man was full of surprises. The Turraburra crowd gave a collective groan as the ball sailed clearly through the Demons's goalposts, putting them two goals ahead.

The whirr of Gramps's gopher sounded behind her, followed by the parp-parp of his hooter. 'Hi, Gramps, I thought you were watching from the stands with Muriel?'

'I was and then Harry Dimetrious told me he'd seen you down here so I thought I'd come and say hello.'

'Good to see you out and about, Bruce,' Noah said, extending his hand.

Bruce shook it. 'You seem to be enjoying yourself, Doc,' he said shrewdly. 'I know you'll be on your best behaviour with my granddaughter.'

'Gramps!' Lily wanted to die on the spot.

Noah glanced between the two of them, his expression amused and slightly confused. He squeezed her hand. 'I like to think I'm always on my best behaviour with women, Bruce.'

Gramps assessed him with his rheumy but intelligent eyes. 'Long may it stay that way, son.'

Desperate to change the subject lest Noah ask her why, when she was almost thirty, her grandfather was treating him like they were teenagers, she saw a Demons player holding onto the ball for longer than the rules allowed. 'Ball,' she screamed loudly. 'Open your eyes, Ump! Do your job!'

Noah laughed. 'I think she's more than capable of standing up for herself, Bruce.'

She stared doggedly at the game, not daring to look at her grandfather in case Noah caught the glance.

By half-time the Turraburra Tigers trailed by fifteen points. 'Cheer up,' Noah said. 'It's not over until the final siren. I saw a sign in the clubrooms that the Country Women's Association are serving Devonshire tea. Come on, my shout.'

Still holding her hand, they walked towards the clubrooms and she felt the eyes of the town on her.

'Hey, Doc.' Rod Baker, her mechanic, pressed his hand against Noah's shoulder. 'You know Lily's special, right?'

Lily's face glowed so hotly she could have fried eggs on her cheeks. Before she could say a word, Noah replied without a trace of sarcasm, 'Without a doubt.'

'Just as long as you know,' Rod said, before removing his hand.

When she'd suggested the footy to him, she'd never anticipated Noah's public displays of affection. Granted, they'd done a lot more than handholding in his car and the other night she'd kissed him so hard she'd seen stars, but in a way it had been private, hidden from other people's eyes. She'd never expected him to act as if they were dating.

Not that she didn't like it. She really did but it put her between a rock and a hard place. If she pulled her hand away it would make him question her, and if she didn't then the town would.

A movement caught her eye and she saw Kylie Ambrose being pulled to her feet by her husband. 'Kylie, you okay?' she called out automatically, a shiver running over her skin.

'She's fine,' Shane said. 'Aren't you, love?'

'Yes,' Kylie said, brushing down her maternity jeans but not looking up. 'I just tripped over my feet. You know, pregnancy klutz.'

'I think I should just check you out,' Lily said, 'Just to make sure you and the baby are fine.'

'For God's sake, Lily,' Shane said. 'You were a panic merchant at school and you're still one.'

Before she could say another word, Noah stepped forward. 'I'm Dr Noah Jackson, Kylie. Were you dizzy before you fell?'

'Kylie's healthy as a horse, aren't you, love,' Shane said, putting his arm around his wife.

'She's also pregnant,' Noah said firmly. 'Have a seat on the bench, Kylie, and I'll check your blood pressure.'

Lily expected Kylie to object but she sat and started pulling up her sleeve, only to flinch, stop and tug it back down before pushing up the other sleeve.

Was she hiding something? Not for the first time, Lily wondered if she should tell Kylie a little something about her own past. 'Did you hurt your arm, Kylie?'

'No. It's just this one's closer to the doc.'

And it was. Two minutes later Noah declared Kylie's blood pressure to be normal, Shane teased his wife about having two left feet, and Lily felt foolish for allowing her dislike of Shane to colour her judgement. She really must stop automatically looking for the bad in men. Good guys were out there—Noah and her grandfather were perfect examples of that—and although Shane wasn't her type of guy, it didn't make him a bastard.

'We still have time for those scones,' Noah said, putting his hand gently under her elbow and propelling her into the clubrooms.

Linda Sampson served them with a wide smile. 'Lily, it's lovely to see you out and about.'

'I'm always out and about, Linda,' she said, almost snatching the teapot out of the woman's hands.

'You know what I mean, dear,' Linda continued, undeterred by Lily's snappish reply. 'Treat her nice, Dr Jackson.'

Lily busied herself with pouring tea and putting jam and cream on the hot scones. When she finally looked up, Noah's gaze was fixed on her.

'The town's very protective of you.'

'Not really. Have a scone.' She pushed the plate towards him.

'At first I thought all these warnings and instructions were about me. That I'd ruffled a few feathers.'

'I'm sure that's it,' she said desperately. 'But word will get around fast that you've improved out of sight. Claire Burke's a huge gossip and after this morning she'll be singing your praises.'

He didn't look convinced. 'The thing is, the more I think about it, every piece of advice I've been given is about you.' He leaned forward. 'Why is the town protecting you?'

'They're not.' She gulped her tea.

'Yeah, they are, and I can't afford any negative reports about me getting back to the Melbourne Victoria.'

Something inside her hurt. 'I guess we should stop whatever this is, then.'

His eyes darkened with a mix of emotions. 'That's not what I'm suggesting at all.'

She stood up, desperate to leave the claustrophobic clubrooms, leave the game, and leave the eyes of the town. 'Let's get out of here.'

He grabbed a scone and followed her outside as she half walked, half ran, able to outrun the eyes of the town but not the demons of her past.

'Where are we going?' Noah finally asked as they passed through the gates of the recreation reserve.

'Your place.'

CHAPTER EIGHT

THE MOMENT NOAH closed his front door Lily's body slammed into his, her hand angling his head, and then she was kissing him. *Yes!* His body high-fived and he was instantly hard. This was it—what he'd been dreaming about for days was finally going to happen. He was about to have sex again with Lily. He was so ready that he risked coming too soon.

Her lips and tongue roamed his, stealing all conscious thought. Nothing existed except her touch, her scent and her taste. Her wondrous, glorious, intoxicating taste that branded itself onto every part of his mouth. He went up in flames in a way he'd never done before.

She kicked off her shoes and then pulled his T-shirt over his head, sighing as she pressed her hands to his chest. 'I've been wanting to do that for hours.'

He pulled her T over her head and smiled at the filmy lace bra that hid nothing. 'You're gorgeous.'

She seemed to almost flinch and then she dropped her head and kissed his chest before licking his hard and erect nipples. For a second he lost his vision.

'Let's go have some fun,' she said, glancing around. Her gaze landed on the kitchen bench.

'Oh, yeah.' As he moved towards the kitchen his brain suddenly fired back into action. *Fun scares me.*

His body groaned. *Don't do this to me. Now is not the time to start thinking and acting like a girl.*

But try as he might, he couldn't banish Lily's words from his head. *Fun scares me.*

He thought about the time in the car when she'd let go of all restraint and how she was doing it again with such intensity, as if she was trying to forget something.

It was a mistake.

That's what she'd said last time and for some unfathomable reason he didn't want to have sex and then watch her run again.

Why? Usually that's exactly what you want—wish for even. But today it felt wrong. He didn't want to have Lily close up on him again and he knew as intimately as he knew himself that he sure as hell didn't want to be considered a mistake.

He held her gently at arm's length. 'I want so badly to have sex with you right now that it hurts.'

She grinned, her eyes wild. 'I'm glad.'

He stared down into her bluer-than-blue eyes and regret hammered him so hard it hurt to breathe. 'But I'm not having sex with you until you tell me what's going on.'

Panic spread through Lily's veins, pumping anxiety into every cell. She opened her mouth to say, 'Nothing is going on,' but immediately closed it. As much as she didn't want to tell him anything, he didn't deserve lies. Her brain whirred, trying to find a way to give him enough to satisfy him without opening the floodgates to a past she refused to allow back into her life.

She scooped up their shirts from the floor and threw his at him. 'Put that on so you don't distract me,' she said, trying to joke. It came out sad.

He silently obliged and by the time she'd pulled her T over her head he too was fully dressed. She'd hit the point of no return. *Say it fast and it won't hurt so much.* 'The town's protecting me because I was married.'

'You were married?' His echoing tone was a combination of horror and surprise.

'I was.' The memory of those pain-filled twenty-four months dragged across her skin like a blunt blade.

'And you're a widow?'

I wish. Oh, how I wish. She was tempted to say yes, but Turraburra knew that wasn't true. Although only her grandfather knew the full story about her marriage, everyone else knew she'd come home a faded version of her former self and without a husband. She was sure they'd speculated and talked about it amongst themselves, but instead of asking her what had happened, they'd circled her in kindness. 'No. I'm divorced.'

He looked seriously uncomfortable. 'Sorry.'

I'm not. She shrugged. 'It is what it is.'

'Am I the first guy since…?'

At least she could give him the absolute truth to one question. 'Virtually. There was one drunken episode the day my divorce came through but nothing since.' She wrung her hands. 'I'm sorry about my erratic behaviour,' she said, hoping the topic was almost done and dusted because she wasn't prepared to tell him any more. 'My libido's been dormant for so long and you've exploded it out of the blocks. I guess it scared me and I'm really sorry for saying you were a mistake. You're not at all, but you don't need to panic. I'm not looking for anything serious. We can enjoy whatever this is for what it is.' *Please.*

His keen gaze studied her and for a heart-stopping moment she thought he was going to ask her more questions. Questions she didn't want to answer. Information she never wanted him to know.

He wrapped his arms gently around her and pulled her into him, pressing a kiss to her forehead. 'As much as I find the out-of-control Lily a huge turn-on and sex in a car and on a kitchen counter reminds me I'm not past spontaneity, I want to make love to you in a bed. I want to be able to see you and touch you without the risk of either of us getting injured. I want your first time in a long time to be special.'

She hastily dropped her head onto his chest, hiding an errant tear that had squeezed out of her eye and was spilling down her cheek. *Oh, Noah, why do you have to be so caring?* But before she could overthink things he ran them down the hall to the bedroom.

'Sorry,' he said with an embarrassed grin as he pulled her into the room. 'I'd have made the bed if I'd thought I had a chance of being in it with you.'

She laughed. 'I only make mine on laundry day.'

'But I bet you do hospital corners.' He whipped off his shirt. 'I believe we were up to here when we hit pause.'

She gazed at his taut abdominal muscles, delineated pecs and a smattering of brown hair and sighed. 'I remember.'

'You're overdressed.' As his hands tugged on the hem of her shirt she raised her arms and let him pull it off. 'As much as I love pretty underwear, this has to go as well.' His fingers flicked the hooks on her bra and the straps fell across her shoulders.

As she stood there half-naked in the afternoon light without the cover of darkness, she suddenly felt extremely vulnerable and exposed. She dived for the bed, pulling at the sheet for cover, but it came away in her hand. 'And you don't do hospital corners at all, do you?'

He laughed. 'Obviously not very well but that's in my favour today.' He rolled her under him, gazing at her appreciatively. 'No hiding your beauty under sheets, Lily.' He lowered his mouth to her left breast and suckled her.

A flash of need—hot, potent and addictive—whooshed through her so fast and intense that she cried out and her hands rose to grip his shoulders.

He paused and raised his head, a slight frown on his face. 'You okay.'

'More than okay.'

His smile encapsulated his entire face. 'Excellent, but tell me if something's not working for you.'

He was killing her with kindness and she didn't know how to respond so she did what she always did when she got scared—she took control. Pulling his head down to her mouth, she kissed him, only this time he kissed her back. Hot, hard, sensual and electrifying, his mouth ranged over hers while his hands woke up the rest of her body.

She was hot but shivery, boneless with need yet taut with it too. She wanted his touch to go on for ever and at the same time she screamed for release. She ran her fingers through his hair, down his spine and across his hips. She soaked him in—the strength of his muscles, the hardness of his scapula, the dips between his ribs,

the rough and smooth of his skin—all of him. Her legs
tangled with his until he'd moved down her body and
she could no longer reach them. By the time his mouth
reached the apex of her thighs, she was writhing in
pleasure, burning with bliss and aching in emptiness.

'Noah.'

He raised his head. 'Yes?'

'As much as I appreciate your focused ministrations,
I feel I owe you after last time.'

'No hurry,' he said lazily. 'We've got all afternoon.'
He dropped his head and his tongue flicked her.

Her pelvis rose from the bed as her hands gripped
the edge of the mattress. 'What…what if I want to
hurry?'

'You sure?' His voice was as ragged as hers.

'God, yes.'

He moved, reaching for a condom, but she got there
first. 'Let me.'

'Next time,' he grunted, plucking the foil square
out of her hand.

'How do you want to do this?'

'I want to see you.'

She cupped his cheek. 'So do I.'

She tilted her hips and with her guidance he slowly
moved into her. Slick with need, she welcomed him
with a sob. 'I'd forgotten how good it could feel.'

'Let me remind you.'

He kissed her softly and she wrapped her legs high
around his hips, moving with him, feeling him sliding
against her, building on every delicious sensation he'd
created previously with his mouth and hands. She spi-
ralled higher and higher towards a peak that beckoned.
Pleasure and pain morphed together and she screamed

as she was flung far out of herself. Suspended for a moment in waves of silver and grey, she hovered before falling back to the real world.

Noah, moving over her, his face taut with restraint and his breath coming hard and fast, finally shuddered against her. She wrapped her arms around him as he came and she realised with a jolt that, once again, he'd put her needs first. No man had ever done that for her once, let alone twice.

It's just sex, remember.

It could only ever be sex.

Noah's blood pounded back to his brain and he quickly realised his limp and satiated body was at risk of flattening Lily. He kissed her swiftly on the lips, before rolling off her and tucking her in beside him. 'That was wonderful. Thanks.'

'Right back at you.' Her fingers trailed down his sternum.

He drew lazy circles on her shoulder. 'So how long has it been?'

'If I told you that I'd lose my air of mystery,' she said lightly.

Her tone didn't match the sudden tension around her mouth. 'Fair enough.' He wanted to know what was going on but most of him didn't want to lose the golden glow that cocooned them both. 'Let me just say, though, for the record, you haven't forgotten a thing.'

She gave a snort of embarrassed laughter. 'Thank you, I think.'

'I can't believe you're blushing,' he teased her. 'You're a conundrum, Lil.'

Her body went rigid. 'Don't ever call me that.'

Like the strike of an open palm against skin, her tone burned. 'Duly noted.'

She sighed and pressed a kiss to his chest. 'I'm sorry. I just hate that contraction of my name. It's so short that it's over before it's started. All my friends call me Lily.'

He wasn't exactly certain what he was to her or what he wanted to be. Lover? Yes. Colleague? Yes. 'Do I qualify as a friend?'

'A friend with benefits.'

A zip of something resembling relief whizzed through him with an intensity that surprised him. Usually, at this point, the snuggling with a woman was starting to stifle him and he was already planning his exit strategy.

'I need the bathroom,' she said, sitting up with her back to him.

Jagged, pale pink scars zigzagged over her shoulder and across her back. He automatically reached out to touch them. 'What happened here?'

She flinched then utterly stilled.

'Lily?'

'I fell through a plate-glass window. I'll be right back.' He expected her to elaborate on how the accident had happened but she didn't say anything more. He watched her disappear into the bathroom. When she returned and kissed him soundly, he totally forgot to ask.

Lily was pottering around the kitchen, supposedly cooking an omelette—something she did most Sunday nights—only tonight she was struggling to remember how to do it. She was struggling to remember anything prosaic and everyday. Usually by this time on a Sunday evening she had her list drawn up for the coming week, her work clothes washed and ironed, and if a baby wasn't on the way she was ready to sit down and relax.

Not tonight. Every time she tried to focus on something her brain spun off, reliving Noah's mouth on her body and his gentle hands on her skin—and they were always gentle—yet they could make her orgasm with an intensity she'd never experienced. Sure, she'd had sex before, thought it had been good even, and then when everything with Trent had started to change in ways she'd never anticipated—irrevocably and devastatingly final—it had taken the joy of sex with it.

It was a shock to discover she now craved sex with a passion that scared her. To crave sex was one thing—and in one way she was fine with that. What she didn't want was to crave Noah. She didn't want to crave any man because it left her wide open to way too much pain and grief.

Don't overthink this. Like Noah said, it's just temporary and for fun. It has a definite end date in less than two weeks when life returns to normal. Enjoy it and bank it for the rest of your life.

And she was enjoying it. They'd spent Saturday afternoon in bed and then she'd been called in to deliver a baby. Noah had visited the midwifery unit on Sunday morning to do the mother and baby discharge check and had brought with him pastries from the bakery and coffee he'd made himself. Once they'd waved goodbye to the Lexingtons and their gorgeous baby, they'd taken a walk along the beach and ended up in his bed. Again.

Distracted, she stared at the egg in her hand before

glancing into the bowl, consciously reminding herself how many eggs she'd already cracked. The ding-dong of the doorbell pealed, its rousing noise rolling through the house. Before she could say, 'I wonder who that is?' her grandfather called out, 'I'll get it.'

A moment later she heard, 'Hello, Doc.'

Her hand closed over the egg and albumen oozed through her fingers. *Noah? What was he doing here?*

His deep and melodic voice drifted down the hall, friendly and polite. 'Call me Noah, Bruce.'

'Right-oh. Come on in, then.' Footsteps made the old floorboards creak and then her grandfather called out, 'Lily, you've got a visitor.'

By the time she'd washed her egg-slimed hand, Noah's height and breadth was filling the small kitchen. 'Uh, hi,' she said, feeling ridiculously self-conscious because the last time she'd seen him he'd been delectably naked.

Now he was dressed deliciously in soft, faded jeans and a light woollen V-neck jumper, which clung to him like a second skin. She swallowed hard, knowing exactly how gorgeous the chest under the jumper was and what it tasted like. 'I... I thought you were studying?'

He put the bottle of wine he was holding on the bench. 'I was but your grandfather called and invited me to dinner. I have to eat so I thought...' He suddenly frowned. 'You knew I was coming, right?'

She shook her head slowly, wondering what her grandfather was up to. In three years he'd never invited someone around without telling her and he'd never once invited a man under the age of sixty. 'Ah, no. Gramps kept that bit of information to himself.'

'If it's a problem, I can go.'

Was it a problem? 'You being here's not a problem but I might need to have a chat with Gramps.'

He rounded the bench and reached for her. 'I'm glad he invited me.'

She stepped into his embrace, enjoying how natural it felt to be in his arms yet at the same time worried that it did. 'You say that now, but you have no clue if I can cook.'

His thumbs caressed her cheeks and his often serious eyes sparkled in fun. 'It's a risk I'm willing to take. I mean, how bad can it be?'

She dug him in the ribs. 'For that, you're now my kitchen hand.'

He grinned. 'I'm pretty handy with a knife.'

She pushed the chopping board towards him. 'In less than two weeks you'll be back operating,' she said, as much to remind herself as to remind him. 'How many hours away is that?' she teased, remembering his first day in Turraburra.

He pulled his phone out of his pocket. 'Two hundred and ninety-four hours and three minutes, twelve seconds.'

'Seriously? You've got an app?'

He had the grace to look sheepish. 'I was pretty ticked off when I first arrived here.'

'Were you?' She couldn't help laughing. 'I had no clue.'

'And that takes the total of the sarcasm jar to one hundred and forty dollars.' He got a self-righteous glint in his eye. 'You've now put more money in it than me.'

'That's a bit scary. That jar was for your problem, not mine.'

He gave her a look that said, *You can't be serious.*
'You use sarcasm like a wall.'

Did she? Before Trent, she hadn't been sarcastic at
all. Then again, she hadn't been wary and fearful either. The fact Noah had noticed she used sarcasm to
keep people at a distance worried her. She plonked an
onion on the chopping board to change the subject.
'Dice this.'

'About the app.' He started peeling the onion. 'When
I arrived I was taking my frustrations out on the town.
I thought I was being singled out from the other surgi-
cal registrars and being punished for no good reason.'
His warm eyes sought hers. 'It took you to show me
I had a problem and that I really needed to be down
here. I've hardly looked at the app since our trip back
from Melbourne.'

Trent had destroyed personal compliments for her—
she never completely trusted them and Noah's sat un-
easily. 'But you must be happy that your time's more
than half over. That you'll be back in Melbourne soon?'

'Put it this way...' He slid the diced onion off the
board and into her warmed and oiled pan. He stepped
in behind her, his body hugging hers, 'I have a strong
feeling the next twelve days are going to fly by.'

They settled into companionable cooking—he stood
next to her, sautéeing the fillings for the omelettes—
and his arm brushed hers as he moved, his warmth
stealing into her and settling as if it had a right to belong. He asked her about the music she liked, the books
she enjoyed—the usual questions people asked as they
got to know each other. It was so very conventional.
Normal. Terrifying.

'I've set the table,' Gramps announced, as he walked into the kitchen.

'I'm just about ready to serve up,' Lily said, pulling warmed plates out of the oven.

Bruce picked up the bottle of wine. 'This is a good drop, Noah,' he said approvingly. 'Might be a bit too good for eggs, though.'

'Never.' Noah smiled. 'I think it will go perfectly with our gourmet omelettes.'

'In that case, I'll open her up.' Gramps, who loved big, bold, Australian red wines, gave Lily a wicked wink before cracking the seal on the bottle. By the time they sat down at the table he'd poured three glasses. 'Cheers.'

'*Salute*,' Noah said easily.

It was a surreal moment and Lily silently clinked her glass against the other two, not knowing what to say. She was struck by the juxtaposition that Trent, whom she'd married, had never sat down to a meal in her grandfather's house and now Noah, who was nothing more than a wild and euphoric fling, was at the table, sharing their casual Sunday night meal. It was nothing short of weird.

Despite her discombobulation, conversation flowed easily around the table and both Noah and Gramps drew her into the chatter. Slowly, she felt herself start to relax. When the plates were cleared, Bruce suggested they play cribbage.

'Gramps, Noah has to study and—'

'I'm rusty, Bruce,' Noah cut across her, 'but, be warned, I used to play it a lot with my father before he got too sick to hold a hand.'

Bruce clapped his hand on Noah's shoulder in a

gesture of understanding. 'Tell you what. I'll give you a couple of hands to warm up then but then it's on for young and old.'

Noah laughed. 'That's a fair deal.'

Lily stared at him, once again flummoxed by his thousand sides—so many that he kept hidden from view. With his tailored clothes, his city sophistication and penchant for gourmet foods and wine, no one would ever guess that he loved footy and played cards. 'Do you play other games?'

'Does the Pope have an art collection?' He gave her a grin. 'My parents didn't have a lot of money but we had an annual beach camping holiday for two weeks every summer. If it rained and I couldn't surf, we'd play cards and board games. You name it, I've played it.'

'Me too,' she said, remembering her own childhood summers and Gramps teaching her the card game Five Hundred, 'but I bet you played to win.'

'Of course.' A bewildered look crossed his face. 'Why else would you play?'

This was pure Noah. 'Oh, I don't know. What about for the sheer enjoyment of it and the company?'

He shuffled the deck of cards like a professional. 'It is possible to do both.'

'The man's right, Lily,' Gramps said, rubbing his hands together. 'Enough of the talk, let's play.'

Over the next hour Lily watched, fascinated as the two men battled it out both determined to win. Despite the heady competition and the good-natured trash and table talk, a lot of laughter and fun ensued. It had been a long time since she'd seen her grandfather quite so animated.

To Gramps's delight, he beat Noah by the barest of

margins. 'You'll have to come back another time and try again.'

Noah rose to his feet and shrugged into his jacket with a smile. 'Next time we'll play poker.'

Bruce shot out his hand. 'You're on.'

Lily walked Noah outside. 'It was generous of you to give up your evening and play cards with Gramps.'

A slight frown marred his forehead. 'You think I was just being polite?'

'Playing cards with an old man? Yes, I do.'

He sighed. 'Lily, surely you know me well enough to know that I wouldn't have accepted Bruce's invitation for dinner or cards if I didn't want to.'

But that was the problem—every time she thought she had him worked out he'd go and do something totally unexpected. Every time it happened it humanised him for her, making her think way beyond the sexy guy and skilled lover. Making her want to hope.

And that scared her more than anything.

CHAPTER NINE

NOAH STRODE ALONG the main street, eating his ham and salad baguette as he went and enjoying the sunshine on his face. Unlike his first week in Turraburra, when he'd actually sat on a park bench and taken in the ocean view, today he was walking directly from the bakery to the clinic, because his morning visit to the nursing home had run a long way over time.

He'd got distracted with the birthday morning tea for Mrs Lewinski, who was celebrating her one-hundredth birthday. The local press had been there and the staff had put on a party with balloons, mugs of tea, a cream-filled sponge cake and bingo. It was Mrs L.'s favourite game and it had seemed wrong not to stay and play one game with her. He'd lost.

His week had been a busy one—Lily had been right about word getting out. His third week in town had passed so fast he could hardly believe it was Friday.

'Dr Jackson. Dr Jackson, slow down.'

He turned towards the female voice and saw Claire Burke hurrying towards him. 'Hi, Claire, great day, isn't it?'

'Yes, it is!' Unlike the scowling woman she'd been last Saturday, now she was positively beaming. 'Karen

just called me and told me the news. I can't believe it.
I really thought you were just spinning me a line the
other day to placate me. I never expected you to be a
miracle-worker.' She pushed a carton of eggs into his
hands. 'These are free-range eggs from my chooks as
a thank-you.'

He accepted the eggs. 'You're welcome, and I'm not
a miracle-worker. I just made a few phone calls and
spoke with my boss at the Melbourne Victoria. I suggested to him that as the hospital had sent me down
here to work, it was only right and proper that I finish
the work I started. I'll be removing your gall bladder
on my first day back in Melbourne.'

'Well, the fact I'll be operated on in eleven days is
a miracle to me and I'm not your only happy patient,
Dr Jackson. Rita Hazelton and Len Peterken told me
their news too.'

Noah matched her smile. 'Like I said, I'm happy to
be able to help.' And he meant it.

In his telephone conversation with the prof, the experienced surgeon had been hesitant about the idea
of Noah bringing back a patient load with him from
Turraburra. Noah had surprised himself at how pas-
sionately he'd pushed for the surgical cases. He always
saw his surgery in terms of making a difference but,
seeing people in their home environment, those dif-
ferences were even starker.

His life in Melbourne, his income and his access to
services had given him a certain amount of immunity
to his past. It was easier to forget the difficult stuff
but his time in Turraburra had brought back a lot of
memories—life in a town without services and hard-
working people in low-paid jobs who couldn't afford

health insurance. The reminder that he'd lost contact with his roots came with a shot of middle-class guilt and going in to bat for four patients had seemed a valid way of easing it. It surprised him just how much pleasure he was getting out of being able to help.

'We all thought you were a bit of a cold fish, Doctor,' Claire said, her tone bemused, 'but you've totally surprised us, in a good way.'

Thank you? It was time to go. 'It's been good talking to you, Claire, but I need to get back to the clinic. Thanks for the eggs.'

He arrived back to find Lily sitting at Reception with a huge box of vegetables. He leaned in for a quick kiss. 'Are you starting a food bank?'

She laughed and kissed him back. 'Actually, they're for you, along with this tub of honey, a leg of lamb and some filleted flathead. The town loves you.'

He gave a wry smile. 'Claire Burke just told me the town thought I was a bit of cold fish when I first arrived.'

Lily dropped her face in her hands before looking up at him. 'She seriously said that after you've just organised her surgery?'

'It's okay. I know she meant it as a compliment and we both know I wasn't exactly enthusiastic when I first arrived. The funny thing is, Turraburra grows on you.'

A stricken look crossed her pretty face. 'But Melbourne's better, right?'

'Melbourne is without a doubt the absolute best.' He hauled her to her feet, wrapping his arms around her waist. 'Do you want to come over for dinner tonight and help me eat some of this stuff?'

Her brows rose teasingly. 'Cook it, you mean?'

'Well, if you're offering…'

She laughed. 'How about you barbecue the fish and I'll make ratatouille with the veggies. Deal?'

'Deal.' He glanced around and with no sign of Karen or the afternoon session patients he kissed her long and hard, loving the way she slumped against him. 'And just maybe you could stay the *whole* night?'

Shadows rolled across her usually clear eyes. 'It's not like I have a lot of control over that. Women have a habit of going into labour in the early hours of the morning.'

Only he knew irrespective of a labouring woman, Lily always left his bed before dawn. 'Is it your grandfather?'

'Is what my grandfather?'

'The reason you always leave.'

She spun out of his arms. 'I'm a grown woman, Noah. Gramps doesn't question my comings and goings.'

So why do you leave? He didn't know why it bugged him so much that she did, because in the past he'd always been the one to depart first. In fact, he'd made sure his trysts with women occurred at their place or in a hotel so that he could always make his exit when it suited him. With Lily, staying at her grandfather's house was out of the question so they used his flat. He couldn't say exactly why he wanted her to stay a whole night but he did know that when she rolled away from him, swung her legs out of bed and padded out of the room, a vague hollowness filled him.

An idea pinged into his head—the perfect solution to this problem. 'You have this weekend rostered off, right?'

She nodded. 'Someone's down from MMU this afternoon through Sunday. Why? Do you want to visit that winery I told you about?'

He caught her hands and drew her back in close. 'Better than that.'

She gazed up at him, her expression quizzical. 'Better than a studio room high in the gum trees with a view clear to Tasmania?'

He grinned. 'Yep.'

Her eyes sparkled with excitement. 'Where?'

'My place.'

'Um, Noah, the hospital flat doesn't come close to the accommodation at the winery.'

He shook his head. 'No, I mean *my* place. Come and spend the weekend with me in Melbourne.'

Her eyes dimmed. 'Oh, I don't th—'

'Yes,' he said enthusiastically. 'Come and experience *my* world. Let me show you my Melbourne. We can go to the Queen Vic market for the best coffee in the country, take in the exhibition at the National Gallery, see a show at the Melbourne Theatre Company, anything you want.'

She stiffened in his arms. 'No.'

The quiet word carried gravitas. He tucked some hair behind her ears. 'Why not?'

'I don't like Melbourne.'

He kissed her hair. 'But you've never had me as a tour guide before.'

She pulled away. 'It's not like I haven't seen or done those things before, Noah. None of it's new to me.'

Her quick dismissal of his idea felt like a slap in the face. 'So you'll spend the weekend at the winery where you've been before but you won't come to Melbourne?'

She shrugged. 'What can I say? I'm a country girl.'

Her dismissive manner was at odds with her usual interest in things. 'Aren't you at all curious about seeing my place?'

She sucked in her lips. 'Not really, no.'

Her rejection flared a jagged, white-hot pain, which burned him under his ribs. *No.* His hand rubbed the spot. It had been a long time since he'd felt something like that and he hated it was back. Hated that he'd allowed himself to care enough to be hurt. 'So this thing between us doesn't extend beyond Turraburra?'

She stared at him, her face filling with pity. 'Noah, you were the one who said sex doesn't have to mean a lifelong commitment. I took you at your word. We enjoy each other while you're here and then we go back to our lives.'

His own words—ones he'd always lived by when it came to women and sex—suffocated him with their irony. For the first time in his life he didn't want to walk away. Lily made him laugh, she called him on his arrogant tendencies and as a result he'd become a better doctor and a better person. She understood him in a way no one else ever had, and because of that he'd opened up to her, telling her more about this life than he'd told anyone.

He wanted a chance to explore this relationship, an opportunity to see where it would take them. Hell, he wanted more than that. He wanted to come home to Lily, tell her about his day, bounce ideas off her, and hear about her day.

I love her.

His breath left his lungs in a rush, leaving him hauling in air against cramping muscles. *No, I do not love her. I can't love her.*

He didn't have time to love anyone, didn't want to love anyone, and he didn't want to feel tied down to another person. Loving meant caring and caring meant his life wasn't his own to do as he pleased.

It's already happened, mate. That empty feeling when she leaves the bed—that's love.

Wanting to show her Melbourne—that's love.

Wanting her to share your life—that's love.

He ran his hands through his hair but the ragged movement morphed into something else. Panic eased, replaced by a desperate need to tell her exactly how he felt. 'What if I told you that when I said all that stuff about commitment I truly believed it, but getting to know you has changed everything?'

'Noah, I—'

'Shh.' He pressed his finger gently to her lips. 'I want to take this to the next level. I want commitment, exclusivity, the complete deal. I want us to be a couple because I've fallen in love with you.'

A look of pure horror crossed her face and she brought her arms up in front of her like a protective shield. 'You don't love me, Noah.'

He opened his hands palms up, hoping the gesture would reassure her. 'It's a surprise to me too but I most definitely do love you.'

'No.' Her voice rose, tinged with a sharp edge. 'You don't.'

Every cell in his body tensed and he worked hard at keeping a leash on his temper. 'Don't tell me—' he immediately dropped his slightly increased volume '—what I think and feel.'

Her face blanched, suddenly pinched. 'Don't yell at me.'

He stared at her, confused. 'You think that's yelling?' He laughed, trying to make a joke to lighten the moment. 'If you think that's yelling, don't come near my operating theatre when a patient's bleeding out.'

'And that's so very reassuring.'

Her sarcasm—her default defensive setting—whipped him, burning his skin. Bewildered, he reached for her, needing to touch her and fix this. How had his declaration of love landed him in emotional quicksand?

She ducked his touch. 'People don't fall in love in three weeks, Noah, they just think they do. You're a doctor. You know about hormones and lust. You've seen the MRI films of the effect of lust on the brain but it's not love.' Her face implored him to understand. 'Think about it. You arrived here angry and disenfranchised, like an alien from another planet, and I made you feel good. You're projecting those feelings onto me but it's not love.'

The logical side of his brain grappled with her argument while his bruised heart quivered, telling him she was wrong. Very, very wrong. 'If it was only lust, I wouldn't be thinking past the next time we had sex or a week from today, but I am. What we have is so much more than sex, Lily, you know it too. I've never felt this way about anyone and for the first time in my life I want to try. We have a shot at a future and it starts with me showing you my real life.'

Her mouth flattened into a grim line. 'I glimpsed it when we spent the day at the Melbourne Victoria.'

'My life's more than just the hospital.'

Her brows rose. 'You're a surgical registrar about to sit your part-two exams. Your life is work and study.'

He immediately jettisoned that line of argument, knowing he couldn't win it, and tried something else. 'I've had the luxury of getting to know you. You invited me into your world and last Sunday, cooking with you and then playing cards with Bruce, was really special.'

'Gramps invited you, Noah, not me. Don't read more into it than country hospitality.'

Her words hit with the force of a king punch and he gripped the reception desk. Something was definitely off. He scanned her face, searching for clues that told him why she was behaving this way. Sure, she had moments of whipping sarcasm but he'd never known her to be so blunt. So mean.

He sighed and tried again. 'All I'm asking is for one weekend, Lily. After all, you've lived in Melbourne so you know one night won't kill you.'

Her already pale face turned ashen and her pupils dilated so fast that the beautiful blue vanished under huge, ebony discs.

A shiver ran over his skin. 'Lily? What's wrong? You look like you've just seen a ghost.'

Her chin shot up and she shook her head. 'I'm sorry, Noah. There's no point me coming to Melbourne with you because we have an end date. My home is here and yours is in the city. These last few weeks have been great but that's all they can ever be. An interlude. We agreed to that and you can't change the rules on me now.'

Incredulity flooded him. 'You're letting geography get in the way of something that could be amazing?'

She folded her arms over her chest, as a slight tremor

rippled across her body. 'Geography has *nothing* to do with it, Noah.'

'I know something's going on, something I don't understand. Please tell me what it is so I can help. Whatever it is, together we can fix it.'

She closed her eyes for a moment and when she opened them again their emptiness chilled him. She swallowed. 'There's nothing to fix, Noah.'

'Why?'

'Because I don't love you.'

His lunch turned to stone in his stomach. 'Well, there's nothing ambiguous about that answer.'

'No. There's not.' She wrung her hands. 'I'm sorry it couldn't be different.'

'You're sorry?' Feelings of foolishness curdled with hurt and despair. 'Am I supposed to be grateful you threw me that bone, because, let me tell you, I'm not.' He tapped his chest directly over his heart. 'This hurts.'

Lily heard Noah's anguish and it tore at her, shredding her heart. She'd never intended to hurt him but he wanted more of her than she was able to give. Loving him was too much of a gamble. It would open her up to a huge risk and she'd worked way too hard at rebuilding her life to chance losing everything all over again. 'I said I was sorry.' And she truly meant it.

'Yeah. I heard.' The deep words rumbled around her, vibrating in controlled anger that flicked and stung her like the tail of a switch. 'Did sorry cut it with your ex-husband?'

She gasped as his bitter words spun her back in time. *I'm sorry, Trent. I apologise. I was wrong.* Fighting for control, she managed to grind out, 'This has *nothing* to do with my marriage.'

His expression turned stony. 'I wouldn't know, seeing as you've never told me anything about it.'

Fear and embarrassment rose on a river of acid, scalding the back of her throat. *And I'm never going to tell you.* 'There's nothing to tell. I was young and stupid. I had a whirlwind, high-octane romance with all the trimmings—flowers, chocolates, horse-and-carriage rides and a proposal straight out of a Hollywood movie. I thought I'd found my great love and I got married. Turned out it was neither great nor love, just lust, and it wore off fast. For Trent, it wore off even faster.' *If you'd been a better wife, I wouldn't have had to look elsewhere.*

She sucked in a steadying breath to push the memory of Trent's vicious voice away. 'It turns out the affair I discovered he was having was actually his third since we got married. I filed for divorce. End of story.'

His keen and piercing eyes bored through her. 'So you were young, you made a mistake and, just like that, you're not prepared to take a second chance?'

Panic skittered through her. She had to stop him asking questions, digging and probing, in case he got close to the truth. *Do what it takes to stop him.*

Her gut rolled. The only choice she had was to hurt him. 'We're too different, Noah. We'd never work so there's no point trying. Believe me, when I tell you that I'm saving us the heartache.'

'You're wrong.'

No, I'm so very right. 'I have to get back to work.'

'Of course you do.' He swiped his phone. 'Don't worry. I've only got one hundred and seventy-two hours left in town and then I'll be out of your hair. I'm sure we can avoid each other if we try hard enough.'

His generous mouth thinned to a hard line. 'Believe me, I'll be trying.'

With his back straight and his shoulders rigidly square, he walked away from her before disappearing into his office.

As she stood staring at the closed door, desolation hit her and, like an arrow slicing through the bullseye on a target it pierced her straight in the solar plexus. Searing pain exploded into every cell, setting up a vibrating agony of wretchedness. She'd just wounded a good and decent man to save herself.

She doubled over in agony. Playing it safe had never hurt so much.

By Monday morning, back in Turraburra after the weekend, Noah struggled not to hate Lily. He'd spent his two days in Melbourne, preparing for his return the following Saturday. Once he'd lodged the necessary paperwork for the Turraburra patients at the Victoria and booked the operating theatre, he'd concentrated on doing all his favourite things. He'd gone to a game at the MCG, he'd run through Yarra Park, bought coffee beans from his favourite deli to replenish his Turraburra supply, and he'd spent Saturday night at the Rooftop. He'd hated every minute of it.

At the footy, he'd kept turning to tell Lily something, only to find she wasn't there, and later, at the Rooftop, his usual coterie of flirting nurses and interns had seemed bland and two-dimensional. For the first time since arriving in Melbourne six years ago, his shiny and beloved city had seemed dull and listless.

He blamed Lily. He didn't belong in Turraburra but now Melbourne didn't seem like home either.

In his more rational moments he could see that perhaps by telling her he loved her he'd caught her by surprise and rushed her. But it was her reaction to his declaration that hurt most. It was one thing not to love him. It was another to be aghast at the thought and look utterly shocked and horrified by it. She'd looked at him as if he was a monster instead of a deluded guy who'd stupidly fallen in love.

He glanced at the two tins on his desk filled with home-baked lamingtons and shortbreads and at a small cooler that contained a freshly caught salmon—all gifts from grateful patients. The irony was that Turraburra had embraced him. He had more fresh produce than he could eat, Chippy had taken to sleeping under his desk, and the biggest surprise of all was that Karen was throwing him a going-away party. Everyone loved him, except the one person he wanted and needed to have love him back.

He picked up the phone for the tenth time that day, determined to call Bruce and ask him about Lily's marriage—to try and get the real story. He set the receiver back onto the cradle just like he had the nine other times. He didn't have the right to stress an eighty-five-year-old man with a heart condition, and deep down he knew it wasn't Bruce's story to tell.

He thumped the table with his fist. Why wouldn't Lily tell him?

Accept it, buddy. There is no story, she just doesn't love you.

Not possible. But even his well-developed sense of self had started to doubt that shaky belief.

We're too different. He shook his head against the thought as he'd done so often over the weekend. They shared so much in common—love of footy, medicine, sense of humour—the list went on. The only thing they really disagreed on was country versus city living and surely there was a way to negotiate on that? But if she didn't love him there was nothing to negotiate.

The intercom buzzed, breaking into his circular thoughts. 'Yes, Karen?'

'Looks like you might get to do some stitching. Lachy Sullivan's cut his hand climbing over a barbed-wire fence and it's nasty. He's waiting in the treatment room.'

'On my way.' He had ninety-eight hours to fill and with any luck this might just kill sixty minutes.

CHAPTER TEN

LILY'S HEAD ACHED. Her day had started at three-thirty a.m. with Sasha Ackers going into labour. Baby Benjamin, the third Ackers child, had arrived by breakfast, knowing exactly how to suck. From that high point the day had gone downhill fast.

On her postnatal rounds, she'd got a flat tyre in a mobile phone dead zone and, unable to call for assistance, she'd fallen in the mud, trying to use the wheel brace to loosen the wheel lugs. She'd been late back for clinic and had spent the afternoon trying to claw back time, but today every pregnant woman was teary and overwhelmed. She felt much the same way.

The only good thing about the day was the fact she hadn't run into Noah. She wasn't up to facing those brown, angst-ridden eyes that accused her of being a coward. At this point she was just counting down the days until Turraburra returned to being the safe refuge it had always been for her.

All she wanted to do was go home and fall into bed, and that was exactly what she was going to do now Sasha had insisted on an early discharge twelve hours after the birth. Sasha claimed her own bed was more comfortable than the birth centre's and, with her mother minding the other children, home was more peaceful.

Karen had closed the clinic at seven and so all Lily had to do was set the security sensor. As she started entering the numbers a frantic banging made her jump. Someone was pounding on the external doors.

'Hello?' a female voice called out. 'Please, help me.'

Lily rushed to the door, threw the lock and opened it. The woman fell into her arms and she staggered backwards into the waiting room and the light. 'Kylie? Are you in labour?'

Kylie's head was buried in her shoulder but Lily heard a muffled, 'No.'

She automatically patted her back. 'What's wrong?'

The woman raised her head. Black bruising spread across her face like tar and congealed blood sat in lumps on her split bottom lip.

Oh, God. Panic swooped through her. She knew only too well what this meant—all her worst fears about Shane Ambrose had come true. *Safety first. Lock the door. Now!*

In her haste, she almost pushed Kylie into a chair. 'Sorry, I just have to…' Her hands trembled as she bolted the door and started pulling chairs across the doorway.

'What are you doing?'

'Keeping you safe.' *Keeping us safe.* 'From Shane.'

Kylie shook her head quickly. 'No, you've got it all wrong, Lily. Shane wouldn't hurt me on purpose. This…' she gingerly touched her lip '…was a misunderstanding. He was tired and I shouldn't have let the kids annoy him.'

You brought this on yourself, Lily. You only have yourself to blame.

The past thundered back in an instant, bringing fear and chaos. She wanted to put her hands over her head and hide, only she couldn't. Kylie needed her. She needed to deal with this situation. She needed to make Kylie understand that the devil she knew was worse than the devil she didn't.

She kneeled down so she was at eye level with the trembling woman. 'Did he hit you?'

Kylie's mouth stayed shut but her eyes filled with tears.

'He has no right to do that, Kylie. Did he hit you anywhere else? In the stomach?'

'He…he didn't mean to hurt the baby.'

Nausea made her gag and she hauled in deep breaths against a closing throat. *Hold it together. You can do this.* Every part of her screamed to call the police but triage came first—check the baby, check Kylie, call the police. She extended her shaking hand. 'Come with me.'

Like a compliant child, Kylie allowed herself to be led to the treatment room and she got up onto the emergency trolley. Lily handed her an ice-pack for her face then helped Kylie shuffle out of her yoga pants. Two bright red marks the size of a fist stained the skin of her pregnant belly.

Fury so strong blew through Lily taking the edge off her fear.

'Is…is there any bleeding?' Kylie asked, her voice so soft and quiet that Lily could barely hear her.

'Your undies are clean.' Only that didn't mean there wasn't any bleeding. Her hands carefully palpated

Kylie's abdomen and the woman flinched. The area was tight. 'Does this hurt?'

'A bit.'

Lily turned on the hand-held Doppler and the baby's heartbeat thundered through the speakers. The heartbeat was way too fast.

'Oh, thank God.' Kylie immediately relaxed, falsely reassured by the sound.

'Kylie, I'm going to put in an IV and call Dr Jackson.'

The woman's face paled. 'Why? What's wrong?'

Lily opened her mouth to reply but the loud sound of fists banging on the door made her freeze.

'Kylie! Are you in there?' Shane's voice sounded frantic and filled with concern.

Kylie struggled to sit up.

'No.' Lily shook her head as she gently pushed Kylie back against the pillows. Snapping a tourniquet around her arm, she said, 'Stay there.'

'Kylie, honey, I know you're in there,' Shane cajoled. 'I'm worried about you.'

'He's not coming in here,' Lily said, sounding a lot more certain than she felt. She forced her fingers not to tremble as she palpated Kylie's arm for a vein.

'But he's my husband,' Kylie whispered, fear filling her voice. 'I made a commitment to him.'

Hearing the words she'd once spoken tore her heart. She understood the power of strong memories—those of a loving, caring man duelling with the new version of the one who inflicted pain. All types of pain—emotional, financial, sexual and physical—that left a woman blaming herself and questioning everything she believed through a fog of devastated self-esteem. Pain that was *always* followed by recanting, declarations of love and the promises of *never again*.

'Kylie, loving husbands don't put your life and the life of your unborn baby in danger. I have a duty of care to protect you and your baby and that means that right now Shane's not coming anywhere near you.' The cannula slid straight into the vein and she connected up the saline drip.

Kylie slumped as tears poured down her face. 'Th-thank you, Lily.'

'Kylie.' Shane's charming and caring voice was fast developing an edge. 'I just want to check that you're okay. Come on, darl, let me in.'

'I'm scared,' Kylie whimpered, as her hand gripped Lily's arm with bruising force. 'Can you talk to him? Please?'

Don't poke the dragon. 'I'm not sure that's—'

'I know him, Lily,' Kylie implored. 'He won't leave until he knows I'm okay.'

She felt herself caving. 'Okay, but you stay here. Do not get off the trolley.'

Kylie released her hand, nodding her acquiescence.

Lily walked slowly back to the foyer, already regretting her offer. When she arrived at the front doors she didn't open them. 'Shane,' she said, trying to sound calm and dispassionate as her heart thundered in her chest so hard it threatened to leap into her mouth. 'Kylie needs medical attention. I will call you as soon as Dr Jackson's seen her.'

'I want to be with her.'

'I know you do but…*forgive me, Noah*…Dr Jackson wants to see her on her own. As soon as he's made his diagnosis, we'll call. For now, it's best if you go home and wait.'

'You stuck-up bitch.' Shane's charm vanished as he continued to scream at her, calling her names no one should ever have to hear. His poisonous words slid through the cracks in the old building, sneaking under the window seals, their vitriol a living, thriving beast with intent to harm. 'Open the goddamn door now, before I kick it in.'

Lily, you're scum. Lily, you're useless. You're a worthless whore. You ruined my life.

The past bore down on her so hard she gasped for breath, trying to force air into rigid lungs. The edges of her mind started to fuzz.

'Lily, I'm scared.'

Kylie's voice penetrated her panic making her fight back against the impending darkness. *I'm a good person. Kylie needs my help. I have to protect Kylie and the baby.*

Somehow her trembling hands managed to press in Noah's number on her phone.

As his rich, warm voice came down the line, the crack of a gun going off had her diving for safety. With her belly on the floor and adrenalin pouring through her, she commando-crawled for cover under the reception desk.

'Lily?' Noah's voice was frantic. 'What's happening?'

The sound of crashing glass deafened her.

'Get the police. Come to the clinic,' she whispered, barely able to speak against the terror that was tightening her throat. 'Kylie Ambrose is bleeding.'

She left the phone connected, hoping against hope

that Noah would use the landline to call the police and keep his mobile connected to hers. That he'd stay on the line and be her lifeline.

He's already your lifeline.

The thought pierced her with its clarity and she gasped. Over the past few weeks Noah, with his love and caring, had brought her back into the world. Noah, who argued with her but never punished her if she disagreed with him. Noah, who loved her but didn't want to control her. Noah, who hadn't run from the hard, hurtful facts that he had a communication problem or blamed her but had worked to change how he dealt with people. How many men would do that?

Some. Not that many. He was one of life's good guys—truly special—and she'd tossed him aside, too scared to trust her future to him because of the fear scumbags like Trent and Shane Ambrose had instilled in her. And for what? A hysterical laugh threatened to burst out of her. She was back to hiding again.

I don't love you, Noah. She shoved her fist in her mouth at the memory of what she'd said to him, biting down on her knuckles to stop herself from crying out in pain. Fear had driven those words from her mouth and she'd do anything to have the chance to take them back.

The crunch of glass under boots boomed in the silence—threatening, ominous and terrifying—taking her back to another dark night and shattered glass. *You survived that and you'll survive this. You have to live so you can save Kylie and tell Noah that you love him.*

The footsteps got closer. Louder. A moment later Shane Ambrose was towering over her with a gun pointed straight at her. 'Next time, bitch, open the bloody door.'

His arrival turned her panic to ice. Now she knew what she was dealing with. Trent had taught her the unpredictability of men and this whole event was all about power. She'd told Shane he couldn't come inside the clinic so to show her he was the one in charge— the man in control— he'd broken in to teach her a lesson. If she wanted to get out of this situation in one piece, she had to do what she'd vowed she'd never do again.

She agreed. 'Yes, Shane.'

He grunted. 'That's more like it. I'm taking Kylie home.'

She kept her gaze fixed on his hateful face and concentrated on keeping her voice toneless and even. 'Kylie's bleeding, Shane. If you take her home, she'll die.'

The gun wavered. 'Don't bullshit me.'

She swallowed, praying that she could get through to him on some level. 'You're holding a gun at my head, Shane. You hold all the cards here, you have all the control. Why would I lie to you?'

'Shane, it's Ross Granger.' The police sergeant's voice, loud and distorted by a megaphone, carried into the clinic from outside. 'I know you're in there, mate, and you've got a gun. We got a call from the clinic saying Kylie and the baby need the doctor. He's here but we need you to come to the door first and bring the gun.'

Shane's cold eyes assessed her. 'Take me to Kylie and don't do anything stupid because I'm right behind you.'

Forcing her jelly legs to carry her, she walked straight to the treatment room. She'd expected the pregnant woman to be sitting up, quivering and terrified, but instead she was lying on her side. 'Kylie?'

Her eyes fluttered open and her hands pressed her belly. 'Hurts.'

Lily opened the IV full bore and checked her blood pressure. It was dangerously low. 'She's bleeding, Shane. She needs a Caesarean section or she and the baby will die.'

The bravado of the cowardly man faltered for a moment. 'Get the doctor.' The gun rose again. 'No police.'

'I have to get in there now, Sergeant.' Noah paced up and down outside the clinic, frantic with worry. 'Gunshots have been fired, there's a pregnant woman who's at risk of bleeding out, a baby who might die, and there's Lily…' His voice cracked on her name. Some crazy guy had his Lily bailed up with a gun.

'Doctor, you can't go in until Ambrose is disarmed. I can't risk any more lives. I've got the medical evacuation helicopter and skilled police negotiators on the way.'

'We don't have time to waste—'

The clinic door opened and Lily stood in the doorway with Shane. He had one of his hands clamped on her arm and the other held the gun pointing at a pale and silent Lily.

'Get the doctor,' Shane yelled.

As if reading Noah's mind, the sergeant said, 'Noah, wait.'

But he wasn't waiting any longer and he bounded forward. Better that he be inside with some control than outside with none. No way in hell was he leaving Lily alone with that bastard. As he approached, Shane stepped back to allow him to pass.

Noah made his second split-second decision for the

day—he decided to just be the doctor and not mention the gun. 'Where's Kylie?'

Shane waved the gun towards the treatment room. 'You have to save her.'

Relatives often said that to him, only they weren't usually holding a gun. 'I'll do my best but I might need more medical help.'

'No one else is comin' in here,' Shane said with a menacing growl.

Noah strode directly to the treatment room. 'Lily,' he said firmly, hating how terrified she looked. He wanted to wrap her in his arms and keep her safe but gut instinct told him not to. Men like Shane Ambrose considered women inferior. Noah needed to keep the bastard on side. 'What's Kylie's BP?'

'Ninety on forty-five,' she replied, her voice oddly emotionless. 'She needs a Caesar but we can't do it here.'

'We don't have a choice,' he said grimly. 'If I don't operate, she dies. We may not have operating theatre conditions but at least we have antibiotics and plasma expander. What about surgical instruments?'

Her eyes widened in momentary surprise before filling with confirmation. 'I can put together an emergency set from the clinic supplies and we have a cautery pen, but I've never given an anaesthetic before.'

'I'll talk you through it. We can do this.' He sounded way more confident than he felt. What he was about to do was combat surgery, only he was a very long way from a war zone. He glanced at the gun. Maybe not.

Calling out instructions to Lily for the drugs he needed, he quickly intubated the barely conscious Kylie. As Lily took over the bagging, he administered the muscle relaxant and that's when reality hit him. They were short one set of hands. He needed another nurse but he couldn't ask anyone to step into this dangerous situation and even if he could, Shane wasn't going to allow it.

He glanced at Shane and the gun. The fact the guy had insisted Noah save his wife made him hope he wanted her to live. 'Shane, can I call you Shane?'

The man nodded. 'Yeah.'

'See how Lily is pressing that bag in and out, giving Kylie oxygen? Do you think you can do that?'

His eyes narrowed. 'Why can't the bitch do it?'

Every part of Noah wanted to dive at Ambrose's throat but he needed the low-life's help and right now saving Kylie came ahead of trying to disarm the creep. 'There's a big chance the baby is going to have trouble breathing when it's born and Lily has the skills to care for it. I'm not asking you to put the gun down. You can bag her one-handed.'

'Fair enough.' Shane sat down at his wife's head and took over from Lily, the gun still in his other hand.

Lily walked over to Noah, her face impassive like she was on automatic pilot. He got the sense she'd gone somewhere deep inside herself to get through this. He surreptitiously squeezed her hand. 'Time to gown up.'

'Time to gown up,' she repeated softly, saying the words like a mantra. 'We can do this. You can do this.'

Her belief in him slid under him like a flotation device, holding him up out of the murky depths of fear. He was operating in a makeshift operating theatre on a woman who might die on the table, a baby who might be born dead, and he was doing it all in the presence of an unpredictable guy holding a gun.

Don't go there.

Panic didn't belong in surgery and as the mask, gown and gloves went on, everything superfluous to the surgery fell away.

Quickly draping Kylie's abdomen, he picked up the scalpel. 'Making the incision. Have the retractors ready.'

A minute and half later he was easing the baby out of the uterus. Lily double-clamped the cord and he cut it, separating the baby from Kylie.

'He's blue.' Shane's panicked eyes followed Lily as she carried the baby to the cot and gave him oxygen. 'Is he alive?'

God, he hoped so, but right now he was battling with keeping the surgical field free of blood and he needed another pair of hands.

'He's got a pulse,' Lily said, relief clear in her voice. 'Come on, little guy, breathe.' A moment later the baby gave a feeble cry.

'That's my boy. Finally after three useless girls I get a son.' The pride in his voice was unmistakable.

Noah almost lost it. He wanted to vault the table and take the guy down. Instead, he bit his tongue to stop the fury that boiled in him from spilling over and putting him and Lily in even more danger.

The baby's cry thankfully got stronger. One saved. One to go. He battled on, trying to find the bleeder in a surgical field awash with blood.

The automatic blood pressure machine beeped wildly, the sound screaming danger and flashing terrifyingly low numbers. He refused to allow Kylie to die. 'Lily, put up another bag of plasma expander, administer oxytocin and re-glove. I need you here with suction. Now.'

A stricken look flared in Lily's eyes as she placed the cot next to Shane and he understood her dilemma. This bastard had caused this mess and now they had to depend on him.

'Please, Shane, will you watch the baby to make sure he doesn't stop breathing?' Lily said evenly and devoid of all the fear that burned in her eyes. 'Your wife and son need you.'

'Of course they need me,' he said, his shoulders straightening with warped pride. 'They depend on me for everything.'

Noah could only imagine the chilling smile that Shane's surgical mask was hiding. The complicated web of emotions that was domestic violence was anathema to him. How could men profess to love a woman and children and yet cause so much damage and pain? If he had his way, after all of this was over, he'd be appearing in court, giving evidence against this man and hoping he got jail time.

First things first. Save Kylie, disarm Ambrose.

The reassuring and tantalising whirring noise of the emergency evacuation helicopter sounded overhead and Noah prayed Kylie would get the chance to use its services.

Lily adjusted the suction and more blood bubbled up.

He swore quietly and cauterised another bleeder. He held his breath. *Please, let that be the last one*. They had limited supplies of plasma expander and Kylie's heart would only pump if it had enough circulating volume to push through it.

The field stayed miraculously clear.

He raised his eyes to Lily's, whose glance said, *Thank you.*

The blood-pressure machine stopped screaming but they weren't out of the woods yet. 'Shane, Kylie needs blood and she needs to be evacuated to an Intensive Care Unit in Melbourne the moment I've stitched her up.'

'And my son?' he asked, his gaze fixed on his newborn baby.

'He needs to be examined by a paediatrician,' Lily said quietly.

'Why?' Ambrose's eyes darted between Lily and Noah. 'Is something wrong?'

'He seems okay,' Lily said, 'but we just like to be thorough.'

'Shane,' Noah said, seeing a potential weak spot in their captor, 'we want your son to have the best medical care possible.

'Damn right. Get over here and squeeze this bag.' Shane kept the gun pointed firmly on Lily as he used the phone to call the police sergeant, demanding that the emergency medical staff meet them at the front doors.

'How much longer are you going to take, Doc?'

'Five minutes.'

Shane put his finger against the baby's palm and grinned when his son's fingers closed tightly around it. 'Strong little beggar, like his dad.'

'Does he have a name?' Lily asked.

Noah's gaze jerked up from closing the muscle layer of Kylie's abdomen. For the first time Lily sounded herself, as if this were a totally normal childbirth scenario.

'Jed,' Shane said.

'A good choice. A strong name for a fighter,' Lily said almost conversationally.

Lily, what are you doing?

'Look, he's looking for a drink,' Shane said. 'Kylie always breastfeeds them.'

Not this time, buddy. Noah struggled with the normality of the conversation. It was like Shane had conveniently forgotten that his violence had put his wife and child in mortal danger. 'I've finished.' Noah set down the scissors. 'Shane, she needs to go now.'

'What about the baby?' Shane asked, still keeping the gun trained on both of them.

'Can you please bring him?' Lily started walking backwards, still bagging Kylie.

Noah manoeuvred the trolley through the wide treatment room doors wishing he could read Lily's thoughts.

'Don't try anything,' Shane said, keeping the gun trained on the both of them as the police and medical evacuation team met them at the front door.

Noah gave a rapid handover, finishing with, 'She needs blood five minutes ago.'

As the flight nurse relieved Lily of the bagging job and the trolley disappeared out the door, Shane grabbed Lily by the arm, pulling her away from Noah. She stumbled backwards.

Noah's heart flipped and he held up his hands. 'Shane—'

'You go with Kylie, Doc. I trust you.'

No way in hell. 'What about the baby, Shane? I thought you wanted him checked out too?'

'Lily knows about babies and she'll do until you send a baby doctor in.'

'I'll be fine, Noah,' Lily said so softly he barely heard, but her gaze—full of love—loudly implored him to leave. To take this opportunity for his own safety.

His heart ripped into two. She loved him. Despite what she'd told him, despite sending him away, she loved him. What should have been the most wonderful news now rocked him with its devastating irony.

The gun moved directly to Noah's chest. 'Get out, Doc. Right now.'

Noah felt one of the police officer's hands wrap around his upper arm. 'Do as he says, Dr Jackson.'

At that moment the baby, who'd been quiet for so long, started to cry.

'Shane, do you want to hold your son?' Lily asked quietly. 'Give him a bottle?'

Shane hesitated, his hand tightening on the gun. Noah, backing slowly out of the door, could see the man's mind working out all the logistics. 'You pick him up and give him to me.'

Lily did exactly as he asked and settled the baby in the crook of his arm.

Shane jiggled his arm to try and sooth the crying baby but Jed, now awake and hungry, wouldn't be silenced. He kicked his little legs, destabilising his position in his father's arm, and Shane, momentarily distracted, moved his gun-holding hand to adjust the baby.

The baby screamed.

Lily moved.

No! Noah watched, horrified, as she slammed the side of her hand into Shane's wrist.

Shane roared. The gun dropped and somehow Lily had it in her hands. Noah threw himself forward, grabbing Shane before he could do anything to Lily.

The police poured into the building, guns raised, and immediately surrounded Shane. Noah relinquished his grip on the man, stepping back as a police officer took the baby and another handcuffed Shane.

Lily sank to her knees, the gun falling from her hands.

Noah ran to her, wrapping his arms around her, holding her tightly, convinced she was going to vanish any second. He frantically kissed her hair, her face and stroked her back. 'You're safe. You're very safe. It's over, Lily.'

Her huge, blue eyes sought his. 'We're...both...safe.'

'We are.'

Her body shook violently in his arms and the next moment she vomited all over the floor.

CHAPTER ELEVEN

Lily opened her eyes, recognising the bright pattern of Noah's quilt. Vague memories of him telling the police she was in no fit state to give a statement and then being cradled in his arms slowly dribbled back.

'Hey,' Noah said softly. 'Welcome back.'

She turned to find him staring down at her, his face full of concern. Despite the fact she'd stupidly told him she didn't love him, despite the hurt and pain she'd inflicted on his heart, he'd never left her side all night. It overwhelmed her. 'What...what time is it?'

'Seven. You've been asleep for eight hours.'

'Gramps?' Panic gripped her. 'Is he okay? Does he know where I am?'

Understanding crossed his face. 'Bruce is fine. He's relieved you're safe and he knows you're with me, getting the best medical care possible.' He stroked her cheek. 'I said I'd call him when you woke up.'

She still felt half-asleep. Her limbs hung like lead weights and her brain struggled to compute, feeling like it was drowning in treacle. 'What did you give me?'

'A mild sedative. I promise it will wear off quickly

but you needed it. It was really important that you sleep.' He squeezed her hand. 'Any nightmares?'

'No.' She shook her head and struggled up to rest against a bank of pillows before accepting the steaming mug of tea. 'But I know the drill about nightmares. They'll come later.'

His lovely mouth grimaced. 'The trauma counsellor wants to see us both later today and it's important we go.'

His matter-of-fact words pierced her, reminding her that he'd been through the same awful experience. She squeezed his hand. 'What about you? Did you sleep? Are you okay? You had a gun pointed at you, just like me.'

'I'm okay.' He brushed her forehead with his lips. 'I was more scared for you than for myself.'

She didn't understand. 'Why?'

His incisive gaze studied her. 'Shane Ambrose's vitriol was centred squarely on you.'

'Yeah. He's a misogynist.' She stared into the milky tea. 'You have the immunity of a Y chromosome.'

'And I hated every minute of it,' he said, his voice cracking with emotion. 'I would have given anything to change places with you and when you karate-chopped him my heart almost stopped. You could have been shot.' He stroked her hair. 'Promise me you'll never scare me like that again.'

Tears welled up in her eyes. His love flowed into her like a life force, giving her hope that, despite all her fears, she hadn't lost him. But before she could hope too much she owed him the truth. 'Shane was distracted by the baby and I saw a chance and took it.

I had to take it for Kylie and for you. For me. I've spent too many years being scared.'

Worry lines creased his forehead. 'Scared? I don't understand. What you did was one of the bravest things I've ever seen.'

She shook her head. 'That wasn't brave, it was just instinctive survival. I've got a Ph.D in that, courtesy of my marriage.'

His face filled with compassion. 'Perhaps you need to tell me about that.'

She met his warm brown gaze. 'There's no perhaps about it, Noah. There are things you need to know about me, things I should have told you but I was too ashamed to tell you because I've always considered it my dirty little secret.' She licked her dry lips. 'Yesterday, when I had a gun pointed at my heart, I realised I should have told Kylie the story of my marriage weeks ago. I should have told you.'

She gulped down her tea and told him fast. 'You know how I said I'd fallen through a plate-glass window? Well, I didn't exactly fall.'

Noah's skin prickled and flashes of the stoic, non-confrontational Lily from yesterday hammered him, making his gut roll. 'My God, Lily, he pushed you?'

Her gaze seemed fixed on a point on the quilt. 'It was the night I left him. I was stupid. Despite his affairs, despite everything he'd done, I thought I owed him an explanation as to why I was leaving, why I was breaking a vow and a promise I'd made in good faith two years earlier.' Her sad gaze met his. 'But I learned there's no such thing as a rational conversation with an irrational person who thinks that you're his property. His chattel.'

He had the primal urge to kill the unknown man. 'You have nothing to be ashamed about, Lily,' he said, keen to reassure her. 'And neither does Kylie or any other woman in the same situation. These men are sick. Even if I hadn't known that before, yesterday sure as hell taught me.'

'Thanks.' She gave him a wry smile. 'On one level, I knew that Trent's behaviour wasn't my fault but when you're cut off from friends and family, doubt sneaks in and it strips away your self-esteem so slowly that you're not even sure it's going until it's gone. If you're told often enough that you're useless, hopeless, a disappointment, and that everything is your fault, then you slowly start to believe it.'

'Please, believe me, you're none of those things, Lily,' he said gruffly, as a thousand feelings clogged his throat.

She patted his hand as if he was the one needing reassurance. 'I know,' she said softly. 'I truly do.'

'So this Trent.' He spat out the name. 'Please, tell me he got charged for almost killing you.'

'Yes, and there's an intervention order in place against him but I find it hard to trust it. I know that's stupid because he's never once tried to break it.' She wrung her hands. 'Other women aren't so lucky.'

Slowly, things started to make sense to him. Her tension in the car the day they'd driven to Melbourne, her refusal to spend the weekend with him, her accusation that he was yelling when he'd only been emphatic. 'All of this happened when you lived in Melbourne, didn't it?'

'Yes.' Her eyes pleaded with him to understand. 'I met Trent in Melbourne a few months before I started my Master's of midwifery. He dazzled me with romantic gestures, poetic words and gifts. He had a way of making me feel incredibly special, as if I was the centre of his world. It was his suggestion that we elope because—' she made air quotes with her hands '—there's nothing more romantic.'

Her hands fell back in front of her. 'As it turned out, I married him for worse, with two strangers as witnesses in the Melbourne registry office. It should have been my first clue about things to come. How he'd work really hard at separating me from my few friends and Gramps.'

He slid his hand into hers. 'When did things start to change?'

'When I started my midwifery lectures. We'd only been married for five weeks and the first four weeks of our marriage was our honeymoon, backpacking in Vietnam and Cambodia. He resented the time I needed to study. If I got engrossed in an essay and was late with dinner, he'd fly off the handle. Initially, I put it down to low blood sugar and him being tired and hungry after work.'

She barked out a short, derisive laugh. 'I wish it could have been that simple but it was so far from simple it made complicated look easy. The first time I stayed late for a delivery he refused to believe I'd been at work all that time. He called me a slut, told me he knew I was sleeping with one of the registrars, and the more I denied it, the more he accused me of sleeping around. Although I didn't know it at the time, the irony was that he was the one having affairs.

'From that night he insisted on driving and collecting me when I had hospital placements. One night I accepted drinks after work with a group of fellow student midwives to celebrate someone's birthday and he locked me out of the house for two hours. After that, he started to control our money. He took over the grocery shopping and restricted the amount of money I could access to a tram fare. Without access to cash, it was impossible to attend any social get-togethers and if you say no to invitations often enough, people stop issuing them.'

He was battling to make sense of why his strong-willed Lily had found herself in this situation. 'Why didn't you tell someone what was happening?'

'This is the hardest thing for people to understand. I was a small-town girl in a big city with no close friends and in a new course. Every time I got close to making a friend, Trent would sense it and find a way to destroy it.' She squeezed his hand. 'Domestic violence is insidious, Noah. Because your filter is clouded by love and you're not expecting someone who professes to love you to hurt you, you're in the middle of it before you realise. He effectively marooned me on an island of fear.'

'I threw myself into study and work and managed to qualify. I was the team member who took on any extra shifts on offer to avoid being at home.'

'But didn't he hate that?'

She gave him a pitying glance. 'Noah, there's no logic to his behaviour. As much as he hated me not being at home where he could control me, he enjoyed the freedom my absences offered him. He still took me to and from work so he knew exactly where I was. One afternoon I came down with a high fever and work bundled me into a taxi and sent me home early. I found

Trent in bed with a woman who had long blonde hair and blue eyes, just like me. She could have been my double. That night I told him I was leaving him.'

He kissed the back of her hand, hating how much she'd been through.

Her voice took on a flat tone as if remembering the trauma of being flung through a glass door was too much. 'I had five days in hospital to think about what I was going to do. The police and the social worker at the Royal helped me take out an intervention order and they even managed to get my clothes out of the flat. As much as I loved working at MMU, the thought of staying in Melbourne was just too awful so I gave notice on the pretext of being homesick. They suggested I apply for a grant for a birth centre to operate down here. I came back to Turraburra, back to Gramps and love, and I slowly recovered.'

Noah's chest hurt from a mixture of pure, hot anger at Trent for his brutal treatment of her and agonising pain that Lily had endured the slow demise of her marriage, her confidence and everything she'd believed she had a right to enjoy. 'You rebuilt your life. That takes incredible resilience and courage.'

She shrugged. 'There were days I thought I couldn't do it but adopting Chippy helped. He's my kindred spirit. He knows what it's like to live in fear. Although no one apart from Gramps knows the real story, the town knew my marriage had failed and they wrapped me up in their care and I concentrated on staying safe.'

'Given what you'd been through, that makes sense.'

She gazed up at him, her eyes filled with shadows. 'I thought it made sense too and I'd convinced myself I had a full and happy life because it was so much better than what I'd had with Trent. It was all working just fine until you arrived and suddenly it was like waking up from a long hibernation and feeling sunshine on my skin for the first time in for ever. You brought me out into the light and showed me what I'd been living had only been half a life. You showed me what my life could truly be.'

Noah held his breath. Since the moment last night when Lily had looked at him with such love shining in her eyes, along with a desperate need to protect him, he'd been waiting and hoping she'd tell him she loved him. Only now he'd learned exactly what she'd been through in Melbourne and on top of yesterday's trauma, which would have brought everything back in Technicolor, he wasn't going to rush her. He needed to give her time and he was going to take things very, very slowly. Take things one tiny step at a time so he never lost her again.

Exhaustion clung to Lily. Telling her story was always like being put through the emotional wringer, but if she and Noah were to have a chance at a future, he needed to know what she'd been through and how the remnants still clung to her. She swallowed hard, knowing what she said next was vitally important. She had to get it right, had to try and make Noah understand why she'd behaved the way she had when he'd told her he loved her.

'All those wonderful feelings I experienced with you both awed and terrified me. Part of me wanted them badly, while another part of me rejected them out of fear.' She grabbed both his hands, needing to touch him, needing him to feel her love for him in case her words let her down. 'Even though I know on every level possible that you're nothing like Trent, me giving in to those feelings felt like I was stepping off a cliff and free-falling without a safety net. When you told me you loved me, I panicked. I said awful and hurtful things, things that aren't true, just so you'd leave.'

She gulped in a breath as bewildered tears poured down her cheeks. 'And despite me breaking your heart, you still came and risked your life for me, Kylie and the baby. I've been so stupid. I've let that awful secret ruin my chance at happiness with you and I'm so sorry.'

His earnest gaze hooked hers. 'I'm still here, Lily. It's not over until the fat lady sings.'

She gulped in breaths. The time had come for her to put her heart on the line. 'I love you so much, Noah. Can you forgive me and risk loving me too?'

'I love you, Lily,' he said so softly she almost didn't hear. 'That never stops.'

The three little words that had sent her into a tail-spin four days ago now bathed her soul in a soothing, life-affirming balm. She cupped his stubbled cheek with her palm, still struggling to understand. 'How can you love me so unconditionally when I've hurt you so much?'

His brown eyes overflowed with tenderness. 'Because you're you. You're a good person, Lily. You're kind, generous and no-nonsense, and, oh, so very good for a grumpy-bum like me.'

A puff of laughter fell from her lips. 'You over-heard Karen?'

His mouth twitched. 'I might have.'

She smiled and fingered his shirt, secure in his love for her. 'You can be grumpy from time to time but, then again, so can I.'

'I'm a lot less grumpy than I was now I have you in my life.' He kissed her tenderly on the forehead. 'And talking about *our* life, after what happened on Friday I don't want to rush you into any decisions. I especially don't want to after yesterday.'

Her heart ached and sang at the same time. 'We *both* experienced yesterday, Noah.'

His face tensed with the memory. 'We did and we need to go to counselling so it doesn't hijack our lives. We go for as long as it takes. I want you to feel safe, to feel loved and secure. We can get through this together, Lily. We'll find our way to be a united couple, no matter what it takes.'

His heart beat under her hand—strong, steady and reassuring—and she needed to pinch herself that he was part of her life. This wonderful man who understood that rushing into things was the worst thing for her. 'Taking things slowly sounds like a perfect idea.'

He let out a long breath and she realised he'd been scared she might freak out again at the idea of them being a couple. Her heart cramped and she moved to reassure him. 'Exactly how slowly are we taking this? We can still have sex, right?'

He grinned. 'Absolutely. And do fun stuff together like picnics and visiting wineries and—'

She smiled up at him. 'So we're dating?'

The last vestiges of tension on his face faded away. 'Dating and having sex sounds great.'

And it did. It sounded fantastically normal. 'Lots of good times and wonderful experiences and time to really get to know each other.'

She laid her head on his chest and closed her eyes, feeling his love and warmth seeping into her.

'Lily?'

'Hmm…?'

He wound strands of her hair around his fingers. 'I have to go back to Melbourne in a few days.'

She stifled a sigh. 'I know. You have that pesky exam to study for and pass with flying colours.'

'And you hate coming to Melbourne.'

She bit her lip. She hated that those last vestiges of her marriage, which still clung to her, could hurt him. 'I'm going to get better at that. I know Trent's never breached the intervention order here or in Melbourne and, who knows, he might not even live there any more. I'll be asking the counsellor to help me over this last stumbling block because I want to enjoy being in Melbourne again. I want to feel comfortable there, with or without you.'

'That's great but it's not quite what I meant.' His hand stalled on her hair and hesitancy entered his voice. 'Days off excepted, I'll be working in Melbourne and you'll be down here, delivering pregnant women.'

'You're sounding worried.'

'I know we're dating and I'm fine with that but I'm just checking we're on the same page. I know I said I didn't want to rush you and I don't, but we're an exclusive couple, right?'

She propped herself up fast, resting on one elbow with her heart so full it threatened to burst. 'We are most definitely an exclusive couple. I'll take down any woman who so much as bats her eyelashes at you. I won't allow anyone to steal you away from me.'

His eyes, so full of love, gazed down at her. 'That could be the sexiest thing you've ever said to me.'

She laughed. 'Really? I'm sure I can do much better than that.'

He raised a brow as a smile raced from his lips to the corners of his eyes. 'I dare you.'

She leaned up and whispered in his ear. He sucked in a sharp breath before lowering his head to kiss her gently and reverently, as if he was worried he might hurt her. She knew he'd never intentionally do that and she wanted the Noah who'd made love to her before he'd learned what had happened to her in Melbourne.

Wrapping her arms around his neck, she pressed herself against him, kissing him back hard—needing to feel, needing to lose herself in wonder and banish the past, banish yesterday and everything they'd been through.

He groaned and immediately rolled her over, his mouth and hands loving her until she was a quivering mess of glorious sensation. 'Noah,' she panted, 'now.'

When he slid inside her, she knew she was home. This amazing man was her safety and her security. With him, she could take risks, say what she believed, challenge him, but most importantly she could be herself. As the wave to bliss caught them they rode it together, embracing life and forging a new future.

Later, as she lay in his arms, a peace she'd never known before trickled through her. She knew without equivocation that no matter what life threw at them, if they faced it hand in hand and side by side, they could and would come out the other end not only stronger but together. She couldn't wait to start.

EPILOGUE

'THERE'S PLENTY OF food in the freezer so, please, don't feel you have to cook,' Lily told Karen as she ran through her list. 'Gramps and Muriel are happy to take the kids for two hours tomorrow, which is about as much as they can handle in one hit, but it gives you a break and—'

'Just go already,' Karen said, with an indulgent smile. 'Anyone would think this was the first time you'd left Ben and Zoe with me. Just be back here by five tomorrow or I'll turn into a pumpkin.'

'Who's turning into a pumpkin?' Noah asked, appearing in the kitchen doorway holding a curly blonde toddler and with a pre-schooler whose arms were clamped tightly around his legs.

'Ka! Ka!' Zoe squealed, putting her arms out towards Karen with delight.

'Let's go and see my new puppy,' Karen said with a broad smile as she lifted Zoe into her arms then put her hand out to coax the reluctant Ben to let go of his father's legs.

As Lily watched Karen and the children disappear out the back door she pinched herself yet again to remind herself how blessed and lucky she was. Who would have known underneath all of Karen's pedantic office rules and terse texts there lurked a woman who adored messy children. She turned to Noah, who was at the sink, sponging something sticky off his shirt. 'I've got a surprise for you.'

Noah dropped the cloth onto the sink and caught her around the waist, gazing down at her. 'I love surprises. Promise it involves me having my wife to myself for a couple of hours?'

She stroked the distinguished strands of silver hair that had appeared at his temples. Six years had passed since he'd told her he loved her and if anything that look of adoration that flared in his eyes whenever he looked at her had deepened. 'I promise you it's better than that.'

'How can it be better than that?'

'Well, first of all it's thirty-six hours with me and it's in Melbourne with tickets to that new show you wanted to see.'

His face lit up. 'Are you serious?'

She laughed at his enthusiasm. 'But wait, there's more. We're having dinner at our favourite restaurant and—'

He tightened his arms around her, pulling her in close against him so his heat flowed through her. 'Tell me you booked at the Langdon.'

She laughed and slid her fingers between the buttons on his shirt, her fingertips caressing his chest. 'I booked the spa room at the Langdon.'

He groaned with pleasure as his lips sought hers, kissing her long and hard. 'It's a shame we've got a long drive and we're not there right now.'

'Everything comes to those who wait,' she teased.

He stroked her hair. 'Not that I'm not appreciative of this amazing weekend you've planned for us but now you've got me worried that I've forgotten some important date. I know it's not my birthday or your birthday and it's definitely not our wedding anniversary so...?'

She rested her head on his shoulder the way she liked to do, loving the feeling of being cocooned in care. 'It's five years since you officially became Mr Jackson, General Surgeon, and we polished your new brass plaque and opened the surgical practice in Bairnsdale.'

'Is it?' He ran his hand through his hair as if he couldn't believe it. 'The time's gone so fast.'

Five years ago she'd offered to go to Melbourne to live but he'd been adamant he was coming to join her in the country. 'No regrets?'

'Not a single one. It was the best decision I ever made. With my one day a fortnight at the Victoria I get to keep up to date with the latest techniques, and with my patient load down here I get plenty of chances to refine them. The practice has grown so fast that I need another general surgeon to join me.' His eyes lit up. 'And I just got an email with some fabulous news.'

She tapped him on the chest. 'Don't keep me in suspense. Spill.'

'With the rural medical course at the uni being affiliated with the hospital, you're looking at the new associate professor of surgery.'

With a squeal of delight, she threw her arms around his neck. An aging Chippy, resting in his basket, looked up in surprise to see what all the noise and fuss was about. 'That is so fantastic. Congratulations. I'm so proud of you.'

'Thanks, but it's because of you.'

'No, it's because of all your hard work.'

'Let's agree it's both.' He gave her a quick kiss on the nose. 'All those years ago I thought that being sent to Turraburra was the worst thing that could have ever happened to me but in reality it was the very best thing. I was embraced by a community in a way I'd never experienced in Melbourne and I learned there's something intrinsically special about being able to give back.' He cupped her cheeks. 'And then there was you. You and the kids are what I'm most proud of in my life. You're the best thing that ever happened to me.'

Her throat thickened with emotion as his love circled her. 'And you and the children are the best thing that's ever happened to me. We've been so blessed.'

'We have. And although I love Zoe and Ben more than life itself, they're exhausting on a scale that makes back-to-back surgeries look like a walk in the park.' He grabbed her hand and tugged her towards the door. 'Let's not waste another moment of our thirty-five hours and fifty minutes of freedom.'

She laughed. 'You're not going to set a countdown app on your phone, are you?'

He gave a sheepish grin. 'No need. By the end of breakfast tomorrow both of us will be desperate to come straight home to see the kids.'

'We're pretty hopeless, aren't we?'

He kissed her one more time. 'True, but I wouldn't have it any other way.'

And neither would she.

* * * * *